IN SICKNESS
AND IN HEALTH

IN SICKNESS
AND IN HEALTH

A Physician Remembers

Richard Bayliss

Book Guild Publishing
Sussex, England

First published in Great Britain in 2007 by
The Book Guild Ltd
Pavilion View
19 New Road
Brighton, East Sussex
BN1 1UF

Typesetting in Times by
Keyboard Services, Luton, Bedfordshire

Printed in Great Britain by
Antony Rowe Ltd, Chippenham, Wiltshire

A catalogue record for this book is available from
The British Library

ISBN 1 84624 049 2

'From inability to let well alone; from too much zeal for what is new, and contempt for what is old; from putting knowledge before wisdom, science before art, and cleverness before common sense; from treating patients as cases, and from making cure of the disease more grievous than its endurance. Good Lord deliver us!'

The creed of Sir Robert Hutchinson
(1871–1960)

Contents

Foreword

Dick Bayliss's remarkable and distinguished career in medicine spanned nearly 70 years. It began in medical school in 1934 at the time of the discovery of the sulphonamide antimicrobials, some years before that of penicillin and at a time when the physician had all too little with which to treat his patients. This was the era in which the art of the physician was all important. It finished in the modern age of scientific high-tech medicine with Dick, so evidently the master of both the art and the science, combining the two with an elegance few could rival. Memories from such a period are bound to be interesting, the more so when the author has had so eventful a life and when his memory has remained so vivid.

Although there are large parts of the book which are truly autobiographical, reminiscences often take the reader down some fascinating byways, some social, some medical and all great fun. These diversions arise from life at home, at school, at Cambridge and St Thomas' Hospital, as a visiting student in the Munich of 1934, in the Blitz, in the army in India, as a researcher and a wise physician serving both the NHS and private practice and who was to become Head of Her Majesty's Medical Household. The whole becomes an unusual and delightful mixture.

Dick was a man with a real zest for his own life and that of others. Much of this comes over in this book. It has been a pleasure to read and an honour for one of his old pupils to have been asked to provide a foreword.

John G G Ledingham, MA, DM, FRCP
Emeritus Professor of Clinical Medicine, University of Oxford

ix

Preface

For a doctor of medicine, particularly one in clinical practice, to write a selective autobiography of his professional life is not easy if the enduring ethics of the profession, as important and as applicable today as when Hippocrates first prescribed them, are to be observed.

Such comments and reflections as are made on the practice of medicine and the delivery of health care during the last sixty years or so are based largely on personal experience. Whether you agree or not will depend upon your own experiences and upon external views, particularly from the media, that may have influenced you. The veracity of what is recorded here should not be questioned simply because, where necessary, the name of a patient or a colleague has been changed to maintain confidentiality. The more clinical asides are as true as my memory can make them, but who can say that the passage of years may not have added to or subtracted from their accuracy.

Richard Bayliss
London, 2005

Thank you to Jane Rankin for her help in checking the proofs

1

An Early Decision

'Must you?' Pamela asked rather crossly. She was aged eight in 1922 and the younger of my two older sisters. She glanced up from the book she was reading as I, two years her junior, tried to work my way round the playroom without touching the floor. It was from her that I had learnt this exciting game which now no longer amused her. Only recently had the playroom been redecorated and its name changed from the 'day nursery', which reflects something of the size of the house we lived in.

'Yes,' I said as I steadied myself on the lid of a plywood toy-box, standing underneath the window, in preparation for my next, more difficult, upward leap onto an oak chest of drawers. With a slight thump as my woollen stockinged feet landed on the polished surface I arrived safely and avoided falling off the other side. The next jump was easy – on to the sofa where Pam was reading.

'Oh, go away!' she said as I landed on the cushions beside her.

I climbed round her back as she leant forward, reluctant to let me pass. I stood poised on the arm of the sofa and jumped onto a low rush-seated nursing chair, steadying myself by grasping its ladder back as I landed.

'There,' I said triumphantly, 'I've done it.'

'You cheated.'

'I did not.'

'You did. I saw. Moved at least two chairs.'

'I did not.' I raised my voice because I was fibbing. 'Anyway you used to cheat.'

Pam ignored the accusation and went on reading.

As I stepped down onto the floor, Nanny opened the playroom

door, banging it against the chair I'd moved – only a tiny bit – to make the wide traverse across the doorway possible.

'Time for tea, children,' she announced. 'Put your shoes on and brush your hair. Your mother's waiting in the morning room for you.'

Tea with my mother in the morning room was rather formal – thin crustless, triangular, delicate sandwiches filled with cucumber, Marmite or strawberry jam, and a three-tier wooden cake stand holding a sponge cake, an orange cake covered with white icing and some chocolate biscuits. The tea from a silver Georgian teapot was poured carefully through a silver strainer to retain any Earl Grey tea-leaves that might escape. At the age of six, sitting on the edge of a sofa and eating and drinking without making a mess were all too often a test of coordination and dexterity that I had yet to develop.

After tea we were allowed to listen to the five o'clock news on the wireless. We were only about fifty miles from the longwave 2LO radio transmitter at Daventry and the crystal set was powerful enough to operate three sets of earphones. My mother assured me that I was better than my father at adjusting the crystal cat's whisker, as it was called, no doubt as today one's grandchildren can with infuriating consummate ease put right some seemingly insuperable problem with one's computer. After the news our mother would read aloud or sit beside us as we looked at *The Illustrated London News* or *The Tatler*.

Nanny put her head round the morning-room door. 'Bedtime, young man,' she said.

I wriggled on the sofa in protest. 'One minute *please*, Nanny. We haven't finished.'

Nanny waited patiently at the door. I was always sent up to bed and had supper in the playroom an hour or more before my sisters, who were old enough to bath themselves.

'That's enough for this evening,' my mother said. 'We'll finish looking at this tomorrow. Goodnight, darling.' She bent over to kiss me.

'Aren't you coming to say goodnight?'

'Not this evening. Daddy and I are going to a cocktail party.'

'When will Daddy be home?'

'Soon I expect. Now run along, there's a good boy.'

I did not dare ask if my father was coming to say goodnight. It would have been too disappointing to be told he wasn't.

2

All the bathrooms in the house were, with one exception, large because they were converted bedrooms. The house had been extensively modernised before I was born; the old direct current electrical wiring had been replaced, central heating had been installed, but only on the ground floor, and three new bathrooms – one for the staff, one for the children and one for guests – had been achieved by sacrificing two bedrooms.

I enjoyed being bathed by Nanny; she was less rough than my mother who insisted on thoroughly washing my ears and between my legs with a stiff abrasive loofah. Afterwards, in flannel pyjamas and a brown Jaeger piped dressing-gown, I ate supper in the playroom. My favourites were Force or Grape-Nuts, a boiled egg into which I dipped 'soldiers' of thin bread and butter, followed by a banana mashed up with cream, and a glass of milk. (What a formidably high-cholesterol meal it was, but cholesterol hadn't been heard of in 1922.) While I ate Nanny read to me or, better still, told me a story. She was good at telling stories. I had progressed from nursery rhymes to story books – *Winnie the Pooh*, Kipling's *Just So Stories*, *Alice in Wonderland*, *The Water Babies* and Arthur Mee's two-volume *Children's Encyclopaedia*, in which I particularly liked 'What is wrong with this picture?'. The picture, a pen-and-ink drawing filling a whole page, would show a number of different mistakes which the viewer was meant to spot. The only one I can remember now is a pillar-box with the opening for letters pointing towards the road instead of to the pavement. Comics I was not allowed.

'What shall I read you tonight?' asked Nanny as I started on the Grape-Nuts.

'Tell me a story.' I liked *Water Babies* but it was a bit frightening; I really didn't understand *Alice in Wonderland* but the pictures were funny.

Nanny's stories were not made-up fantasies but accounts of true events that had occurred in the Bayliss family during the ten years she'd been with us since my older sister, Di, was born.

'Well, I remember when your Uncle Norman and Auntie Dilys got engaged.'

I listened intently. Both of them were favourites and even to a child Uncle Norman was a romantic figure. He was my youngest uncle – and different from other grown-up men. He treated me as an equal, not a child. At his suggestion Di, Pam and I had stopped

3

calling him 'Uncle' and simply called him 'Norman'. He had a private income but I was not really sure what that was, except I knew that Uncle Norman did not go to work like other men. He did so many different things and all of them supremely well, we were told. He had a good eye for ball games, good balance and was a natural athlete. He had a single handicap at golf, was skilled at trout and salmon fishing, and was an expert ballroom dancer. To me he was a special hero because he drove Sunbeam racing cars at Brooklands. His wife, Auntie Dilys, ran the nursery school I went to every day. She was the daughter of a Welsh clergyman and had a degree in classics from Aberystwyth University, my mother told me; I didn't know what classics were but she said Dilys was very clever. She was a pretty, vivacious woman, and even at the age of six I admired her legs.

'On the Sunday after they got engaged,' Nanny started, 'they came to lunch with your grandfather – your father's father. It was also our turn to have lunch with the Governor that Sunday.'

At the beginning of each year my grandfather, known as the Governor, sent to his eight children, most of whom lived in the neighbourhood, a little printed card setting out on which Sundays they were expected to come for lunch at his house. It was drawn up, my mother had explained to me, like an American tennis tournament so that a different uncle or aunt and their children, my cousins, lunched each time with different other members of the family.

'We arrived after church as usual,' Nanny went on. 'Your father's old nanny opened the front door to us as she always did. She'd looked after your father and his six brothers and sisters for years and years – ever since they were born. She had her own sitting-room and bedroom near the front door. As long as your uncles and aunts lived at home, no matter how old they were, they were never allowed a front-door key. Old Nanny waited up for them at night however late they came home. Until your Uncle Norman got married, she always bought him his shirts and underwear, his pyjamas, socks and handkerchiefs.'

I had heard this story several times before, but 'Go on,' I said, 'what happened next?'

'Well,' said Nanny, the engagement caused a lot of excitement and congratulations. Your grandfather opened a bottle of champagne. You and Di and Pam, of course, were given stone ginger beer in

4

those pretty pink pony glasses with an etched Greek key pattern just below the rim. Auntie Dilys was sitting beside Uncle Norman on the sofa, with her legs tucked under her, her skirt an inch or two above her knees, showing a lot of silk-stockinged leg. The Governor turned quietly to your grandmother and whispered something in her ear – they were sitting side by side as they always did in their two identical upholstered armchairs facing the fireplace. Granny got up and left the room. A few seconds later she returned with a light cashmere rug. She went over to Auntie Dilys. "The Governor thought you might feel the cold, dear," she said quietly, as she draped the rug over Dilys's elegant legs.'

'What happened then?'

'Well,' said Nanny, 'nobody laughed. Everyone went on talking as though nothing had happened. Your aunt passed it off by smiling sweetly and saying, "Thank you".'

*   *   *

We lived on the fringe of the village of Tettenhall which is unusual in having two village greens, something shared only, I believe, with Clifton near Bristol. It is located to the west of Wolverhampton on the road that leads to Shrewsbury and Hollyhead. The village lies at the bottom and the top of a steep rocky escarpment. The Upper Green is on level ground beyond the top of the wooded red sandstone cliff, and the Lower Green at its foot. Most of the village, and certainly in my youth the more prosperous part, lay at the top of the escarpment.

Scaling the cliff are two roads. The original one throws itself boldly at the cliff face to ascend at an angle sufficiently steep to merit on the upward journey a road sign declaring a gradient of 1 in 4, and on the downward a warning that advises engaging a low gear. On either side of this Old Hill trees had been felled and ledges cut deep into the soft rock on which houses are perched with dark caves tunnelled into the red sandstone behind them. As a child this was one of my favourite walks, and Nanny would tell of the days when horse-drawn coaches climbed the hill with difficulty, and showed me the half-timbered public house that had provided the extra horses, ostlers and grooms to assist the carriages and wagons.

The other road was built much later and runs almost straight up the escarpment through a deep cutting in the rock to reduce its gradient. With conviction Nanny told us that the road was built by French prisoners of war captured in the Napoleonic Wars. Later I learnt that it was part of Telford's grand design in the nineteenth century and constructed by the rough seasoned navvies who had dug the canal and levelled the ground for the railway in the valley below.

When I was a child, on one side of the Upper Green there was a muddy, foul-smelling duck pond in which I, unlike some children in the village, was not allowed to paddle or sail a toy boat. Years later the accession of Queen Elizabeth II was a golden opportunity, grasped by my father who was chairman of the Rural District Council at the time, to convert the malodorous pond into a toddlers' clean paddling pool. The cost of draining and enlarging the pond with a bulldozer, lining it with clay and facing the side walls and surround with artificial stone was modest compared with the subsequent annual maintenance by the council's workmen who regularly had to cleanse the pool of discarded empty packets of Smith's potato crisps, wrappers from bars of Cadbury's milk chocolate and submerged spent cans of Coca-Cola.

From the west corner of the Upper Green, following the line of the escarpment, runs the village high street flanked for a few hundred yards by small shops – in my day Mrs Shilling the green-grocer, the post office, Mr Tandy the butcher, Mr Bond the newsagent, a grocer, a baker and a confectionery shop. Thereafter the road ran through woods of beech, lime, oak and chestnut. Half a mile down this road, hidden behind a high holly hedge and set back behind a dense copse of huge beech trees and rhododendrons, was our house with fields beyond it. Sadly it has now been demolished and replaced by a nursing home for the elderly.

* * *

Sundays always started badly. The trouble began after breakfast, and the conversation was predictable.

'Who's coming to church? Are you?' my mother asked my father brightly, knowing full well what the answer would be. My father looked up at her with pained mock surprise as he sat in a low chair in the bay window of the dining room, changing from his indoor slippers to his brogues and tying the laces.

6

'No, I'm due at the golf club at ten o'clock,' he always said.

My mother pursed her lips. 'Well, children, be ready in the hall at half past ten. Di, don't forget your gloves and your prayer book. Dick, remember your prayer book and brush your hair – properly.'

Di was always late and at the last minute, just as we were about to leave the house, she invariably ran back upstairs to her bedroom without explanation or apparent reason.

'Di's gone again,' I said trying to stir up trouble, and shouted after her, 'What have you forgotten now?', knowing there would be no answer.

We were formally dressed for the occasion. My mother, Di and Pam wore hats and carried white kid gloves; I in a grey flannel suit with short trousers. We climbed into my mother's Austin Seven and after a ten-minute drive parked the car beside the stoutly built oak lychgate to Saint Michael's and All Souls Church beside the Lower Green. Flanked by white-marble tombstones, we walked, the four of us in a line, up the long wide gravel path that led to the porch of the red sandstone church with its earlier Norman tower. Here we were met by one of the church wardens, whom my mother would greet warmly and who tried to guide us to a reserved pew at the front of the nave near the pulpit. To my mother, who always held that snobbishness or social precedence was a sin, this smacked of class distinction, although secretly I think she rather enjoyed it.

'Thank you, but I think today we'd better sit at the back. We may have to leave before the sermon.' We seldom did.

I squirmed as the cold seat of the polished wooden pew pressed against the back of my bare knees. Dutifully I pulled the hassock towards me and gingerly knelt on its rough prickly surface. I buried my face in my hands, imitating my mother beside me. I didn't like church. It was dark, cold and had a curious smell – of stale incense and beeswax polish. You had to talk in a whisper and not smile. A slight nod to friends was allowed but you never waved. I understood little of what went on. I knew that I'd been bad; everyone told me I'd been bad, all week long. If I hadn't done anything wrong, I certainly must have had bad thoughts, they told me. That was why, my mother explained, I had to say, 'Forgive us our trespasses and lead us not into temptation.' I didn't know what trespasses were and was not sure what temptation was either, but it was something you didn't talk about – something not quite nice. Why did members of the congregation suddenly lower their voices and look even more solemn when they said, 'He did not abhor the Virgin's womb'? What was the Virgin's womb and why this fuss about it? It must be pretty bad too. I had also learnt from my mother that women in general were bad; they led men astray, whatever that might mean, as Adam was by Eve over an apple.

I enjoyed those Lessons that I could understand, like the one when three men were put in a burning fiery furnace. But why was the name Abednego pronounced Abendigo by some of the men who read the first Lesson and as Abedneego by others? Why didn't Daddy come and read the Lessons like the other men Mummy was friendly with? If my father didn't go to church, why should I?

* * *

I had nothing more serious than whooping cough but during the day I was moved to my parents' bedroom – larger, lighter and more airy than mine – and put in my father's bed from which there was a splendid view of two long herbaceous borders flanking a wide grass path that led to a tall yew hedge. In the top of the hedge was shaped a deep semicircle through which, over the neighbouring green fields and just visible some seventeen miles to the west in Shropshire, was the blue-grey silhouette of the Wrekin Hill reaching more than a thousand feet towards the sky.

Our general practitioner called every morning to see me. My sisters and I mischievously sensed that our mother had a 'thing' about him, and well she might. Many women form an attachment to their obstetrician, and Dr Dent had skilfully delivered the three of us at home; it was not surprising that she liked him. We could not fail to notice that she did her hair more carefully, applied a little more lipstick and wore her smartest clothes whenever he came to the house. In addition to being a good general practitioner and accoucheur, Dr Dent was a Fellow of the Royal College of Surgeons and an honorary unpaid surgeon at the Royal Hospital in Wolverhampton some ten miles away.

He stood beside my mother at the foot of the bed in which I sat propped up with a very popular and gentlemanly thriller called *Berry & Co* by Dornford Yates open on the counterpane. I was trying with all my might to stifle a cough. The effort of this and the tickle inside my chest made single tears course slowly down my cheeks.

Dr Dent watched intently. 'Poor boy,' he said quietly. 'He's trying not to cough, but in a second or two he won't be able to help himself.'

Unable to resist any longer I coughed – on and on until I felt I was suffocating. When at last I was able to breathe in, with the inspiration came the characteristic drawn-out high-pitched whoop of whooping cough.

'There,' said Dr Dent with satisfaction. 'What did I say!'

I wanted to know more about whooping cough. My mother brought me *Pear's Encyclopaedia*, and I read the medical section from beginning to end. When I grew up, I was going to be a doctor, I decided. No doubt subconsciously I realised that to be like Dr Dent would please my mother, but I was more impressed that my illness was caused by a micro-organism that bore the impressive name of *Bordetella pertussis*, which I repeated several times until I had it tongue perfect.

Thereafter there was no doubt about what I would do when I grew up. After I'd recovered from whooping cough, Dr Dent offered to show me how to dissect a frog. On an agreed afternoon I captured one of the many in the garden and put it in a jam jar with holes punched in the lid. My mother set up a collapsible bridge table covered with a sheet of American oilcloth on the lawn beside the tennis court. Into the jam jar Dr Dent put a wedge of cotton wool soaked in chloroform which he'd brought from the hospital. The frog was anaesthetised and, as Dr Dent started the dissection I was fascinated to see its little heart still beating.

Two years later my grandfather gave me a second-hand brass Leitz microscope. All that summer holiday I studied the contents of the foetid water from different levels of the pond beside a willow tree in our kitchen garden.

In one of the several empty attics at the top of the house I was allowed to build a laboratory so that I could study things under the microscope, develop, print and enlarge photographs taken with my Box Brownie camera and do chemical experiments. Had I not worn spectacles for short sightedness I might well have been blinded when a round-bottomed glass flask exploded while being heated by a roaring bunsen-burner.

I can't now remember what was the chemical experiment I was trying to do, but many years later I read in *The Lancet* an article from the Hospital for Sick Children in Great Ormond Street claiming that a high fever in the young could distort the shape of the eyeball and thus cause short-sightedness. Whether true or not, at my prep school, the Wells House in Malvern Wells, soon after an attack of measles which gave me a temperature of 105°F (40.5°C), I certainly developed myopia. At the time I and four other boys were incarcerated in the school sanatorium, and I had a nightmare in which I was on board the sinking *Titanic* liner. I jumped out of bed, shouting 'God Almighty save us', and ran down the dormitory to get into the nearest lifeboat. As this happened to be a bed occupied by another nine-year-old boy, my arrival was not exactly welcomed.

Early days at Rugby School brought my first introduction to proper science. This initial experience was associated with a physical accompaniment that reflected the intensity of my excitement. A skinny youth, I was standing in the entrance hall of the Science School, with its dark-blue terrazzoed walls and vaulted ceiling, waiting to be allocated for the first time in my life to a real laboratory. My heart began to pound; my head felt as if it were going to burst; I was shaking and bathed in a cold sweat. I suppose it says something that instinctively I realised I was not ill and that this was an emotional reaction. Not until later at Cambridge did I understand that it was the response to an exaggerated outpouring of adrenaline and noradrenaline.

Then, as now, Rugby was a thoroughly sound and enjoyable school. With hindsight the teaching was dedicated, sometimes didactic, rarely dull, but with some notable exceptions seldom inspirational. Wire or tape-recorders had not been invented so there was no language laboratory, although one master used gramophone records of French conversation to leaven his lessons. Another made history more alive, by passing round postcards of portraits of politicians, sovereigns, generals and admirals, and sometimes their wives and mistresses. Art was taught by a much loved master, R. Talbot Kelly, who in World War I had been a camouflage expert and whose wildlife and bird paintings were later reproduced for many years as posters on the London Underground. Science was particularly well taught; we were blessed in having an outstanding young biology beak, Peter Falk, who had just come down from Oxford and had been on a biological exploration of Greenland before joining the staff. He taught us to think for ourselves. Also we learnt from him that nature was not immutable. I first discovered this when dissecting a dogfish, the cranial nerves of which did not run exactly as depicted in the textbook. I tried to arrange them so that they conformed with the picture in the book, but Peter Falk immediately spotted the congenital aberration. This was an important lesson; textbooks are sometimes wrong and biological variation is common.

I owe much to Rugby School. It taught that essential lesson in life – how to teach yourself. Although I suspect this was deliberate policy, it is not an easy lesson to instil and was an invaluable one which has stood me in good stead all my life. Peter Falk usually answered a question directly, but sometimes he would claim he didn't know. 'Go and look it up,' he would advise. 'And when you've found out, come and tell me the answer, will you please?' He was a paragon of courtesy; he treated us as grown-ups; he was a beautiful dissector and he trained generations of future doctors.

When he retired from schoolmastering, I and those of his other old students who were medically qualified gave a dinner in his honour at the Royal College of Physicians in London which was attended by some fifty people. He did not stop working though. For many years he did research on the biology of cancer cells at the Royal Postgraduate Medical School at Hammersmith Hospital in London.

During one of the school holidays, Dr Dent invited me to watch him operate at the Royal Hospital in Wolverhampton. Wearing a green sterile gown, white theatre boots and a sterile cap and mask I followed every step as he removed a kidney, approaching the site through the patient's flank. As he clamped the renal vein, Dr Dent somehow managed to puncture the inferior vena cava into which the vein from the kidney drains. Instantly the deep wound in the patient's flank flooded with blood. I could feel the cold perspiration on my brow; I was going to faint. Fortunately one of the theatre nurses had her eye on me; she led me away to a corner of the theatre and made me sit down and put my head between my knees. I watched the rest of the operation unperturbed and did not dismiss surgery as a possible future calling.

This experience of fainting grew when someone introduced into our house at Rugby what many years later was called in the *British Medical Journal* 'The Mess Lark or Fainting Trick'. This involves standing behind another boy who hyperventilates by taking deep breaths in and out. After about a minute of doing this, the boy takes in as deep breath as he can and holds it. At this point the

11

boy standing behind puts his arms round the lower thorax of the victim in front and gives his chest a long hard squeeze. The 'experimental subject' loses consciousness and is then lowered gently to the dormitory floor, where he lies unconscious for a few minutes during which you can stick pins in without him feeling any pain. This 'game' had short-lived popularity and then, just as well, lost its interest. Later at Cambridge none of my tutors or supervisors could explain the mechanisms involved in this phenomenon and it was not until ten years later that Peter Sharpey-Schafer, a physician at the Postgraduate Medical School in London, investigated the fainting lark, showed what happened and why, and explained how potentially dangerous it was. Nevertheless the fainting trick persists and sometimes, I understand, is practised today at Pony Club camps and doubtless elsewhere.

2

A German Interregnum

As my grandfather's Sunday luncheons will show, we were an extended family. On my father's side, I had fourteen aunts and uncles and eight cousins, most of whom lived within a ten-mile radius. We shared many common interests. From an early age we played tennis and golf together, were professionally coached in these activities and became quite proficient. We rode, my sister Pam hunting regularly with two local packs – the Albrighton and the Wheatland – but this held little appeal for me, and only with reluctance did I look after and exercise her horses when she was away from home.

Music played a large part in our lives. What would be the drawing-room in most houses was called in ours the music room, replete with a beautiful Bechstein concert grand piano, Di's cello and various wind instruments that I borrowed from my Uncle Norman but never learnt to play properly. From an early age we were all taught to play the piano. Bad pupils are likely to blame their teachers and until I went to boarding school I had a succession of, to me, unattractive ladies who did not fail to show their boredom at my incompetence and lack of commitment. The thought of Czerny's exercises, derived from his three-volume *Complete Theoretical and Practical Pianoforte School*, sends, even today, a shudder down my spine. By the age of sixteen I quit taking formal piano lessons and learnt harmony and counterpoint from a gifted music master at Rugby, Marcus Berisford.

My mother was a good pianist and a competent singer, who delighted in entertaining us in the Edwardian style. Her brother, Wilfred Sanderson, who had been trained at the Royal College of Music and was the organist at Durham Cathedral for some years, had become the successful composer of many popular, if rather sentimental, Edwardian or World War I ballads, such as 'Friend of Mine' and 'Until'. Particularly at weekends when we all were at home for the holidays, we enjoyed musical evenings when my mother played the piano and sang arias from operas by Puccini or Verdi and Uncle Wilfred's songs. My sister Di played her cello and also sang, accompanied by our mother; I seem to remember Roger Quilter's 'Now Sleeps the Crimson Petal'. And to finish the evening – and the decanter of port – my mother would regress in years and sing with panache the popular songs from the operettas and musical comedies of her youth, not least *Choo Chin Chow*. Perhaps surprisingly, none of us much liked Gilbert and Sullivan.

I left Rugby after passing my First MB in December 1934 and was faced with what is nowadays called a gap year, which in my case was nine months before going up to Cambridge. For the first trimester of 1935 I went daily to the Department of Anatomy at Birmingham University and dissected an arm and attended the anatomy lectures. This brought a new freedom and was my second step on the long ladder of being a medical student. Every morning my father, on his way to work, dropped me off at the railway station in Wolverhampton, and I travelled the fifteen miles to Birmingham in the company of two friends who were studying accountancy there. The old Birmingham University Anatomy School in Mason College was a short walk from New Street railway station. The head technician told us with pride that Dr Francis Brett Young, at that time the author of many popular novels, including *My Brother Jonathan* and *The House Under the Water*, had once studied anatomy there. My two Tettenhall friends and I would sometimes meet in a local pub for lunch, comprising a hunk of bread, butter and Gorgonzola for six pence and half a pint of Ansell's bitter beer.

In March, after being accredited for dissecting an arm, I went to Munich for six months. My sister Pam, who was a strong candidate for the British equestrian team in the next Olympic Games, had been there for some time attending a riding school near the Residenz to improve her dressage. What better than to join her and do some more anatomy under that great master Spalterholz, whose textbook was held on the Continent in as high regard as Gray's *Anatomy* was throughout the English-speaking world. I might even improve the rudimentary German I'd learnt at school.

14

Travelling abroad on your own for the first time is exciting. The crossing in a half-empty boat to Ostend was calm. On the train I secured a corner seat in a third-class carriage with slatted wooden seats, and ate dinner in the *Wagonlits* restaurant car punctiliously attended by a steward in pristine uniform. During the night I slept fitfully and was woken in the early hours at Basle railway station by workmen with hammers on long hafts tapping the carriage wheels to be sure they weren't cracked. The station with its wide expanse of platforms was deserted. Shafts of light from the shaded lamps shone through the smoke-laden haze and the silence was broken by the intermittent hiss of steam escaping from the stationary locomotives.

Pam met me at the Hauptbahnhof in Munich. I hadn't seen her for several months. She looked more self-confident and attractive in her Bavarian green Loden coat and skirt with smart piping and antler buttons. We kissed as perfunctorily as English brothers and sisters do. Certainly she was even better groomed and more elegant than when last I'd seen her. Her dark hair had a natural wave, page-boy length and swept back from her forehead. She seemed to have a better figure. Her eyes twinkled above her long smiling mouth with its upturned corners.

'You're looking well,' I said.

'I am, and why is it that Englishmen always say "You're looking well" when they mean you're looking attractive or pretty?' She laughed. 'It's odd but the moment I'm abroad my morale – my confidence – perks up.'

'And what exactly d'you mean by that?' I asked.

'Here I'm made to feel like a proper woman. At home men seem almost afraid to look at you – as though it was sinful, whether you're married or not. Here men take a proper look at you instead of the furtive glances you get at home. They're not afraid to show their approval or whatever it is.' She laughed.

Lugging my two suitcases we climbed into a tram which noisily ground its way through Maximilianplatz and across Odeonplatz before turning north at the Feldherrnhalle. A lot of people on the streets were wearing swastikas on their arms.

'How's the dressage going?' I asked.

'Marvellous! I've learnt a lot but will I be able to school my horses at home? That remains to be seen. In the Olympics the Germans will be outstanding at dressage but they've still got a

15

long way to go in showjumping, I think. They haven't got the right horses – at least not for showjumping.'

'Why not?'

'Not enough Arab in them, I think. Hitler thinks the Herrnvolk should be able to breed the best horses in the world without importing new bloodstock.'

'Like breeding the best human beings,' I commented disparagingly.

I stayed with a middle-aged couple in Schwarbing – an upper-class district in Munich where many writers, artists and singers lived and which was likened to the Chelsea of those pre-war days. The Fürsts had a medical student son – one reason for staying with them – but he was away in Italy the whole time I was there. Their flat was gloomy with squeaky parquet floors and heavy beige net curtains over the windows, but they looked after me well. The main problem was that Herr Fürst, the managing director of a company that made petrol from potatoes – so essential for the future German war effort – was an ardent Nazi. Most evenings at supper I was subjected to Nazi propaganda and some-times a diatribe against *die Juden*; it was my first experience of anti-Semitism. Certainly Hitler was closing his grip on the country but, as a visitor, it seemed unwise to comment too openly on your host's politics, particularly when everyone was enthusiastic about the economic benefits and the improved standard of living, not to mention the restoration of national pride that the Führer had induced.

At the university I joined the student union which gave remarkable financial concessions for attending the opera and even having a haircut. I could afford to go to the whole of Wagner's *Ring* – but in the most uncomfortable cramped seats high at the back of the uppermost balcony. Unwittingly I had joined the Hitler Youth Movement.

* * *

Pam, a girlfriend of hers called Elizabeth Bromwich, and I were sitting in the basement of a Schwarbing bar after dinner. Elizabeth, two years older than I, was an attractive girl and a paying guest with the same family that Pam was staying with in a rather grand house in Karl Theodor Strasse owned by Freifrau von Dobbeneck, the widow of a former German ambassador to Greece. As we

16

sipped our Lowenbrau beer, a basso profundo with a splendid voice and reputedly from the opera company sang '*In Keller Kühler*', lingering on the lowest notes so long that one of the windows in the bar vibrated with the slow frequencies.

We were discussing whether we should go on a skiing holiday that had been advertised on a noticeboard at the university – a week over Easter in a *Gasthaus* in Rettenberg in the Allgau Alps for the equivalent of £10, including all meals and the train journey there and back. Di, Pam and I had been skiing the year before in Gerlos in Austria with a group, led by two masters, of schoolboys and their sisters from Rugby and Harrow. It had been a great success. Liz Bromwich hadn't skied before but it was too cheap an opportunity to miss.

*   *   *

We slithered and laughed as we heaved our bags off the horse-drawn sleigh that had brought us from Rettenberg station. The Gasthaus Steiner looked inviting in the late afternoon sunshine. Its whitewashed facade had heavy overhanging timbers to support the verdigrised copper roof covered with a dusting of snow. The windows were flanked with louvred green shutters pinned back like butterfly wings; above them was painted a decorative architrave which at first glance looked as though it were fashioned from pewter. On the wall, beside the arched front door decorated with large black iron studs, was a mural in muted colours of a man in Tyrolean *Lederhosen* and an apron scything hay.

We stomped into the warm entrance hall with its smell of wood smoke. Herr Steiner, the proprietor, was elderly and a little bent. He greeted each member of the party with a courteous smiling '*Grüss Gott*', disregarding the loud *Heil Hitlers* that the German students gave. There were nine of them – seven men and two girls – and all wore swastika armbands. Only one was a typical Aryan – good looking, well-built with a wide flat jaw but an unpleasant twist to his thin lips. The two girls were also blonde and as sturdy as Welsh cobs. Formal introductions were made as the registration forms were filled in at the reception desk.

'Welcome everybody,' the Aryan student addressed us authoritatively, 'and a special welcome to our foreign friends. My name is Walter Standenhardt; I am your leader. We look forward to good skiing. Supper we eat at seven o'clock this evening. Tomorrow we parade at nine o'clock in front of the *Gasthaus*. Lunch we take in our rucksacks up the mountains. Now we will be shown our bedrooms. Afterwards any of you who have not got skis, boots and skins will get them at the sports shop across the road. Being members of the Hitler *Jugend*, you will pay a specially reduced price. Now follow, please.'

Herr Steiner led the way, the others humping their bags along the wide hallway hung with antlers and chamois heads. Pam and Liz Bromwich were sharing a room on the first floor, the two German girls sharing another. I followed the male students to their dormitory on the second floor under the eaves.

'Ah, the young foreigner!' Herr Steiner smiled apologetically at me. 'You are down on the first floor, *mein Herr*. Come please.' He led me downstairs again to a door at the end of the corridor.

'You will be warm in here.' He opened the door to let me pass. The room was spotless with a plain wooden floor, the boards so scrubbed that the grain stood out. There were two small dormer windows, an armoire, a bed, and a wash bowl on a stand with a large china jug resting in it. I started to unpack. The little room was certainly cosy and warm but it had a curious smell – of rotting or damp hay. I opened one of the windows and saw that I was in an annex at the back of the main building. From beneath the floor came strange noises and then, unmistakably, the sound of a cow munching. I knelt down and through a gap in the floor-boards peered into the darkness below. As my eye adapted to the dim light I could make out three cows and a calf standing in their byres, their hocks deep in wet trampled hay.

I joined Pam and Liz in their room before dinner, Pam had brought her hunting flask filled with schnapps. We sat on the beds having a swig.

'Walter Standenhardt is pretty competent, I think,' said Pam. 'He said he would act as *Ski lehrer*.' She hesitated and then continued rather glumly, 'And as *Führer* too, it seems.'

'Well we're certainly in a proper Hitler *Jugend* group, aren't we?' Liz said with a laugh. 'You couldn't miss all those *Heil Hitlers* downstairs, could you? I felt rather embarrassed for poor old Herr Steiner.'

'It's nearly seven; we'd better go down to dinner,' I warned, and we hurried down the creaking staircase to the dining room.

The others had already started; at one end of the table were three empty places with bowls of liver *Knödel* soup awaiting us.

Some of the party already seemed a little tipsy; they talked loudly, casting glances at the two waitresses. I heard one of the students say, 'She's Jewish,' and tapped his nose knowingly.

Rebecca was Herr Steiner's quiet eighteen-year-old daughter. She had olive skin, a long face, wide green eyes and black glistening hair held at the back of her head in a tortoiseshell slide. She reminded me of a figure in an icon in the Alte Pinakothek gallery in Munich. The other waitress, Ingrid, was a dumpy jolly girl with a spotty face and thick legs; she moved quickly as she expertly collected the empty soup bowls and balanced them on her upturned left forearm.

Bratwurst, red cabbage and *sauté* potatoes followed. The party sat back afterwards drinking their steins of beer. Rebecca began collecting the plates, politely asking every one if they'd like any more.

The crash occurred as she bent over Walter Standenhardt's shoulder to take his plate. He was sitting at the head of the table, and a cascade of plates, knives and forks fell – onto the table, into his lap and onto the tiled floor.

Walter leapt to his feet, his face flushed with anger as he vigorously mopped his trousers with a napkin. In the sudden silence he shouted, 'You idiot' and struck Rebecca a blow across the face.

She stepped back, her face impassive except for the fear in her eyes. 'I'm so sorry, so very sorry,' she said and began gathering up the broken plates.

For a moment I thought Pam was not going to intervene; her face was grey with anger and her lips taut. But she got up and walked down the table. 'Sit down,' she ordered Standenhardt in German. 'It was an accident; anyone can have an accident. Here, you help,' she said to one of the female German students and began picking up the shards of china from the floor.

The *Apfelsdtrudel* was eaten in uncomfortable silence.

*   *   *

Next morning I came down to breakfast a few minutes after eight o'clock to be greeted with friendly 'Good-mornings' as I sat at the only empty place, set with a plate and an empty eggcup. I looked round; every one else was eating two boiled eggs. I glanced over my shoulder to see whether Rebecca or Ingrid was around. I helped myself to coffee from the urn on a side table, sat down again and waited. Some of the group cast furtive glances in my direction and went on eating. Pam and Liz on the other side of the table concentrated on their eggs and didn't look up.

Standenhardt said, 'You were late for breakfast, Herr Bayliss. Others have eaten your eggs.' There was a roar of laughter. I felt very small – and rather angry. I smiled, probably not very convincingly, but I wasn't going to show my feelings.

Standenhardt continued, 'Collect your pack lunches from the table over there. We meet outside the main entrance at nine o'clock promptly. Don't forget your skins.'

Well before nine I was in the boot room in the cellar, checking the spring cables on the skis, carefully lacing up my leather boots, and then adjusting the leather thongs on the long wooden ski poles. I packed the skins, which in fact were made of canvas, and our pack lunches in my rucksack. Pam, Liz and I climbed the few steps from the cellar to the front of the hotel. The others joined us in dribs and drabs. Walter appeared, rather theatrically, through the front door and grinned with his narrow lips.

To our astonishment, as the village clock struck nine, he shouted 'Parade!' We formed up in a straight line, the English trio on the left.

'Number,' ordered Standenhardt.

'God, we're back in the OTC!' I whispered loud enough for Pam and Liz to hear.

'*Ein, Zwei, Drei...*' they numbered off down the line.

'*Zehn!*' I shouted.

There was an appreciable pause for a second while Liz remained tongue-tied, and then came a faint '*Elf*'; she laughed nervously.

Walter scowled. 'Quicker,' he shouted. 'Again, number!' This time it was better.

We walked to the end of the village and put on our skis. Liz had never skied before and began to slither. She fell over. She got up and tried to take a step forward; her rear ski slid backwards. She laughed and tried again. I showed her how to plant the front ski firmly in the snow and not to push off with the rear one without first transferring her weight. Walter led us in single-file, making a long traverse across the lower slopes. We zig-zagged up but each

20

change of direction was a major undertaking for Liz. After an hour I put skins on Liz's skis which made the ascent easier for her. The sun was warm and the slope increasingly steep. 'How is Liz ever going to get down?' I asked myself. After climbing for two hours, we stopped at a hut.

'Now we rest for twenty minutes,' directed Walter. 'It will be steeper now, so everyone put on their skins.'

An hour later we stopped at another hut. I was tired and knew how Liz must be feeling. The three of us sat on my navy-blue gaberdine ski jacket spread on the snow and leant against the side of the hut. That Pam was furious I could tell from her drawn mouth.

'This man's mad,' she said. 'God know's how we're going to get Liz down. None of the others are total beginners.' She walked over to talk to Walter and returned looking even crosser. 'He says he didn't realise that Liz had never skied before, but I made it perfectly clear in Munich.'

We ate our salami rolls and hard-boiled eggs, and then an apple. The students handed round their army water bottles and Pam gave Liz a nip of schnapps from her flask.

'Now we will ski down,' announced Standenhardt. 'Elizabeth, you follow me.'

I waited at the back of the line with a good idea of what was going to happen. Walter started down the fall-line, made a snow-plough turn and shouted over his shoulder to Liz, 'Like this.' She tried to copy him and fell. The man behind helped her up. We started off again. Three falls later Standenhardt waited with ill-disguised contempt. Liz was in tears and Pam looked even angrier. I skied down to the front of the line.

'Wouldn't it be better,' I suggested to Walter, 'if you and the others went ahead and Pam and I brought Liz down?'

For a moment he hesitated, wondering if this was a threat to his authority. 'Okay,' he said. 'It'll take us about half an hour to get down and then we'll be going up again; we've enough time before the light fails if we don't have you foreigners with us.' The Germans disappeared over a shoulder on the mountain-side.

When they'd gone, I showed Liz how to edge her skis, how to stem and how to make a snow-plough turn. We were weary when we reached the *Gasthaus* at three o'clock.

'Thank you,' Liz said as we took off our skis. 'Thank you very much indeed.' She put her arms round my neck and kissed me on the lips – something that had never happened to me before!

Thereafter the three of us skied on our own.

* * *

It was Liz who broke the news because Pam and Walter were not on speaking terms. 'Walter says we're expected to do something tomorrow night.'

'Why?' asked Pam.

'Because it's Easter Sunday. He wants us to sing a song or do a dance – anything. It's expected of us.'

We put our heads together. There was no point in telling funny jokes in English which they wouldn't understand. We'd better do some sort of song and dance routine.

'I know a silly little song,' offered Liz and sang

'Do we come from the North,
From the land of ice and snow...'

She finished the inconsequential ditty. We rehearsed in my bedroom with me in the middle and Pam and Liz on either side, our arms linked round each others' shoulders doing a simple step routine. Pam went down to the Gasthaus kitchen and returned with three Camembert cheese lids and a length of white string.

'Would you ask Herr Steiner if he has a red and a blue pencil?' she asked me. 'And bring some plain paper, a pair of scissors and three toothpicks.'

We drew three little Union Jack flags, threaded the toothpicks through them and stuck them in the middle of the Camembert cheese lids. With a piece of string threaded through each side of the lids and tied under our chins we had made ourselves three miniature page-boy hats.

It was a real Tyrolean *Abend*. A lot of beer was drunk before we sat down to a dinner of Wiener *Schnitzel* and *Sachertorte* with plenty of Liebfraumilch to drink. When we'd finished, the dining-room tables were set to one side and the Hitler *Jugend* arranged themselves as a choir – four men at the back, three in the middle and the two girls in front, one with an accordion. They sang a curious mixture of songs including Gounod's 'Ave Maria' as a solo by one of the girls and ending with the Nazis' much loved 'Horst Wessel Lied'.

'Now it is the turn of our foreign friends,' announced Walter.

Our entrance with the little hats set at a rakish angle was greeted with applause. We danced and sang our little song – more applause.

Walter stood up. 'Ladies and gentlemen, I ask you to drink to the health of our American friends.' As the German students rose, Pam looked in bewilderment at Liz and me. Shyly we bowed.

'Thank you,' it was Pam who replied, '*Ski Heil.*'

Later in the bar I asked Walter, 'Why did you call us Americans? We're English and this is a Union Jack in our hats.'

Walter was puzzled. 'English...' He hesitated. 'I did not know the English could be so uninhibited.'

The lantern-lit sleigh rides round the village were over. We came in from the cold, stamping our feet on the floor and clapping our hands to get warm. Beside the reception desk Herr Steiner, Rebecca, Ingrid and the chef, wearing a white jacket with a kerchief knotted round his neck and check trousers, shook hands with the guests and exchanged greetings.

'Well, I'm off to bed,' announced Pam. 'Coming Liz?'

I interjected quickly. 'Liz and I are going to have a last drink, aren't we, Liz?'

We stood at the bar talking to Walter. Must be friendly, I thought, even though I could never like him.

Then Liz and I moved to the back of the room where it was quieter, and watched Walter and his friends getting more and more drunk and noisy. Behind the bar Rebecca looked radiant in her quiet, composed way, a flush on her olive cheeks. Her father helped fill the grey earthenware steins initialled with the blue HB logo of the Hofbrauhaus in Munich.

'Time for bed,' said Liz. Holding hands we slipped quietly from the bar and climbed the stairs. 'Goodnight,' she whispered on the landing and with a wave of her hand went to the bedroom she shared with Pam.

*   *   *

I was first down to breakfast. The dining room was empty; the table not laid. There was no sign of Rebecca or Ingrid. I sat down and waited.

Pam appeared, her face grim. She scanned the room with angry eyes. 'What a night – appalling. What happened?'

'Happened? I didn't hear anything.'

'You slept through all that?' Pam was incredulous. 'I suppose you might have, being in the annex. Didn't you hear the shouting and the screams? I'll go and see what's going on.' She disappeared through the green leather-clad swing door leading to the kitchen.

Ten minutes later she returned accompanied by Ingrid with coffee and a basket of boiled eggs. Ingrid's face was red and blotchy; she'd been crying. Liz joined us. We sat in silence until Pam said, 'Hurry up! I want to get out of here before those bastards come down. I've got our railway vouchers. Dick, you tell Herr Steiner we're leaving. I knew something awful must have happened. First that singing in the bar and then the raucous laughter. I'm sure there was a fight on the stairs and the screams...'

'Who was screaming?' I asked.

'Rebecca, I think.'

Herr Steiner was sitting in his little office talking quietly to someone; I hesitated to intrude.

'Please come, Herr Bayliss.' Herr Steiner levered himself to his feet with difficulty. He had a black eye, a plaster across his forehead, his unshaven chin was crusted with dried blood and his right arm was in a sling.

'Last night?' was all I could think of saying.

Herr Steiner nodded. 'Herr Dr Meier, may I introduce Herr Bayliss, a guest from England,' he croaked.

We shook hands.

'And Rebecca?' I asked.

Herr Steiner stared at me. 'They said we were ... we were just Jews. They took what they wanted. My poor, poor beloved Rebecca.' His face contorted in tears as he sank back into his chair and with a moan buried his head in his arm.

'Terrible, terrible,' Dr Meier said. 'I love Rebecca like my own child. I brought her into the world. Herr Steiner is too old, too alone, to suffer this.'

'Will she be all right?' I asked naively; I didn't know what else to say.

'All right? She'll be all right if anyone can be all right after being raped – not once but many times by those ... those Nazis.' His face softened as he put his hand on my shoulder. 'Yes, young man, she'll be all right. She has to be. Time is a great healer, but what is happening to our Germany? She was a good Jewish girl.' He sighed.

Herr Steiner raised his head. 'Standenhardt is to blame; he's a fiend.'

* * *

In the train on our way back to Munich Pam noticed Liz's suitcase on the rack. Crayoned on the outside was a large black swastika with *Sieg Heil* written underneath it.

'Who did that?' she demanded.

'Walter – who else,' Liz replied uncomfortably.

'And you let him?'

'Couldn't very well stop him. I met him in the hall just as we were leaving. He said he must leave a mark of his respect for the British; I didn't know what he was going to do.'

Pam gave her a furious look and stared pointedly out of the carriage window as the train wound its way round the Starneberger See.

* * *

Back in Munich I slipped out of the university late one morning to cash a Cook's travellers' cheque at the bank. As I filled it in an obvious Englishman, much older than I, who later turned out to be the aristocratic owner of a London newspaper, asked if he might borrow my Parker pen – it was long before the days when banks provided the cheap ball-point pens invented by Mr Biro. We got to talking and he invited me to tea that afternoon with his wife and daughter at the Regina Hotel.

The Regina Hotel in Odeonplatz was impressive. We ate in the foyer with a three-piece string orchestra playing teatime music. The director, his violin under his arm, called at our table and asked, in perfect English, whether there was some particular music we would like him to play. The newspaper owner's daughter said brightly, 'Oh, how kind. Could we have "Smoke Gets in Your Eyes" and "Lullaby of Broadway", please?' Poor Walter Schacht didn't know, perhaps hadn't even heard of, either because modern American jazz was frowned upon by the Führer.

'I know them,' I said. 'Perhaps I could score them for you if you've got any manuscript paper.'

The next morning, missing a German lesson at the university, I found myself in Walter Schacht's small office in the basement of the hotel. I wrote out both tunes for a small string orchestra and a five-piece jazz band. I played the tunes through to Walter Schacht in the dark empty nightclub and was offered a job – to play the piano with the band every night from ten until two o'clock in the morning. The pay wasn't much but it was the first time in my life I'd earned any money.

For nearly three months I became a professional musician and it proved hard work. Not only did I play the piano at night but by day I scored out many of the popular American tunes of the time, although our main repertoire was jolly German umpty-ump music and Viennese waltzes. Playing one-two-three all night becomes pretty boring and Franz, the alto saxophone and clarinet player, who sat next to me on the bandstand, brought a miniature chess set which he hid on a shelf underneath his music stand and so made the long nights more interesting. *One-two-three*, we would play and then quickly I might move a bishop. A few bars more of *one-two-three* and Franz would move a knight. It was usually he with a move of his queen or a rook who said 'Check mate, I think.'

The nightclub was built like a circular Paduan lecture theatre, steeply raked with the small dancefloor at the bottom, the bandstand to one side, and with four semicircular tiers of tables above. Quite often the guests would offer the band a drink as a *Trinkgeld* for playing the tunes they requested. We would ask for champagne which was, by arrangement with the barman, ginger ale suitably diluted with soda water to give it the right colour. The barman took ten per cent of the takings and we pocketed the difference less the cost of the ingredients.

Three regular guests caught our attention. Judy Porter from Ohio was aged eighteen and had been brought on a cultural tour of Europe by her mother – the first woman I'd ever seen with purple hair. Judy had fallen in love with a major in the *Schutzstaffel* who nightly brought her and her mother, an ardent chaperone, to the Regina. He always wore the black uniform of the SS, spoke excellent English and was a beautiful dancer – we could all see that. Mrs Porter was alarmed at her daughter's relationship and carried the reluctant Judy off to Berlin. The SS major was not happy. Every evening at eleven o'clock he came to the nightclub. He brought an old-fashioned telephone, with the earpiece hanging on its hook, onto the dancefloor and called Judy at her hotel in Berlin. After a short conversation he would ask which of *their* tunes she wanted to hear. On his signal, we played 'Smoke Gets in Your Eyes' or a Gershwin or Cole Porter number – whatever she asked for – into the mouthpiece of the telephone held in front of us. As Noel Coward used to sing, 'I wonder what happened to her?'

3

Cambridge

Cambridge was another world, and brought three very happy and rewarding years. In 1935 it was as though a medieval sixteen-foot wall surrounded the university, separating it from the outside world. The frivolous post-World War I days of the twenties had gone and in the mid-thirties most of us worked acceptably hard and did nothing outrageous.

The Natural Sciences Tripos, comprising anatomy, physiology and biochemistry as the main subjects, brought my life's objective closer but the course was somewhat unrelated to our subsequent clinical needs. In later years medical education, as it always must, underwent a change which reduced this dichotomy and promoted the natural relevance of the preclinical to the clinical constituents.

I continued a discipline learnt at Rugby of reading on my own for at least at hour every day and kept meticulous notes in lectures and the laboratories. It never occurred to me to aspire to a first class degree; all I wanted was to understand what was intellectually so exciting, to pass the exams without too much hassle, certainly avoiding the last minute frenetic revision that some of my friends were to subject themselves to. Our supervisors and tutors unobtrusively made it clear that there was more to university life than work.

During our early weeks at Cambridge we were canvassed by the secretaries of different organisations to join, for example, the Cambridge Intercollegiate Christian Union, commonly known as the 'Kick you', or the Union, the university debating society. Had not the Oxford Union, I remembered, recently voted not to fight for king and country – an outcome, it was later said, to which Ribbentrop, the German ambassador to the Court of St James, had

29

given undue importance when he advised Hitler that the British were unlikely to fight in support of any cause.

After dinner in hall, compulsory on three nights a week, we spent our time in each other's rooms drinking beer and talking the night away. Left-wing Gollancz books in yellow dustcovers written by Oxford economists were passed around; pristine Penguin paperbacks costing sixpence each were just appearing in Heffers and in Bowes & Bowes bookshops. Someone had bought a copy of Havelock Ellis and there was a queue to read this revealing sexual treatise. Homosexuality was not prevalent. We encountered a few dons and fellows of this persuasion but had no knowledge of the notorious spies, Burgess and Blunt, who were to infiltrate the Foreign Office and were uncovered many years later. Only a small minority of undergraduates were 'camp' and most of them were unusually intelligent, artistic and interesting; they tended to be more mature and socially at ease than their heterosexual counterparts – no beer or stale sausage-rolls at their parties but wine and specially ordered aspic-glazed canapés served by a waiter or college gyp.

By placing an order with the local newsagent *The Times* was delivered daily before breakfast at the special concessionary rate of a penny a copy, a sound investment by the publishers which ensured the lifelong loyalty of many undergraduates, certainly me. With hindsight *The Times* was surprisingly pro-Nazi or, perhaps to be fairer, not anti-Nazi. It drew attention to the economic successes of the Third Reich and praised German industriousness. What if they were re-arming? Had not the Treaty of Versailles been unduly harsh? Never was there any mention of Jewish persecution. But my father had no illusions and reluctantly, after my stay in Munich, I had to agree with him.

'Sooner or later there'll be a war,' he said. 'Why else is Hitler re-arming? Eventually he'll go after the Sudetenland and Alsace and all those other German-speaking territories the Allies annexed after the fourteen-eighteen war. Stanley Baldwin's nice enough but as Prime Minister he's too complacent, afraid to face reality. Winston Churchill may be a wild fellow but I'm afraid he'll be proven right in his predictions.'

As undergraduates we had other matters on our minds. During my first two years I spent some 800 hours dissecting a human cadaver and learning about the very early development of the foetus of a pig. The need to remember such detailed anatomy, which was largely divorced from any clinical application, was called into question some twenty-five years later when I was a member of the Medical Faculty Board at Cambridge University. When young doctors were training to become surgeons, most had forgotten their undergraduate anatomy and needed to know a rather different sort of anatomy from the kind that had occupied their minds at Cambridge. Despite the remonstrations of the old guard we reduced the course to a more appropriate 200 hours and ensured a more clinical slant which today is enhanced by the use of new technologies, such as X-rays taken by computer-assisted tomography and magnetic resonance scans.

Nevertheless I enjoyed 'Meaters', the irreverent name given to the anatomy hall with its white porcelain tables, on each of which lay a corpse embalmed and preserved with formalin, covered with a cloth smeared with Vaseline and a thin white rubber sheet to prevent the tissues from drying out. Each cadaver was dissected by eight students – one pair at the head and neck, another pair working on the chest and abdomen, a third on an arm and the fourth on a leg. Contrary to most people's expectations, this is not a distasteful or disturbing undertaking. The bodies bear as little relationship to a living person as a joint of meat hanging in a butcher's shop does to a fleecy lamb baaing for its mother in a field.

The professor of anatomy was a burly Welshman from the Rhondda, much disliked by the handful of female medical undergraduates at whom he directed constant gibes, hugely approved of by their still puerile male counterparts. At the beginning of the term, early in October, some 250 of us packed into the steeply raked creaky wooden lecture theatre in the Old Anatomy School. As was customary the women occupied the front rows. Professor Harris entered through a door behind the podium. He had all the Welsh histrionic talents of a Richard Burton or an Emlyn Williams, and stood smiling to acknowledge the vigorous stamping of feet that greeted his arrival. He raised a hand to quell the noise.

'Ladies...' he beamed at the front rows, '...and gentlemen.' He spoke slowly, wrapping each word in his rich Welsh accent. 'I hope you have all had a splendid vacation. I'm just back from the Gilbert Islands. They are in the Pacific Ocean, you know. A very interesting part of the world and, ladies, of particular interest to you.' He paused – the audience hanging on his every word. 'Of

31

particular interest to you, ladies, because in the Gilbert Islands there are six men to every woman. Just think of that!'

On a prearranged signal made in anticipation of some such insult, the female undergraduates rose in unison and marched up the steep steps to the exit at the back of the theatre. As the last few pushed through the door, Professor Harris raised his hand.

'Stop! There's no need to hurry, my dears. The boat doesn't leave 'til Wednesday.'

The blushes deepened as we stamped our feet until the last girl had left. Not until well after the 1939–45 war did this absurd chauvinistic attitude to women begin to change.

I also read physiology and biochemistry in my first two years. Physiology is concerned with the mechanisms by which the body – all its organs and every cell in each of these organs – works. In most illnesses it is this normal physiology, which operates in health, that goes awry and hence the subject is of fundamental importance. For me it had an additional interest because my grandfather's cousin had been a distinguished physiologist and secretary of the British Physiology Society for twenty-two years. Most of Professor Sir William Bayliss's work had been done at University College in London in collaboration with Starling who was head of the department, and whose sister William Bayliss married. At the turn of the century Starling and Bayliss had discovered a chemical substance that was produced in the wall of the stomach and carried in the bloodstream to activate the pancreas and cause it to secrete digestive juices into the intestines. This chemical substance therefore induced its effect at some distance from where it was produced and was carried there in the blood. In 1906 no name for such a substance existed and it was William Bayliss who coined the word 'hormone' from the Greek verb meaning 'to urge on'.

Sir William Bayliss had two sons, one of whom was a physiologist at Edinburgh University and co-authored a textbook, generally known as Winton and Bayliss, which was one of our standard texts at Cambridge. Sir William's other son was reader in physiology at University College in London. During World War II he was seconded to the army to try to improve the accuracy of anti-aircraft guns and the people who fired them.

Before World War II the advancement of physiology was hampered by the lack of appropriate techniques to study the function of the body at a cellular level. In the mid-thirties the physiology of

32

reproduction in general, and of the ovary in particular, was receiving much attention, and for the first time the exact hormonal sequences that led to the normal female menstrual cycle were being unravelled. But there were no easy or accurate methods for measuring the two major hormones, oestrogen and progesterone, which were secreted cyclically by the ovaries of the normal woman during her reproductive years, nor for measuring the equally essential hormones secreted by the pituitary gland that regulate these ovarian activities. As an undergraduate I remember reading the original article in the *Journal of Clinical Investigation* by Japanese researchers which showed that ovulation took place some twelve to fourteen days before the onset of menstruation, and that fertilisation might occur five days on either side of this time. Thus there was a scientific basis for the unreliable Roman Catholic 'rhythm method' of birth control but there remained the practical difficulty of having to calculate backwards, when the woman could not possibly know when exactly her next period would be.

The scientific inventiveness developed during the war speeded post-war research in departments of physiology and also in many university hospitals where investigative physicians and surgeons began to study the physiology of normal subjects and the abnormal physiology of sick patients.

In the second part of the tripos, in my third year, I read pathology with its more clinical applications. With only fourteen of us on the course, our relationship with professors, readers and lecturers was intimate and relaxed. We were introduced to all aspects of pathology, to immunology and to bacteriology, but particularly to the microscopical changes that different diseases induce in tissues of the body. A newly-appointed Regius Professor of Physic, Sir John Ryle, had come to Cambridge from Guy's Hospital where he had been a distinguished physician and had left, we were led to believe, because he had developed angina. He was the author of *The Natural History of Disease* which contained a series of essays on clinical subjects. Once a week he gave us a fifty-minute lecture without a note or a slide as we sat entranced by this elegant, tall, grey-haired man. One of these lectures was on the nature of pain, and Sir John showed us that there were eleven questions that could profitably be asked of any patient with this symptom. This analysis of a patient's pain is so important, often indeed so essential, that I have taught generations of medical students early in their clinical course how to use this technique for determining the cause of a patient's pain. Ever since becoming an NHS consultant, the eleven questions are printed into my case-notes in the event that the patient is required to answer them. Such a procedure is essential in distinguishing anginal pain from, say, oesophageal or gall-bladder pain, tension headaches from migraine, and intestinal from pelvic or renal pain.

The final examination in pathology was a protracted affair and did not engender a great deal of 'examinationitis'. In the practical we were given the remnants of a pork-pie that had, we were told, been served at a wedding reception. 'Fifteen of the fifty guests subsequently developed diarrhoea. What was the causative organism?'

By the end of the three-day exam we had grown the *salmonella* responsible and with antisera had accurately classified its type. The external examiner was Professor Topley, the co-author of a large two-volume textbook that we looked upon as the bacteriological bible. So as not to interfere with our work too much, lunch during the exam was served each day in the departmental library and each candidate was generously treated by Professor Topley to half-a-bottle of Liebfraumilch.

* * *

Apart from the enjoyment and excitement of the work, Cambridge brought new friends, many of whom were to be lifelong, although sadly some were killed in the war and others have died before their time – some of diseases that today would be treatable.

In the mid-thirties freshmen at Clare College spent their first year out of college, arguably not an ideal arrangement. I had digs near Parker's Piece, occupying the front and back ground-floor rooms of Mr and Mrs Green's terraced house. Mr Green was a booking clerk at the railway station and Mrs Green kindly gave me a cooked breakfast every morning and did my laundry in a tub in her downstairs kitchen. Opposite us, across an asphalted path, was a junior school. At breakfast one fine autumn morning I was exasperated when for the third day in succession the children were summoned to assembly by the music mistress playing that undistinguished piano piece, 'Narcissus'. I opened my sitting-room window as far as it would go and contributed on my piano an extemporised jazzed-up accompaniment. To my surprise I was joined by the strident tones of a Bach trumpet being played by my next-door neighbour, Bill Trethowan, another medical student at Clare. Later that day a note appeared under the front door. 'The headmistress, her staff and the pupils appreciated the musical accompaniment before assembly this morning but it undermines discipline and the solemnity of the occasion...'

My piano was a recent acquisition. All my life I'd had access to a piano and to be in digs in Cambridge without one was unthinkable. I went to Miller's, the music shop in Cambridge, and sought to hire one but the assistant was persuasive in suggesting that it would be more sensible to buy a new upright on hire purchase for £50. My father, when he heard, was not pleased; he thought ill of this recently introduced financial arrangement whereby you bought things which, as he put it, you could not afford – without saving up.

In addition to many other attributes Bill Trethowan was an unusually gifted musician, a talent inherited from his father who had been an orthopaedic surgeon at Guy's and had installed an organ in the basement of their house in London. From his earliest days young Trethowan in the nursery above had grown up hearing his father playing after dinner late into the night. With an astonishing fluency Bill could play any musical instrument but with critical self-honesty only claimed proficiency on the trumpet and the piano. After his first year at Cambridge he abandoned medicine, read music and formed his own sixteen-piece dance band which played for undergraduate dances at the University Arms, the Garden House Hotel or the Corn Exchange. He was so gifted that he was able from memory to 'lift' the music from a ten-inch Parlophone gramophone record. There were six instrumentalists on one particular newly-released 78 disc which ran for a few seconds over three minutes. Bill listened to the record twice and then scored on manuscript paper what each instrument had played. He listened to the record a third time to check what he had written.

'In bar 154 the tenor sax plays B natural and he should have played B flat,' he commented without the slightest hint of conceit.

My understanding and appreciation of all types of music increased when I moved into college at the beginning of our second year. Fortunately without invoking any reprimand, I deliberately broke two rules. The first was that no musical instruments should be played in college, and the second was that nobody in *statu pupillaris* could join any theatrical society or partake in any theatrical activity without first seeking the permission of the Senior Tutor. I ignored both. The new Cramer upright piano was moved from Parker's Piece to my bedroom in the Memorial Court at Clare – there was no room for it in the sitting room – and I joined the Amateur Dramatic Club. Bill Trethowan's rooms, next door to mine, did not face onto the quadrangle; happily his trumpet and my piano, which he often used, invoked no adverse comments from our neighbours. My theatrical activities were not as a Thespian on the stage but as the writer – I would hesitate to use the word composer – of undistinguished tunes for witty lyrics used in reviews and cabarets. I was also asked by the editor of *The Granta*, an undergraduate magazine, to become their gramophone record critic. Every fortnight I met my nice piano salesman in the basement of Miller's music shop where he offered me a selection of recent releases to review.

The first two recordings were Tebaldi singing *Madam Butterfly* and Mendelssohn's Fourth Symphony (the *Italian*), completed when the composer was aged thirty-three. I now have several recordings of the latter – there are about fifty in the catalogue – and have the impression that the older conductors, such as Sir George Solti, play the second movement, *andante cum moto*, at a slower tempo than the younger ones, such as Claudio Abbado and Ray Leppard, so that the weary pilgrims have to climb the steps of St Peter's, as the music suggests to me, at a brisker pace.

After Cambridge Bill Trethowan became the arranger and conductor of a small group of professional musicians which played regularly on the BBC's Light Programme, *Monday Night at Eight is on the Air*. Shortly after Chamberlain's 'Peace in our time' speech Bill resumed his medical studies, qualified and thereafter specialised in psychiatry. After the war he became a professor of psychiatry in Sydney, and then for many years was a professor of psychiatry at Birmingham University, Dean of the Medical School there, and had an altogether distinguished career, being knighted in 1980.

Another close friend at Clare was Billy Fraser, whose father was chairman of the Anglo-Iranian Oil Company, later the British Petroleum Company, and became Lord Strathalmond. Billy was a gentle Scot, as kind and as generous as anyone could be. Tall with a quiet voice and a slight Scots brogue, Billy was a thoughtful man who moved slowly. His expression could be serious, some-

36

times lugubrious, but he had laughing eyes and a keen sense of humour. He read law and later did an important job in the army during the war. Post-war he became chairman of British Petroleum and served the government in many roles both before and after succeeding his father in the House of Lords. He was the college's practical joker.

During our second and third years at Cambridge, Billy Fraser, Bill Trethowan and I had adjacent rooms in the Memorial Court which, built of lavender-grey brick, was a tribute to Clare men who had fallen in the 1914–18 war. The neo-Georgian style with additional Adam details made the building more architecturally appealing than many of the other post-World War I Cambridge buildings. It was constructed, it seemed to me, to last for ever and to require the minimum of maintenance. The doors, staircases, built-in cupboards and bookcases, and window-frames were made of resolutely solid oak – stained, not painted. During the last half-century little seems to have changed except that the original over-sized baths have been replaced with smaller ones and more economical showers. For a time the gas stoves in the sitting rooms were removed because of the risk of suicide, but they have been reinstalled now that carbon monoxide-free North Sea gas is available.

I dropped into Billy Fraser's rooms one night for a pre-bedtime cup of Ovaltine, as perhaps surprisingly was our habit, to find another Clare man there. McLintock, like Billy, was reading law but was in trouble. He'd been caught climbing into college after the gates were locked at ten o'clock.

'Last night, a few minutes after midnight, I was squeezing through the window grill on the staircase on the other side of the court – you know the one. The trouble was the bright moonlight,' he said.

'Go on,' Billy prompted.

'Well, I was halfway through the grill when from below a voice said, "I hope you won't get stuck, McLintock." I knew exactly who it was. He'd been watching me; the Senior Tutor's voice is unmistakable. So I climbed back out again, and there we were standing face to face on the grass.'

'Then?'

'Thirkill told me to come and see him in the morning – this morning – so I went. You know what he's like – an iron hand in a velvet glove. It was a serious matter, he said. During the long

37

vacation he'd give it some thought and write to let me know his decision.'

Billy Fraser's face was sombre. 'I wouldn't be surprised if he rusticates you for a term.'

'Send me down for a term? That would be ridiculous,' said a scared McLintock as we laughed at such an improbable punishment.

Henry Thirkill, the Senior Tutor, knew his students surprisingly well. Every Sunday morning during termtime he asked a small group to breakfast. He sat, his large face creased in an avuncular smile, at the head of the table in his sitting room, proffering juicy kippers followed by rather greasy bacon and eggs. He was a physicist who was reputed to have designed for the navy in World War I a clever method of mine-sweeping, but he never talked about it. He never talked about anything much; he just sat Buddha-like, encouraging others to do the talking – and listened.

The following October, when a few days before the beginning of term I went up to Cambridge, the first person I ran into was a bronzed McLintock.

'Had a good vacation?' I asked and, then remembering, added, 'What did Thirkill do about you climbing into college?'

'I had a pretty wretched holiday, thanks. In July we went to the South of France; we've got a house in Menton. In August a letter came from Thirkill – all official, you know the sort of thing. He said he'd decided to kick me out of college for my last year and had arranged lodgings for me somewhere in the sticks – at the far end of Mill Road. Can you imagine?'

I listened in horror.

'A few days later a letter on Woolworths' scented violet notepaper with deckel edges came from a Mrs Fortune in Mill Road. She was to be my new landlady. She said she was looking forward to having me but felt she should warn me about one or two things. Her son of twelve was learning the trombone and her husband played the tuba in the Salvation Army. No young ladies were ever allowed in their house which, apparently, also lacked certain amenities. The WC is chemical and at the bottom of the garden. You can imagine how I felt – out of college and miles from anywhere with a hundred-yard walk down the garden on a rainy winter's night to have a pee.

'For several days I said nothing and then talked to my father. He thought Thirkill was being a bit harsh and suggested I wrote

38

asking if there weren't some digs closer to college. So I did. Not surprisingly the great man was away for most of the long vac and not a word came until the middle of September.'

'What did he say?'

'He said he didn't know what I was talking about. Apparently he'd forgotten all about my climbing in and had made no arrangements for lodgings for me. He'd never sent me a letter and would very much like to see it. So I sent it him.'

I was beginning to cotton on. 'Billy Fraser's behind this?'

'Billy admitted it when I rang him up. He thought I'd spot that Thirkill's letter was a fake because of the signature, but it was typed on his headed college notepaper. The letter from Mrs Fortune was most convincing.'

It was a few days into the term before the Senior Tutor sent for Billy. Thirkill, all smiles, enquired how he had spent his vacation and how his father was. Still smiling he said, 'Fraser, next time you have breakfast with me, I'd be obliged if you'd refrain from removing any of my stationery. I see the typewriter used for a certain letter to McLintock during the vacation is remarkably similar to the one your father's secretary uses when he writes to me.' Despite that innocent avuncular air Thirkill knew more about what went on in college than many supposed.

Another of Billy Fraser's practical jokes involved Johnny Mallett, a medical student who went on to St Thomas's Hospital for his clinical training as I did. Johnny was a lovable man with a slight lisp, something of a calculated buffoon and a rugger blue. He invited his girlfriend, Elizabeth, who was a physiotherapy student at the London Hospital, to come to the Cambridge University Medical Society's Christmas ball at the Dorothy Café. Johnny arranged a *tête-à-tête* dinner for her in his rooms. The three-course meal was ordered from the college buttery at a cost of ten shillings and sixpence and was carried from the kitchens in the Old Court to the Memorial Court by a porter bearing on his head a large wooden tray covered with a green baize cloth. The menu was a college standard – mock-turtle soup laced with sherry, lamb cutlets with white paper frills on the rib ends, *sauté* potatoes and spinach *en branche*, followed by *crème brûlée*. Johnny had bought the wine from Dolomore's in Petty Cury and persuaded the buttery to lend him a silver candelabra so he could turn off the harsh electric light in the centre of the sitting-room to promote the warming glow from the gas fire and the candles. Elizabeth in an evening dress arrived by taxi from the Garden House Hotel.

That something was amiss became clear to the inhabitants of the Memorial Court ten minutes later. Johnny stormed out of his rooms, his face flushed with anger.

'Where is he?' he shouted for all to hear. 'I know who's done this. Where's the bugger? I'll kill him.' He stormed from staircase to staircase, from room to room, in an unsuccessful search for Billy Fraser.

Soon after Elizabeth's arrival, it appeared, a porter had come from the lodge bearing a box of flowers from Moyses Stevens and a card with 'To darling Elizabeth, with love from Johnny' inscribed on it. Elizabeth was suitably impressed, so much so that Johnny unwisely omitted to mention that he hadn't ordered any flowers.

In the seductive candlelight she had opened the box; from under the lovely red roses scampered a troop of white mice. They jumped onto the dining table and thence to the floor. Elizabeth dropped the box and screamed. She pulled up the skirt of her evening dress and climbed on a chair. She rejected Johnny's declarations of innocence.

When he returned from his fruitless search, Elizabeth with faultless female logic could not understand why he had not immediately disclaimed sending her the flowers.

* * *

I left Cambridge certainly more mature but with a sense of an unrepayable debt for having taught me so much about life and human beings, about science and above all the scientific method. The university gives first, second or third class honours degrees, and the second class honours degree is subdivided into an upper 2:1 and a lower 2:2. I got a run-of-the-mill 2:1 in both the first and second parts of the Natural Sciences Tripos, and was delighted because I hadn't worked all that hard. Even had I worked harder, I doubt a first was ever within my reach.

Years later, when Dean of Westminster Medical School, I looked into what had happened to men who had got firsts and subsequently took a medical degree. Over a five-year period very few, after being qualified in medicine for ten or fifteen years, had achieved any distinction or been appointed to a particularly important post.

This is not to say that these men were not happy in their work or failed to contribute to society; but with few exceptions it appeared that many were not well-equipped to distinguish themselves in academic medicine or even in the more practical aspects of doctoring.

4

A Clinical Student

For some years before World War II, St Thomas's Hospital in London had attracted a sizeable proportion of Cambridge and Oxford's pre-clinical students. What made one London teaching hospital more popular than another was often a matter of fashion. Undergraduates at Oxford or Cambridge might be led by one of their number whose father had been trained at a particular London hospital; sometimes they were influenced by a college supervisor or tutor; sometimes their parents would be impressed by a particular London hospital because members of its staff had achieved notoriety by attending an eminent politician or a member of the Royal Family.

All the London teaching hospitals are affiliated to London University and, although the academic year begins in October, St Thomas's was perfectly happy to admit clinical students in July. Thus a few weeks after we had come down from Cambridge, a group of us, including six from Clare, began our clinical studies there in the summer of 1938. There was no rousing address of welcome from the Dean nor an erudite discourse on medical ethics, the nuances of which would doubtless have passed over our heads. We were simply thrown in at the deep end – being put to work in Casualty, as the hospital's busy Accident and Emergency Department was called.

No doubt the Dean's Office had a carefully worked out curriculum for the three years of our clinical training but we never saw it, and it would have required immediate restructuring with the outbreak of war in 1939. What subjects were taught and how much time was devoted to each was largely decided by the Dean in conjunction with the Academic Board and ratified by the School Council. Overall, but not detailed, approval of the curriculum came from

London University and was also scrutinised by the General Medical Council. The public may think of the GMC solely as a disciplinary body which deals with the misdemeanours of doctors, but it has another important function in overseeing medical education throughout the British Isles.

Many years later as a Dean I learnt how difficult it is to organise a curriculum that has the approval of all parties. The old dictum 'You can't please all the people all the time' was certainly true. There were pressure groups, both inside and outside the hospital. For example, because of the rising incidence of diseases of the prostate gland in an increasingly ageing male population, the British Association of Urologists sought two months, instead of one, for teaching the students, and because skin diseases were so common in general practice, the dermatologists wished to prolong their course from two to three months; the Ministry of Health wanted more time given to teaching matters relating to public health. To have conceded to all such demands would have prolonged the course by at least six months, and to reduce the instruction time given to another department was interpreted by its head as a slight on the importance of his subject or a criticism of the teaching skills of his team.

We attended some lectures but the amount of formal instruction was relatively small compared with what we learnt from the time-honoured apprenticeship system. We had no rigid timetable although a notice would appear on a board in the medical school saying that our group would be working on a general medical or surgical firm for the next three months or for the next month we must go each day to the local fever hospital. Working with patients in Casualty was as good a place to start as any, and certainly held our interest. The contrast between the leisurely academic pace at Cambridge and the practical earthy apprenticeship in London was striking – and at times rather alarming.

Our group was supervised by Dr W.A.R. Thomson, who was aged about thirty-five and was first assistant to the professor of medicine. When you're twenty, someone ten years your senior is positively old and, because of his unfortunate initials, Bill Thomson was universally known as Wart, but not to his face. Short in stature with Brylcreemed, sleeked-down dark hair and a broad Scots brogue he was lively and friendly. He told us which books to buy and read now, and which we should buy to dip into occasionally but

44

to read in full later as we approached our finals. Slowly and thoroughly he taught us the fundamental science and art of how to examine a patient systematically from head to toe, so that every bit of the body and every system was looked at. Equally, if not more, important is to listen to every word the patient says and the sequence in which the history is given, but in 1938 this was less widely appreciated than it is today.

'D'you know why the rubber tubing on your stethoscope is thirteen inches long?' Wart asked.

Like other students before us we had no idea.

He was delighted at the silence that invariably followed this question. 'Because...' he paused for effect, '... because a flea can jump only eleven or twelve inches.' We laughed and remembered this probably inaccurate and certainly unimportant fact for the rest of our lives.

The stethoscope, which early in the nineteenth century had been looked upon as a 'new-fangled and ridiculous plaything' is not an easy instrument to learn to use. At first we found it impossible to hear all the sounds and murmurs we were meant to; this was a new, a strange kind of music. With my eyes closed I can easily distinguish the sound made by a clarinet from that of an oboe, or a bassoon from a French horn but this comes from practice and experience. Not surprisingly it took nearly three years before I was able to identify with any certainty the characteristics of the different sounds my teachers claimed they could hear; today learning is made easier by listening to hi-fi audiotapes.

During our first three months we watched and helped the young casualty officers, themselves qualified only a few weeks or months, who worked under the eye of Sister Annie Beale. Having been for thirty years in charge of the department Sister could instinctively sort out the seriously ill from the not-so-ill. She was a large tireless woman and expected everyone to be as dedicated, quick and single-minded as she. Idleness, lack of attention to detail or failure to act promptly were to her anathema. She was of a generation that considered most psychological disorders the expression of moral turpitude, yet she showed brusque and unsentimental sympathy to those in physical pain or stricken with bereavement. Sister Beale, it seemed, could be in three different places at once as she moved quickly from room to room – supervising, instructing, ordering. She was the key figure, a position only surrendered when a registrar

– if she liked him – or the Resident Assistant Physician or Surgeon was summoned because a casualty officer found himself out of his depth.

We followed the casualty officers from patient to patient. We watched, did dressings, took blood samples – fearfully and badly at first – and we ran errands.

'There's a patient in Room Two with a boil that needs opening. Go and do it, will you?' one of the casualty officers asked me during my second week.

Apprehensively, despite having seen boils lanced on several previous occasions, I went.

'Hello, Travers,' I said, omitting the 'Mister' as was the custom in those days, even though the patient was old enough to be my father. I studied the angry red swelling on the front of the man's thigh. Sister Beale swept into the room. I heard her coming because a slight limp from a gammy leg caused the enormous bunch of keys dangling from her belt to jangle loudly.

'Come along now! Put the patient on the couch. You can't do this with him sitting on a chair, can you? What would happen if he fainted?'

Mr Travers was laid on a couch.

'Now, nurse, take off his shoes. They'll dirty the sheet and what if he kicks...?' Sister Beale left the sentence unfinished.

Another nurse wheeled in a trolley of instruments and I took off my short white coat, rolled up my shirt sleeves and scrubbed my hands and wrists at the sink with a hard brush and a cake of harsh soap. Sister watched every move.

'Never leave your wallet in the pocket of your white coat, Mr Bayliss; it might get stolen.'

I approached Mr Travers. 'I won't hurt you,' I lied, knowing the relative ineffectiveness of the local anaesthetic that was going to be used. I swabbed the skin with iodine, took the ethylene chloride bottle from the trolley and sprayed the boil until it was frozen and covered with a thin layer of frost. With an old-fashioned scalpel that seemed unreasonably blunt and reminded me of the one I had used in Meaters at Cambridge, I made a cries-cross incision; all that happened was that Mr Travers flinched.

'You'll have to make a deeper incision,' directed Sister Beale.

I did and was rewarded with a gush of thick yellow pus. 'All over,' I said, mopping the wound with gauze and then applying a simple dry dressing. On the patient's card I recorded briefly what had been done.

'Hot soaks, as hot as you can bear, four times a day,' I instructed the patient. 'Come and see us tomorrow at ten o'clock.'

'Thank you, doctor. Thanks very much.' Mr Travers knew he had been treated by only a student but seemed grateful.

Sister Beale had the last word. 'Next time,' she said, 'make a deeper incision first time. Now don't stand around; there's plenty to do next door.'

I passed the wooden benches in the waiting area crammed with patients to another white-tiled room where the Resident Assistant Physician was teaching three casualty officers and a group of students. The patient was a ten-year-old girl lying naked on a couch with her mother sitting apprehensively beside her.

'This is absolutely characteristic,' Dr Hector Johnson was saying. 'The rash is everywhere; it covers the trunk, the face and the limbs. She's obviously ill, has a temperature and a splitting headache – don't you, Shirley?' He squeezed her hand but did not wait for a reply. 'She's got nuchal rigidity – look.' He put his hand behind Shirley's head and gently lifted it up from the couch; she winced. 'She doesn't like that; she can't bend her head forward without her neck hurting. This is a sign of meningeal irritation – inflammation of the meninges covering the brain. She has meningococcal meningitis and she has meningococcal septicaemia, hence the rash Now take a good look at the rash – all of you.'

We filed passed, examining the rash carefully. The RAP shepherded us outside the room, away from the patient and her mother. He told them about this usually fatal disease but how there was now a new drug, M & B 693, that would probably cure it. He explained how there might be an epidemic of the disease in any future war when there was overcrowding, just as there had been in World War I.

'D'you know why soldiers sleep head-to-tail in a barracks?' he asked. 'Why does one soldier have his head against the wall and the man in the next bed have his turned round the other way? Because this reduces the risk of droplet cross-infection from one soldier breathing into the face of another.'

A week later I felt unwell; the next day my head was throbbing and I ached all over. My temperature was 101°F (38.3°C). I stayed in bed in my flat in Emperor's Gate off the Cromwell Road in

South Kensington, and took two aspirin. The next day I felt even worse and my temperature was a little higher. I struggled out of bed and read the relevant section in Price's *Textbook of Medicine*. It was not reassuring. The incubation period for meningococcal meningitis was about eight days. My symptoms seemed similar, indeed identical, to those described in the book. Instinctively I drew the curtain because the light hurt my eyes. I lay on the bed and tried lifting my head off the pillow; my neck hurt. Undoubtedly I had meningococcal meningitis.

What should I do? There was no medical student health service at the hospital; I didn't know a general practitioner in London. I could not telephone Wart Thomson at the hospital; he was much too grand. Casualty officers never went outside the hospital. There was nobody to turn to. Then a thought crossed my mind – Sir Maurice Cassidy. He was the senior physician at St Thomas's. By four o'clock my situation was so desperate that I dragged myself to the sitting-room, perused the telephone directory and rang Sir Maurice's consulting rooms in Montague Square. His secretary was surprisingly solicitous. She took down my name and address and elicited a brief history of my illness.

'Will you hold on a minute, please?' She was conferring with the great man. A few seconds later she said, 'Sir Maurice will come and see you this evening,' and confirmed exactly where I lived.

Shortly after six o'clock a large black Daimler saloon drew up outside the house in Emperor's Gate. When I opened the door of the flat to him, Sir Maurice was distinctly short of breath after climbing the four flights of stairs.

The senior physician, for whom I was to work later in my career, was kind and unhurried. He took a meticulous history; he examined me from top to toe. Finally he stood up, arching his back after sitting on the edge of my low divan bed for so long.

'I think,' he said gently, 'you've got 'flu. I appreciate you've been exposed to a case of meningococcal meningitis at the hospital but I'm sure you haven't got that; you haven't really got nuchal rigidity and your photophobia isn't marked enough. There's no rash. You're really too well. There's a lot of 'flu about. Take a couple of aspirins every six hours, drink plenty of water and stay in bed until you're all right again.' He left smiling, without a hint of criticism.

I felt ashamed and deflated. Forty-eight hours later I was much better. Like many a medical student I had had my first, and happily my last, 'fatal' illness! I vowed that if I were ever in Sir Maurice's shoes I would try to be as considerate to a sickly medical student as he had been to me. Fifteen years later at Westminster Hospital we established a comprehensive health service for all the medical students and nurses.

*　*　*

Although after his meeting in 1938 with Hitler in Munich, the Prime Minister had proclaimed 'Peace in our time', few people seriously doubted that war was inevitable. At first the planning and preparations were slow and unobtrusive but the tempo accelerated as the remaining precious months slipped by.

A week before war was declared the students at St Thomas's were posted to various hospitals in Surrey, and the medical school rented a vacant shop in Guildford that became both a lecture theatre, refectory and clubhouse. The Dean dispatched a group of seven of us to the large Victorian mental asylum at Brookwood near Woking. We were accommodated in a previously unoccupied house in the extensive grounds where a 500-bedded emergency hospital had been built of Nissen huts specifically for the reception of the air-raid casualties anticipated in London. At 11.15 on the fateful morning of Sunday, 3 September 1939, we sat listening to Neville Chamberlain's speech on the wireless.

'I am speaking to you from the Cabinet Room at Ten Downing Street. This morning the British Ambassador in Berlin handed the German government a final note, stating that unless we heard by eleven o'clock that they were prepared at once to withdraw their troops from Poland ... I have to tell you that no such undertaking has been received, and consequently this country is at war with Germany.'

Nobody said anything – our faces expressionless – as the words hung in the air of our cramped sitting-room. Seven minutes after the Prime Minister's announcement came the plaintive rising and falling wail of an air-raid siren. Without a word we took our gas masks, each in a cardboard box marked with our name, from the hooks in the hall and hurried to the hutted emergency hospital. In anticipation of air-raid casualties we spent the next hour filling

49

hot-water bottles and putting them into 200 beds – pointlessly because it was a false alarm.

During the nine months of the inactive 'phoney' war when the Germans were preparing for their *blitzkrieg* on the Low Countries and France, we continued our studies as best we could. There were lectures in Guildford and ward rounds at hospitals in Godalming, Guildford, Woking, Chertsey and Epsom. We gave a helping hand at Brookwood Asylum, which was mainly filled with patients suffering from chronic schizophrenia. One Saturday night we attended a fancy dress dance given for the patients. Inevitably there was a Paul Jones, a dance in which the ladies form a circle in the middle of the dance floor and the men form another circle outside them. When the music of 'Here We Go Gathering Nuts in May' begins, the two circles rotate in opposite directions – the men clockwise and the women anti-clockwise. When the music suddenly stops, a man in the outer circle takes as his dancing partner the lady in the inner circle immediately opposite him. After a short dance together the whole procedure is repeated. During the Paul Jones I danced in succession with three young female patients, all claiming to be Marie Antoinette and each pointing out the other two as impostors. They also called my attention to the four Napoleon Bonapartes who were present, only one of whom, they said, was authentic – but each Marie Antoinette pointed to a different man!

We saw no wartime casualties until the evacuation of the British army from Dunkirk at the end of May 1940. Then our group worked all hours helping with the wounded who were brought by special trains to Woking station and transferred to the Nissen huts in the grounds of Botley's Park Hospital near Chertsey which had stood empty for nine months. No one was surprised at the failure of the French Maginot Line to check the advancing Germans because it failed to extend northward to the Channel coast, but the almost immediate surrender of France was to us incomprehensible. Britain felt betrayed as alone, without any allies in Europe, we faced the enemy. Invasion seemed imminent. Concrete pillboxes and anti-tank traps began to appear around the outskirts of London. Signposts were removed from the roads, and place names taken down at railway stations and outside towns and villages.

After Mussolini declared war on us in June 1940, an Italian restaurant in Soho, Quo Vadis – much patronised by students from St Thomas's – had its windows smashed as did several others in

50

the neighbourhood. The gentle courteous Italian proprietor, who had lived in England since childhood, was taken away by the police and interned on the Isle of Man along with thousands of other foreigners. As a registrar at St Thomas's Hospital later in the war, one of my chiefs, Dr Isaac Jones, who was Chief Medical Officer to the Metropolitan Police, asked me out to lunch in the days, of course, of rationing. 'It's a special occasion; I think we'll have a splendid meal,' he said. 'At last I've persuaded the Home Office to release Leoni, the owner of Quo Vadis, from internment.' Our very special lunch lasted two hours.

The Blitz started in September 1940 and early in October our group was moved back to London to help with the air-raid casualties. St Thomas's had undergone many changes; all the windows had been bricked up and the interior was depressingly gloomy in the artificial light provided by low wattage bulbs. New operating theatres and wards had been constructed in the basement where a Women's Voluntary Service canteen, staffed by ladies whose husbands were in the armed forces or had been taken prisoner of war in France, had been opened for patients and hospital staff. Young women from the Voluntary Aid Detachment, with a bright red cross on the white bibs of their nursing uniform, augmented the hospital's own Nightingale nursing staff.

Psychological changes were no less obvious than the physical ones already wrought on the hospital by high explosive and incendiary bombs. There was comforting reassurance in the fatalism of, 'We're here today and gone tomorrow' or 'You're okay if it hasn't got your number on it'.

We worked hard, often with little sleep at night. When not on duty I slept in the Emperor's Gate flat and after the sirens went at about eight o'clock at night, joined the other inmates of the house in the basement flat of the caretakers, Mr and Mrs Morgan. Mr Morgan drove an electric delivery van for Harrods, and such was the service, even during the war, that if you telephoned the store before two o'clock in the morning to order some foodstuff, Mr Morgan would deliver it by nine o'clock that morning.

It was safer to be below ground during the German bombing. Outside the house was an anti-aircraft gun of considerable vintage that fired noisily into the night sky as the Luftwaffe circled overhead; it was unlikely to hit anything but it heightened morale and certainly interfered with our sleep. Deck-chairs are unsuitable for sleeping in; the wooden strut under your knees cuts off the blood supply to your lower legs and feet; the resulting discomfort and pins and needles keep you awake. Nor could we pass the time reading; Mrs Morgan was firmly of the opinion that in the event of a bomb hitting the house the single naked electric light-bulb in her hall, where we all slept, would explode. Hence she insisted the light was turned off.

When on duty we hung around the hospital in the evenings waiting for the Luftwaffe to arrive. Some tried to read wherever they could find a quiet corner; others drank coffee in the basement canteen; and the majority frequented The Rodney, the hospital's local pub. The Luftwaffe came at dusk. After the sirens sounded, it was not long before we had a good idea whether we would have a busy night or whether the main target was further afield, perhaps Whitechapel, the docks or the power station for the Underground in Lot's Road, Chelsea. If the raid was in our vicinity we knew what to expect. First incendiary bombs were dropped, setting on fire and lighting up the target area; then came the high explosive bombs or later, in the early months of 1941, huge naval mines suspended on parachutes that floated down slowly, swaying in the night breeze. One of these, clearly visible in the moonlight, hovered ominously over the Houses of Parliament and, as we watched, a puff of wind deflected it to fall silently into the Thames and sink. The medical and nursing staff had learnt instinctively that the best way to control any fear was to continue to work as though nothing were happening. Surgeons and anaesthetists not immediately required took cover in the basement – a few wearing tin helmets. In our youthful innocence we thought this unfair when patients and nurses were in wards on the ground and first floors with two vacant floors and the roof above – between them and the Luftwaffe.

As the Blitz continued, few people appeared afraid or mentioned their anxiety. Fewer patients with psychosomatic disorders or anxiety states attended Casualty or the outpatient departments. The nurses worked in shifts but the doctors had no structured off-duty and slunk away for an hour's sleep whenever best they could. Irrespective of what the night had brought, either in the number of casualties or bomb damage to the hospital itself, ward rounds started promptly at half past eight. When there were too few beds for the next night's anticipated casualties, inpatients well enough to be moved

52

were sent in Green Line buses converted into ambulances to Guildford, Woking, Godalming or Epsom.

* * *

I took my finals at Cambridge in May and June 1941. It may seem strange that, having done all the clinical training within the curtilage of London University, the passport to practice medicine should be given by a university that had provided only our pre-clinical education. The reasons for this were mainly historical. At that time Cambridge had no clinical school; for generations London had been the predominant medical centre in England and not surprisingly many great teaching hospitals had developed there, some near the major railheads – St Mary's next door to Paddington, Guy's beside London Bridge and St Thomas's near Waterloo. Nevertheless we went back to Cambridge to take our finals and were examined predominantly by those who, like us, had done their pre-clinical training at Cambridge and then proceeded to a London teaching hospital.

Cambridge is at its best in June, and it was a fortnight of undiluted pleasure. We lived in college, and it was good after three years to see old friends who had gone to other teaching hospitals – usually in London but sometimes as far afield as Edinburgh. The sun shone and strawberries and cream were abundant. We wrote many three-hour papers and were examined on patients in what is now the old Addenbrooke's Hospital in Trumpington Street. Often they were outpatients and used as short cases whom we saw briefly and then discussed for five or ten minutes; many came from far afield in the Fens, being brought to the hospital each day by taxi. My examiner took me to look at a patient sitting on a bench who was bent so far forward that his head almost touched his knees.

'What d'you think of this chap?' the examiner said, and then asked the patient to stand up and walk around.

The man, who was about 40, took a few steps. He was bent almost double.

'What d'you think of that?' the examiner asked.

'I think his bent spine is fused and rigid; it's got no movement in it; he's got ankylosing spondylitis.'

'Quite right. He's got ankylosing spondylitis; his spine is completely fixed. What do you think we should do for him? He's not in any pain.'

I pondered; this was one of those social, public health questions I knew little about. Perhaps he should be registered as a disabled person, I suggested, or could he be trained to operate a telephone switchboard?

'Rubbish!' exploded the examiner. 'This feller's an agricultural worker. What d'you think he does? I'll give you a clue – his work is peculiar to this part of the country.'

'I don't think I know.'

'He cuts off the leafy heads of sugar beet and throws the beet into a truck. He keeps his machete sharp and he can work, bent over, all day long without getting backache. He's one of the best paid agricultural workers in the Fens.'

We did not wait for the results of the exam to be pinned on the boards outside the Senate House; confidently we hurried back to London.

5

Life as a Houseman

In 1941 after passing his final examinations and registering with the General Medical Council, a doctor could without more ado begin to practise on his own or be an assistant or partner in a general practice. Although most newly-qualified doctors did gain postgraduate experience by working in a hospital, not until long after World War II ended did the General Medical Council require every doctor to do a year's postgraduate training in approved hospital posts before he could be fully registered and engage in independent work. House physicians and house surgeons are called 'Mister' rather than 'Doctor' and wear short white coats, a convention that has little to commend it because housemen need as much, not less, sartorial protection than their seniors and, with the introduction of the lapel badge showing the doctor's name and appointment, there is no need for a short white coat to emphasise his lowly status.

As housemen – house physicians or house surgeons – at St Thomas's we worked hard. There was no rota system and we were on duty day and night for six months – with no official days or weekends off. If you needed a haircut, you asked a colleague or your immediate superior, the registrar, if he would look after your patients for an hour while you went to the nearest barber's shop; the hospital barber who shaved the patients pre-operatively was not an attractive alternative. Medicine was less complicated in those days; it was easier to reach a diagnosis because fewer diseases had been defined; the notes were briefer; X-rays were simpler and more limited in scope; laboratory investigations, apart from a simple blood count, were virtually unheard of, although we did Wassermann reactions on those we thought might have syphilis. But there was

55

no technician to take electrocardiograms; we trundled a bulky Cambridge ECG machine, almost the size of a bed and about as difficult to manoeuvre on its four small castors, round the wards. Its sensitive string galvanometer was as delicate and as expensive to replace as a piece of Meisen china. The tracings were recorded on glass photographic plates which we developed in the darkroom in the basement of the hospital and then printed and glazed, entering our interpretation of the tracing in a leather-bound ledger. Whereas today recordings are taken from twelve different positions, then they were taken from just the limbs and one from the chest.

We saw no reason to complain; we simply did as others had done before us; we were brought up in the tradition of a heroic stereotype – doctors never failed in their duty and were never ill. Nevertheless we got very tired from interrupted nights. It was alarming to find that after an emergency was admitted in the small hours whom you had clerked, diagnosed and prescribed treatment for, you had no recollection next day of having ever seen the patient. At night when there was a problem on the ward, the nurses were more fearful of calling the head Sister on duty than summoning the houseman. There were no telephones in the residents' bedrooms and a porter had to come all the way from the lodge in Casualty to wake you with the message. We worked forty-eight hours or more without proper sleep, and eventually when you did get to bed a churning overactive mind kept you awake. Many of us resorted to the occasional capsule of Nembutal, a short-acting barbiturate, taken from the drug cupboard on the ward. But despite the appalling hours and the volume of work I do not recall feeling professionally unsupported or insecure. Today in a much more complex medical world the hours that junior doctors work are much too long despite good objective evidence that their judgement does become impaired. Today when on call a third of all housemen sleep less than four hours a night although the government's aim is for junior doctors to work no more than fifty-six hours a week. This is unlikely to be achieved without lowering the standard of care unless more junior staff or more consultants agreeable to being called out at night are employed – at additional expense for the NHS.

Each morning at half past eight we made a ward round with the Resident Assistant Physician, the Medical Registrar and the Sister accompanied by a staff-nurse carrying a white enamel tray bearing a blood-pressure machine, a torch, an ophthalmoscope, a knee-jerk hammer, and cotton wool and pins to test sensation in the skin. The ward was silent and the patients lay, as though on parade, in immaculately made beds, the top sheet turned down the distance from a nurse's wrist to the tips of her fingers and the wheels on the beds all facing in the same direction. Each patient was discussed and the necessary decisions taken. The ward Sister was not silent; she made her invaluable contributions because she knew the patients better than any of us. Often there was surprisingly little interchange with the patient; sadly the need for 'patient communication' was not appreciated and almost invariably the patient was known by the number of the bed he or she occupied. This was not deliberate depersonalisation but a safety measure because there might at the same time be two Smiths and three Joneses in the thirty-eight bed ward. The houseman learnt much from his ward Sister who also knew each consultant's therapeutic likes and dislikes.

'Sir Maurice Cassidy has all his patients with heart failure on digoxin,' she might say and unless there were good reason to disagree I heeded her advice.

There were unwritten conventions that governed the behaviour of College House, a name given to the resident staff as a whole and also to the location of their communal sitting and dining room. The original College House had been destroyed by a bomb in the Blitz and Hector Johnson, the Resident Assistant Physician, had been sitting there at the time relaxing over coffee after dinner.

'I've a mental picture indelibly recorded in that millisecond,' he told us. 'The bomb went through the roof of the hospital and the two floors above us before coming through our ceiling; I can see it now – a large grey bomb with fins on its tail. It went straight through the floor in front of us without exploding, down through the ground floor and exploded in the basement. God, I was lucky because I was sitting in a corner. Poor Spillsbury and Colin Campbell were near the middle of the room. They went head-first through the hole in the floor the bomb had made. I suppose they were just sucked down – blown to smithereens, poor devils.'

Spillsbury was the son of Sir Bernard Spillsbury who had taught us forensic medicine; Colin Campbell had been a year senior to me at Clare.

'What happened to you?'

'Me? Just bashed against the wall. Deaf as a post for a bit –

hopeless trying to use a stethoscope for a few days, covered in dust and rubble, a few bruises and scratches – nothing much.'

An empty children's ward had then been converted into a new College House – a large cheerless room with a grey terrazzo floor and walls covered with Victorian tiles in which were set huge ceramic murals of Little Jack Horner and Puss in Boots. At meal times the two senior residents, the Resident Assistant Physician and the Resident Assistant Surgeon, sat at either end of the dining table. Conversation seldom revolved round the war; mainly we discussed patients – our own and other people's – and learnt a great deal.

As Resident Assistant Physician, Hec Johnson had overwhelming authority. Irrespective of the honorary consultants, it was he who decided which patients should be admitted and which could be discharged. The son of a general practitioner in Newent, Gloucestershire, Hec was a peppery little man who had been in the army as a cavalry officer before studying medicine, which made him our senior by more years than usual; we were a little frightened of him. He was an excellent doctor and teacher; intellectually honest, he hated sloppy thinking or an imprecise diagnosis. His main fault was an aversion to anything new and still unproven. 'We don't want any of that damn'd nonsense,' he would say if some unusual diagnosis or novel treatment were suggested. To him all scientific progress was highly suspect.

One sunny Sunday morning at breakfast while quietly reading the newspaper, restricted in war time to only four pages because of the paper shortage, he exploded. 'I'm fed up with this bloody porridge. Day after day, half-cold watery lumpy porridge. It's the lumpiness I can't stand. It's as lumpy as the disgusting thighs of some fat old tart. Why in God's name can't they make decent porridge? I'm going to talk to Matron and you lot are coming with me.'

He stood up holding his bowl of porridge. A comical procession filed out of College House, with Hec Johnson leading, followed by the Resident Assistant Surgeon, two registrars and eight housemen, each bearing a bowl of porridge. We went down the curving stone stairs to the ground floor and along the wide main corridor to turn into the wing that housed Matron's offices. Like the sovereign she was protected by a series of ADCs and acolytes who stared in astonishment as we marched in.

'I wish to see Matron,' Hec announced to an assistant matron, resplendent in a dark-blue uniform covered with tiny white dots, who constituted the last defence.

'I'll see if she's available.' The assistant matron scuttled into the inner sanctum, and returned to announce, 'Matron will receive you.'

Hec moved in. It was hard at the back to hear exactly what was said in gentle tones interspersed with laughs. Behind her imposing desk Miss Hillyers seemed to be taking the matter seriously but there was the hint of a smile on her face.

Hec turned and led the little procession out of the office, his face pink with triumph. 'She's going to fix it,' was all he said. 'Now get back to College House.'

Fifteen minutes later Miss Hillyers appeared with the assistant matron and two deputy matrons carrying trays. We rose to our feet.

'Please be seated,' Miss Hillyers said. 'We'll only keep you a few minutes.' She conversed with Grant, the much loved butler who looked after us, and then disappeared into the kitchen which had been converted from a sluice room. Grant busied himself getting knives, forks and plates before joining Matron in the kitchen to make toast.

A few minutes later Matron and her assistants emerged carrying plates of bacon and eggs – not one egg but two. Rationing was strict and limited to two eggs a week; College House broke into spontaneous applause. Miss Hillyers smiled in appreciation.

'I'll talk to the cooks about the porridge,' she said as she and her aids left to further applause.

This incident says something about how St Thomas's Hospital, as a voluntary hospital, was run before the NHS. It was a matriarchy founded by Florence Nightingale, and the quality of the food and the standard of cooking were matters for women, for Matron's Office, rather than for the House Governor.

* * *

Just before the war Norman Barrett, our chest surgeon, had returned after many months in Boston, Massachusetts, working with Dr Churchill, a famous pioneer of thoracic surgery. In St Thomas's was a girl of twelve who had a lower lobe of one lung that was little more than a bag of pus. She was frail, undernourished, had a constant fever and coughed up large amounts of green purulent phlegm day and night. The only antibiotic available, M & B 693, was useless. Barrett, who was universally called Pasty because of his complexion, pointed out that the only way to help this young patient was to remove the diseased lobe of the lung, an operation that was being successfully undertaken in the United States. Maureen was the first patient at St Thomas's Hospital to have her chest opened and part of the lung removed. Sadly, two days afterwards she died. We were stunned – sorry for the poor patient and almost as sorry for Pasty Barrett. A pall of mournful silence hung over the ward.

About a week later an unwritten edict emanated from Matron's Office but no one knew its precise origin or authority. 'God did not intend patients to have their chests opened,' the edict went. 'No more patients at this hospital will be subjected to this operation.' Not for a year was Pasty allowed to do another thoracotomy but thereafter the successful surgical treatment of patients with severe bronchiechastasis became more common.

*   *   *

Young doctors are liable to imitate, consciously or unconsciously, the characteristics, the intellectual attitudes and the mannerisms of the consultants for whom they work. As a house physician I had two role-models as they would be called today.

Sir Maurice Cassidy was the older. He specialised in heart disease and his reputation had been enhanced by attending King George V when he had pneumonia, and subsequently looking after King George VI. Sir Maurice was a quiet man; one might say even shy. He was punctilious in his devoted selfless care of the patients of St Thomas's where he was an honorary physician and like the other honoraries received no remuneration – his livelihood being derived from private practice. Sir Maurice claimed that every doctor would be more understanding of his patients if he himself had experienced three things – a serious acute illness, a chronic illness, and an endoscopic examination. In the 1914–18 war Sir Maurice had served in Mesopotamia where he had typhoid fever; after the war he developed pulmonary tuberculosis and spent many months in a sanatorium; more recently he'd had his lower bowel examined by sigmoidoscopy. No doubt these experiences made him more sympathetic to his patients, all of whom he treated with infinite kindness and courtesy.

When later I was his registrar, we were having tea one afternoon in Sister's sitting-room adjacent to the ward. The room was small and dark because the windows had been bricked up against bomb-blast. The hospital supplied a square of carpet and a few pieces of basic furniture, but Sister George took pride in making the room more personal by providing her own upholstered chairs, cushions, curtains, pictures, ornaments, photographs and china. Tea after the ward round was a ritual; Sister produced an elegant George III silver cream-jug for the milk and at her own expense the sandwiches and jam-filled spongecake.

Sir Maurice was being more expansive than usual. 'When I got back from eighteen months in the sanatorium in Davos – the TB had occurred at the worst possible time in my career – I tried to restrict my workload of private patients. I thought I could do this by increasing my consulting fee from £5 to £10. A fat lot of good that was; more patients were referred to me than ever! I felt badly that my secretary had to turn patients away but life would otherwise have been impossible.'

There was a knock on the door, and a porter presented me with some notes from Casualty. I glanced at the two cards.

'These new casualty officers!' I said. 'Been qualified about three weeks and here's one making a diagnosis of leprosy. I'll come down,' I told the porter. 'Leprosy indeed! I've never seen a case. Have you, sir?'

'Yes, as a matter of fact I have – several – years ago in Mes'pot. May I come down with you?'

It was typical of Sir Maurice to be so deferential. We finished tea and went to Casualty. The patient was a waiter aged twenty-three who worked in a Soho restaurant renowned during the war for its succulent horse-meat steaks. There were some curious lumps on his face.

'What do you think, sir?' I turned to Sir Maurice who looked more closely and ran his fingers over the patient's cheek.

'Dr Bamforth has taken a nasal swab,' interjected the keen casualty officer. 'It's positive for ... for...' he hesitated, trying to find the right word that would not alarm the patient, '...positive for Hansen's bacillus.'

The patient, who originally came from Cyprus, was admitted.

Later that evening we explained that he had leprosy and that it was curable. 'I don't know if you're religious but you shouldn't believe all that stuff in the Bible. You are not untouchable or even highly infectious. We'll put you right,' I said.

To keep beds vacant for air-raid casualties, arrangements were made to transfer Mr Christopoulou by ambulance to Guildford next day.

Half an hour before lunch the following morning I had a telephone call from the superintendent of St Luke's Hospital in Guildford.

'What the hell d'you think you're doing sending us a case of leprosy,' an angry voice shouted, 'and infecting everyone else in the Green Line ambulance? Are you crazy? All the other patients are very upset – can't blame 'em.'

'But he's not infectious in that sense,' I protested. 'All that stuff in the Bible about ringing bells and everyone keeping out of the way is rubbish – honestly. D'you know, you have to live with a leprous woman for twenty years before you get the disease? I promise you, it's all right.'

'You may think so, but I don't. I shall ring the Ministry of Health; it's monstrous. I've had to isolate the fellow. You should have sent him to a fever hospital.' He hung up.

Half way through lunch I was called to the phone.

'This is Dr Cochrane. You don't know me but I'm the Ministry's adviser on leprosy. I gather you've diagnosed a case and sent him down to Guildford?'

'Yes,' I said, fearing the worst.

'Perfectly all right,' reassured Dr Cochrane. 'Sounds interesting, and congratulations on isolating the bug from a nasal swab first time. I'll go down and see him in a day or two; probably transfer him to our leprosarium in Kent. Quite a lot of new cases turning up these days with all these foreigners around.'

'He's not infectious, is he, sir?' I asked. 'Not a danger to others in the bus or on the ward?'

'Oh Lord, no,' confirmed Dr Cochrane. 'Don't worry. These superstitions die hard. Oh, by the way I've placated that chap at St Luke's in Guildford; he sounded a bit narked.'

* * *

Dr Evan Jones was the other role-model and totally different from

Sir Maurice. Brought up on a hill farm in Wales, he spoke his native tongue more comfortably than English when he first came to London as a medical student. He was so outstanding that he was appointed a consultant at the unheard of age of twenty-nine. By the age of forty he was overweight – not surprising in view of the amount of beer he drank – and had a round cherubic face with sparse untidy sandy hair. His laugh was like a foghorn and he was never without a cigarette. He was untidy in his dress – the tail of his shirt often hanging outside his trousers. He was a master of administrative chaos with unopened letters stuffed in his jacket pockets. His eccentricities were legion and worn so naturally that no one for a moment thought they were affected. He called everyone, from his aristocratic private patients to the hospital cleaner, by their Christian name. People either accepted and loved Evan or disliked him; there was no in between. But those who disliked him were few and their distaste arose from Evan's apparent inability to conform with what was considered the correct, the appropriate, behaviour of a consultant to a major, rather snooty, London teaching hospital. Unconventional though he might be in his behaviour, all had to concede that he was outstanding as a physician, although even here his approach to patients was sometimes unusual. Some of his juniors thought his legendary diagnostic skills came from some magical Welsh intuition but in fact he managed to incite his patients to give him a clearer picture of their symptoms and problems than they did to anyone else, and it was this extraordinary rapport that I sought to emulate. He was late, not by a few minutes but by an hour or more, for everything – his ward rounds, his outpatient clinics and his private patients, but not for committee meetings because he never attended any. If something important to him, like the choosing of his houseman or registrar, was at issue, he nobbled the chairman of the committee ahead of time and told him who he was going to have. He was a law unto himself. Never did he write a scientific or clinical paper or report, but he was up-to-date with the literature although nobody had ever seen him read anything other than a newspaper.

*   *   *

From early days as a house physician I decided to become a physician; it was as general and non-specific as that – a physician

63

as opposed to being a surgeon. In 1941 relatively few physicians specialised in cardiology or in neurology; you had to be a generalist, and this required a lot of training and experience which culminated in passing a higher medical examination, Membership of the Royal College of Physicians of London. In those days this could be taken after being qualified for only twelve months. The exam was spread over a fortnight – two written papers, a clinical examination involving the diagnosis of patients, a *viva voce* exam, followed a week later by a final *viva.* Success in the clinical part was mandatory and failure at this early stage brought a halt to the candidate's further progression.

'Man, you'll pass the Membership; I did first time,' Evan said in his strong Welsh accent and put his hand as big as a bear's paw on my shoulder. 'Just be yourself. The Membership's no more difficult than the qualifying exam except you mustn't make any mistakes. D'you know it's quite good fun – really!' and he roared with his foghorn laugh.

It was cold and still dark when the alarm clock rang. Reluctantly I climbed out of bed and the clutter of books on the floor was a reminder of the previous night's last-minute revision. In College House I ate in silence, the improved porridge sprinkled with a little sugar from an ointment-jar that bore my name and contained the week's eight-ounce ration. The strong tea had the metallic taste of the large dented unscoured aluminium teapot. The two fried potato cakes swimming in grease were left untouched.

I hurried back to my bedroom to collect a bottle of Quink and the Faber slide-rule I'd had at Rugby. I closed Price's *Textbook of Medicine* and gave it a friendly pat; I'd read its 1600 pages and many other books and articles in *The Lancet, The Quarterly Journal of Medicine* and the *New England Journal of Medicine.*

Outside the hospital I caught a tram, with steep narrow steps leading to the top deck, which carried me, as it jolted and screeched arguing with the rails, to Holborn. It was a short walk through an alley to the examination halls in Queen Square.

Other candidates, apprehensive and uncommunicative, were waiting on the pavement.

'Hello Bill! Fancy seeing you.' It was a surprise to find Bill Trethowan there. I'd last heard him on the BBC.

'Hello,' he said in a quiet, lugubrious, worried voice. Further conversation stopped as the doors opened.

I found my desk. Evan Jones had told me the score. The morning and afternoon papers each had four questions, carrying equal marks, plus an optional few sentences of medical French and German to translate. At 12.15 the bell tinkled. The chairs were pushed noisily back as the candidates stretched themselves.

'Come and have lunch.' Bill and I pressed through the door onto the street. In a nearby pub was wartime potato-rich meat-deficient shepherd's pie. As Bill lifted his half pint of beer, he remarked, 'This exam is surrounded with mystique; it's as much a test of character as of knowledge.' A not entirely inaccurate assessment by a budding psychiatrist.

A glance at the third question in the afternoon paper made me groan. I read it again in horror. 'Discuss the Cause and Treatment of Writer's Cramp'. I was stumped; I hadn't the faintest idea. There was half a page on writer's cramp in Price's Textbook of Medicine but for some inexplicable reason I'd never bothered to read it. If I wrote nothing, I'd get no marks. I had to have a stab. On reflection I decided it was a psychological disorder that occurred in underpaid clerks who worked long hours in cramped offices with poor lighting and used quill pens. I painted a Dickensian picture of underprivileged scribes. Any literary eloquence belied confidence in the correctness of my answer.

Soon after five o'clock a tram took me back to St Thomas's – too weary to climb to the top deck. I gave tuppence to the conductor. In the seat in front sat a man with a pipe in his mouth.

'No smoking down 'ere,' ordered the conductor, 'only upstairs.'

The offender took the pipe out of his mouth and waved its empty bowl.

'I've got me shoes on but I ain't walking, am I?' he growled.

Back at the hospital I hurried to look up writer's cramp in Price's textbook. I was right; it was a psychological condition. Not wholly reassured I turned to another textbook. In this, to my alarm, writer's cramp was considered a physical illness due to some dysfunction of the muscles of the hand. I was even more surprised to find that the accounts in the two textbooks had been written by the same neurologist. I could only hope that whoever marked my paper was aware of this dichotomy.

At seven o'clock I put my head round the door of the porters' lodge.

'Going to the Rodney,' I said.

'Right you are, sir,' said the ever-cheerful Jones. 'Dr Evan Jones and some of the others are already over there.'

In the Blitz the Rodney had lost its windows, each of which was boarded up and looked like a black patch over a sightless eye. I opened the door to the saloon bar and hesitated on the threshold long enough to accommodate to the dimness inside. Fred Thrower, the landlord, waved from behind the bar. There was a lot of noise coming from the corner where the house staff usually sat. A roar of laughter confirmed that Evan was there. I went to the mahogany bar; the gashes inflicted by the shards of glass from the blown-in windows had been sandpapered, re-stained and polished. It was just as well the bomb had landed after closing time when Fred Thrower and his wife were asleep in the cellar. They were excellent publicans and enjoyed the comings and goings of the hospital staff. They enjoyed a little gossip and were beginning to relax the unwritten rule that no unaccompanied woman, and particularly no unmarried woman, was allowed, unless of a certain age, in either the public or saloon bars. Wisely the 'certain age' was undefined but the Throwers were not going to have their pub used as a pick-up point by the local tarts.

'Hello, sir!' greeted Fred. 'Let's see what I've got for you.' He thumbed through a wad of paper. 'There's a pint of best bitter from Mrs Horsely yesterday and a Scotch from Mr Brinley. Oh! and a sherry from the day before.'

'I'll have the pint of bitter, please.'

It was nearly always thus. Outpatients or relatives of inpatients dropped in, had a drink and left a present for the doctor. Not surprisingly Evan Jones got the most.

'How'd it go?' called Evan.

'Not bad. Want to see the papers?'

Evan studied them. 'God, what a bloody silly question – this one on writer's cramp.' He roared with laughter.

I told him what I'd read in the two textbooks.

'There you are!' Evan was dismissive. 'Wouldn't matter what you wrote, would it? That's why it's such a bloody silly question, man.'

Fred Thrower was clearing the empty glasses from the table. 'What the missus and I really like...' he drew in a long breath between his teeth. '...is a large bowl of mussels and shrimps (he pronounced it 'shiire-imps') washed down with a bottle of dry white wine while we listen to some Tchaiii-kovsky on the gramophone.' He took the empty glasses.

A week later I presented myself for the clinical part of the Membership at the London Hospital in Whitechapel where the bomb damage was even worse than around St Thomas's. To avoid giving information to the enemy, the newspapers were not allowed to reveal the location of an air-raid, but it was common knowledge that the docks and the East End had suffered more than their fair share.

Again Evan Jones had prepared me. 'The cases you'll be shown will be current inpatients or old outpatients. There'll be no doubt about the diagnosis. For God's sake don't think you'll be shown anything esoteric.'

I was taken to my long case. 'You've got an hour,' the registrar said. 'I'll ring the bell ten minutes before your time is up.'

Miss Fingerhut was aged eighteen and even before examining her I knew what was wrong. I could hear Evan saying, 'D'you know, if you don't have a good idea of the diagnosis after taking the history, you probably never will.'

Miss Fingerhut had a very overactive thyroid gland. When I'd finished examining her, I dismissed the chaperoning nurse and sat on the edge of her bed.

'D'you know what brought this on, Miss Fingerhut?' In 1942 the cause of hyperthyroidism was as much a mystery as it largely is today.

Miss Fingerhut hesitated. 'Well, my boyfriend and I and Mum and Dad used to go to the air-raid shelter together, see?' she said in a rush. 'It's a surface shelter – a big 'un; holds about 400 people. It had a direct hit – not at our end but the other. Lots of people were killed. We weren't hurt much but I couldn't stop screaming. My boyfriend got cross with me – said I was behaving 'ysteric-like. "If you don't pull yerself together, I won't fetch you to the shelter again" – that's what he said.'

'And . . . ?'

'He didn't. He made me stay home.'

'On your own?'

'No, him and me. We're on the sixth floor of a Peabody. When the bombs came down, the whole building swayed; I swear to God it did. That's when my eyes started popping out . . .' She burst into tears.

* * *

A few days later a letter came, its origin immediately discernible because of the unusual oversized bold typeface used by the Royal College of Physicians. Inside was a card saying that the President, Censors and Examiners were satisfied with my performance in the written and clinical parts of the examination and would I please attend for the *viva voce*.

Evan was more optimistic than I was. 'They've weeded out about eighty per cent of the candidates, but don't forget only ten per cent are going to pass,' he said.

The exam itself a week later was almost enjoyable. Evan had warned against speaking too fast. 'The quicker you answer, the more questions they've got time to ask. You'll be unlucky to fail now,' he said. 'With the first question you'll know how you're doing. If they ask you a relatively simple straightforward one, you're borderline; if they ask you some esoteric way-out question, you're home and dry.'

I stepped from the bright spring sunlight of Trafalgar Square through the columned entrance into the grandeured gloom of the Royal College of Physicians. The hall with a wide strip of red carpet laid across the marble floor was cool and silent. I climbed the shallow steps of the wide staircase with its ornate gilded wrought-iron banisters. At the top stood Miss Cook, a stocky woman with short grey hair, holding a clipboard. I handed her my card. The College Secretary took it, ticked my name off her list and said simply, 'Wait here,' as she guided me to a small room.

After what seemed eternity Miss Cook put her head round the door.

'This way, please.'

The long table in the Censor's room was covered with green baize. At the far end, with his back to the light from a window overlooking Trafalgar Square, sat the President, Lord Moran, stirring a cup of coffee, flanked by the censors and examiners. I stood beside the vacant chair at the end of the table – waiting. Never before had I seen the inside of the beautiful Censor's room with its linen-fold oak panelling, salvaged during the Great Fire of London from the College's original home in Warwick Lane in the City and destined in later years to be moved again to the College's new building in Regent's Park.

'Sit down.' Lord Moran shuffled some papers on the table in front of him. 'Tell us about phlebotomus fever.'

My heart gave a lurch. What a question – phlebotomus fever! Surely this was one of Evan's esoteric ones. My voice was slightly shaky as I began.

'Phlebotomus fever, sir, is a virus disease that occurs in the Middle East and India. It's transmitted by a particular mosquito – the *Aedes Aegypti*.' (How could anyone forget an insect with such a pretty name?) 'The condition is also known as dengue or break-back fever.' I went on until, unable to think of any more to say, I stopped rather lamely.

'Good.' Lord Moran's smile was snake-like. 'Ever seen a case?'

What a stupid question; of course I hadn't. He's teasing me, I thought.

'What do you know about *la maladie du petit papier*, also known as *la maladie du morçeau de papier*?' The President prided himself on his French accent.

For a moment I was dumbfounded. 'The illness of the bit of paper?' I queried, playing for time. 'I've ... I've never heard of it.' It was safer to be honest.

Lord Moran smiled with evident delight. 'Osler said ... you know who Osler was?'

I nodded.

'Osler had an aphorism: a patient with a written list of symptoms is neurotic. What's your view about patients who bring a little piece of paper with all their symptoms written down, eh?'

'Well,' I began slowly, now knowing what was being asked. 'It's difficult to generalise. In my limited experience when a patient has more than about ten complaints, she – and I think it's usually a woman – probably doesn't have much wrong with her.'

The examiners had started arguing amongst themselves, each with his own ideas about patients with a *morçeau de papier*.

'Gentlemen, please!' The President silenced them. He held a hushed conversation with the two Censors on either side, and then stood up. 'Thank you. We're quite satisfied. Pray step outside and have a word with Miss Cook.'

I walked the length of the long table passed the smiling Censors and examiners. Lord Moran shook my hand. Outside the steely Miss Cook was more affable.

'There you are,' she said like a nanny for once pleased with her charge. 'Sit down and write a cheque for £50.'

My hand shook a little as I did so.

6

Steep Learning Curves I: Anorexia Nervosa

My immediate future in 1942 was likely to be with the armed forces. As I walked down the main corridor of St Thomas's I ran into the Dean.

'Congratulations on your Membership. Well done,' he said. 'How long have you been qualified?'

'Just over a year, sir.'

'So you've taken the exam after the shortest allowable time, eh? Good. I'd like you to start as medical registrar next month.'

I mumbled my thanks.

'Right. I'll discuss it with the medical committee and let you know.'

Today such an appointment could never be made in such an irregular way – without formal application, ten copies of your *curriculum vitae* and the names of two consultants for whom you had worked and who were willing to give a reference.

Passing the Membership Examination of the Royal College of Physicians does not imply you have become a specialist in medicine. On the contrary it is nothing more than a passport to further training. Today this takes some six or more years' experience in approved hospital posts as a senior house officer, then as a registrar and finally as a senior registrar before you can apply to the Joint Committee on Higher Medical Training for accreditation as a specialist physician and, if this is granted, become registered as such with the General Medical Council.

Thus for the next two years I worked at St Thomas's, answerable to the consultants and to Hec Johnson, who remained Resident Assistant Physician. There was no official contract, no rota, no official time off duty, and I was on a steep learning curve.

* * *

I picked up the telephone within seconds of it starting to ring.

'This is Sister City. A patient with anorexia nervosa has been admitted to my side room. She's eighteen and under the care of Dr Gardiner-Hill. His houseman has just seen her; you will too?'

'Of course, Sister. I'll be down this afternoon.' I put the phone back on its cradle. You could read a good deal more into what Sister City had just said. City was a male surgical ward and Sister would not take kindly to having a female patient admitted to her side room nor to one with a medical rather than a surgical condition.

Sister City – all the Sisters at St Thomas's were known by the name of the ward they were in charge of rather than by their surname – approved of Dr Gardiner-Hill despite her low esteem of physicians in general; by her standards they were too inactive. Sister City had been in charge of the ward for twenty-five years – 'pre- and post-menopausally' as Evan Jones had once remarked one evening in the Rodney. She was a nurse of whom Miss Nightingale would have been proud. She was a no-nonsense, straightforward lady who many years ago had made it known that she would never seek promotion to an administrative post. Being a ward sister was her *métier.* Whenever she considered the number of nurses allocated to her ward were insufficient to maintain her high standards, she did not accept the situation as a *fait accompli* as others might have done. She went straight to Matron's office and was so persuasive that one of the assistant matrons mustered the extra nurses deemed necessary.

In her mid-fifties she was still strikingly good-looking. Most of her contemporaries wore no make-up but Sister City saw no reason to accept the anaemic appearance so common in wartime when there was little time for exposure to fresh air and sunshine. Her lips and cheeks had an unobtrusive pink tinge and her eyelashes the benefit of a touch of mascara. Her slender figure was the envy of many of her junior staff. Her face had a certain beauty with its deep blue eyes that twinkled and a mouth that rose at the corners in a ready smile. She was scrupulously fair to her nurses without having favourites. Unlike some of her colleagues Sister City encouraged each member of her team to develop their own individuality, but they had to conform by always being punctual, and while on duty they had to give their undivided attention to

72

the patients. She would not allow two junior nurses, making a patient's bed, to discuss their previous evening's social adventures. Her patients revered her. Without being stand-offish she never addressed an adult patient by his Christian name nor, if he were elderly, called him 'Dad'. Many of her charges had cancer and suffered multiple operations which they survived in large part because of her dedicated nursing skill. Her patients were never allowed to suffer pain. Some discomfort was inevitable during the process of recovery but Sister City did not believe this was 'character forming'. From her long experience she could anticipate uncannily a patient's requirement for morphine or pethidine before the effects of the previous dose had worn off. She ran each successive house surgeon with a firm hand but never undermined his self-confidence, and he learnt as much from her as he did from the registrar and consultants. She moved quickly on light feet like a dancer but never appeared in a hurry. She had time for everyone's problems. Her nursing staff, even the most inept, adored her for she was no harridan.

When I'd been a house surgeon on City ward, I'd wondered about this strange powerful woman. How was it that she had never married? She was, I realised, no desiccated spinster who was frightened of men; her management of the ward thrived on her femininity. One evening in the pub I had raised this with Evan, who had simply shrugged his shoulders and said, 'Good God man, how would I know? She did have a feller but he was killed – riding in a point-to-point, I think. D'you know, it's bloody sad really...' and he mopped his eyes with the back of his wrist.

Margaret Borden was sitting tense and bolt upright in bed when I saw her later that afternoon. Her straight straggly black hair hung down to her shoulders. She had large brown eyes that seemed to stand out from her purple pinched face with its beaky blue nose and sunken cheeks covered with fine down. She was wrapped in a dark-brown woollen Jaeger dressing gown edged with light brown piping. We shook hands and I sat on the edge of her bed to read the houseman's notes. Margaret's father was a general practitioner in Cheltenham and a friend of Dr Gardiner-Hill. Clearly she had anorexia nervosa. Dr Harold Gardiner-Hill specialised in endocrinology and although anorexia nervosa is not primarily an endocrine disease he was referred many patients with this complaint. He was a charming man with a ready sense of humour and a golf handicap

73

of scratch; he later became Captain of the Royal and Ancient at St Andrew's. He had his own particular mannerisms and feigned a poor memory.

'This is the man you saw last week, sir, with jaundice,' we might say on a ward round.

'Ah! yes, the yeller feller.'

Or, 'This is the patient with diarrhoea, sir.'

'Ah! yes, I remember – the crappy chappie.'

I left Margaret and went into the ward to tell Sister how she would have to be treated. She listened carefully.

'We'll do our best. I've never nursed a case of anorexia nervosa before but I'm sure we'll manage.'

In City ward patients were routinely weighed once a week. When the houseman and I went to visit Margaret at the end of her first week, we called at Sister's desk in the middle of the ward. She looked puzzled as she stood to greet us.

'I don't understand. That girl's not gained an ounce – not an ounce. In fact she's lost a pound. She's eaten everything we've given her – always leaves a clean plate.'

We went and examined Margaret. She was just as thin as she'd been on admission. What made me move her bed away from the wall and pull up the lower sash of the window behind her I don't know. I stuck my head out into the warm summer sunlight. City ward was on the ground floor and underneath was the basement. Splattered on the flag-stones that paved the well below was an unpleasant grey mess – the meals that Margaret had thrown out of the window. Sister also took a look. The faintest trace of a smile, which the patient did not see, crossed her face.

'Margaret, look at this,' I said.

Reluctantly the patient climbed out of bed, pulling the dressing gown around her, and walked to the window but hardly looked outside. 'Nothing to do with me,' she said.

'It is, you know. From now on, Sister, we'll weigh Margaret every morning at the same time and in the same clothes before breakfast and before she's had anything to drink.'

It worked. Every day Margaret gained half a pound. After two weeks she'd gained seven pounds. Everyone was pleased, despite Margaret remaining uncommunicative and monosyllabic.

At the beginning of the third week Sister City was badly and uncharacteristically out of sorts.

'What's bugging you today, Sister?' I asked.

'The patients didn't sing this morning. The chaplain took the weekly ward service at eight-thirty; staff nurse Tomkins played the piano, but very few of the patients joined in the hymns – all the old favourites they know perfectly well.'

As we walked to the side room to see Margaret, we passed a patient I'd known when I was a house surgeon on the ward. 'Hello, how are you getting on?' We stopped to chat and just before moving on I asked him, 'Did you sing the hymns this morning?'

'No, sir,' said the patient.

'But why not? You know all the hymns, surely?' Sister asked.

'Course I do – at least the tunes. But I can't remember the words, can I?'

'But the words are in the hymn book.'

'Didn't have no 'ymn book, did I?'

'No hymn book? Why not?'

''Cos there was a shortage, Sister.'

Sister stopped a passing probationer. 'You handed out the hymn books this morning, nurse?' she asked.

'Yes, Sister, as many as I could find – but the cupboard was half empty.'

We moved on to the side room. As usual Margaret was sitting upright in bed enveloped in her brown Jaeger dressing-gown.

'Good morning, Margaret.' I took down her weight chart from its hook on the wall. She had gained another half pound since the day before. 'I want to take a look at you. Would you mind taking your dressing gown off, please.'

Margaret gave a look of defiance and folded her arms across the front of her chest. 'It's too cold – much too cold. *Please,* Sister,' she pleaded.

'Margaret, we do have to look, you know,' Sister said.

Strung around Margaret's waist, attached with thin gauze bandages, were fifteen hymn books.

We had learnt that in future Margaret must be watched as she ate each meal.

Four months later Margaret left hospital, and five years after that she was married. So was Sister City; she married a widower with two young children.

* * *

75

Anorexia nervosa is not a new disease but its incidence is increasing. In 1689 Dr Richard Morton described a girl of eighteen 'like a skeleton clad in skin' who died of what he called 'atrophia nervosa' (nervous wasting). He also described a clergyman's son aged sixteen who 'fell gradually into a total want of appetite, occasioned by his studying too hard and the passions of his mind, and upon that into a universal atrophy, pining away more and more'. This patient survived, and was much improved by taking ass's milk and a change of scene.

A larger number of patients with anorexia nervosa were described by Sir William Gull (1816–90), a physician to Guy's Hospital and at one time President of the Royal College of Physicians, when he spoke on 'Hysterical Apepsia' at the Annual Conference of the British Medical Association in Oxford in 1868. Sir William described a 'peculiar form of disease' that occurred in young women aged sixteen to twenty-three who refused to eat and became extremely emaciated. After further experience of the condition, he changed the name in 1874 to anorexia nervosa.

During the last fifty years the incidence of anorexia nervosa has trebled in many western countries. When I was a medical student the disease was largely confined to a particular age group drawn from a narrow stratum of society. They were the daughters, aged twelve to twenty-four, of fathers who were members of a profession or officers in the armed forces. Today the condition occurs in all socioeconomic groups and the age range is wider, occasional patients being aged thirty or over and rarely married women who have had children. As Gull noted, the disease rarely occurs in men. The first man I saw with anorexia nervosa was a contemporary medical student who during our time together at hospital characteristically never submitted himself as a patient.

Anorexia nervosa is a protracted disease, often spanning many years. The patient is usually intelligent and often attractive. She is animated and active – nowadays often athletic or attends a gymnasium. Characteristically she develops a particular distaste for all starchy foods. Initially the weight loss is gradual and may not incite parental comment. Concomitant with the weight loss, or frequently preceding it, menstruation stops. This amenorrhoea is not weight-related; it is psychological in origin. Any emotional upset can stop menstruation; in World War II sixty per cent of women stopped having periods as soon as they were incarcerated in a prisoner of war camp, long before they became malnourished. By the time the patient with anorexia reluctantly agrees to see a doctor, she is likely to be substantially underweight. Despite being skin and bones, she protests that there is nothing wrong with her. Most will explain they are dieting to lose weight; others say that their reason for not eating is that food gives them a tummy ache or causes nausea.

The physical appearance of a girl with this disease is so characteristic that the diagnosis may be made on sight. Her extremities are cold and reddish-purple in colour, her face is pinched and her scalp hair lacks lustre. Often her dry skin is covered with a fine fuzz of delicate hair as though nature were trying to provide extra insulation to counteract the loss of the normal insulating layer of fat that lies under the skin. The heart rate is slow and the blood pressure low. Without treatment the worst affected patients may succeed in starving themselves to death.

It is not the disease so much as the treatment that proves so distressing, both to the patient and, particularly, to her family. Attempts by the parents to encourage their daughter to eat more invariably end in failure. The parents become increasingly frustrated, sitting down to meal after meal which their child refuses to eat. Increased pressure leads to extraordinary subterfuges on her part and the parents cannot believe that their daughter would deliberately lie or deceive them. Mealtimes become a battlefield, with one parent likely to complain that the other is being too harsh. The whole family is in disarray.

Often several factors cause anorexia nervosa. Today slimness is very much in fashion and its persistent visual promotion by women's magazines and television may contribute to the increased incidence. Many patients with anorexia have a morbid overwhelming fear of becoming fat. They have a distorted perception of their body image leading them to believe they are fatter than they really are. Younger patients may not wish to grow up; they are frightened of their emerging sexuality and seek to avoid becoming physically and sexually mature.

Patients, reluctant to be treated, make endless excuses as to why they cannot come into hospital. But hospitalisation is essential and Sir William Gull was well aware of this. 'The inclinations of the patient must in no way be consulted,' he wrote. 'The patient should be fed at regular intervals, surrounded by persons who would have moral control over her; relatives and friends being generally the worst attendants.' Success depends on the patient being admitted to hospital and to a ward where the doctors and nurses have experience of the condition. The role of the nurses is of paramount importance; they may be the same age or a little older than the patient, with whom they may identify because they too wish to be slim, and allow themselves to be manipulated by her.

Initially the patient is confined strictly to bed and visitors of any kind, including the girl's parents, are banned. With the first small meal in hospital it is firmly made clear that the patient will eat all that she is given. The eating of every meal must be supervised by a nurse. Gradually the daily food intake is increased. A reward system allows the patient to earn certain privileges as her weight rises to mutually agreed levels. The first target is being allowed up to use the lavatory; thereafter, with increasing weight, come in succession bathing, use of the telephone, visitors, dressing in ordinary clothes and being allowed home for a weekend. Psychological improvement may only become apparent when the patient has achieved about eighty per cent of her ideal weight; the time has then come to explore the underlying psychological causes of the anorexia. Finally, when the patient's weight is stable, she is allowed home but further outpatient supervision is essential. Major or minor relapses are common but an encouraging milestone is the return of menstruation.

Anorexia overlaps with an allied condition, bulimia. Sir Edward Gull noted that some girls with anorexia might, after refusing food for a long time, indulge in phases of compulsive eating. Today we are familiar with the girl or woman who goes on eating binges during which she eats vast amounts of food and then makes herself vomit. Patients who have seemingly recovered from anorexia nervosa may also resort to bulimia nervosa.

7

II: Gout

'Next please,' I shouted loudly.

One of the main duties of the medical registrar at St Thomas's in 1943 was to be in charge of Sorting Room, the title given to a clinic held every weekday between ten o'clock and noon. It took place in two identical large windowless white-tiled rooms, one for women and the other for men, each reminiscent of some vast Victorian lavatory. Bare wooden benches with hard backs were arranged in neat rows on the tiled floor. The registrar sat at the far end of each room in turn, perched on a high chair with a tall narrow sloping desk in front of him and the patient far below on an ordinary chair – an arrangement hardly conducive to a good doctor-patient relationship. Intimate conversation was impossible because the words exchanged reverberated off the tiled walls into the ears of those waiting on the crowded benches.

Medical Sorting Room fulfilled an important function in the care of the inhabitants of Lambeth and South London. During the war, few general practitioners were left in the neighbourhood and they were elderly and overworked. If a GP took an evening off, patients attending the evening surgery would simply be handed by the receptionist his visiting card on which was written, 'Please see and advise', and told to go next day to St Thomas's at ten o'clock where they would be seen in Sorting Room. Other patients were referred from Casualty, unless they were considered suitable for the attention of a consultant in a more formal outpatient clinic, and there was a considerable passing trade of sick people from inner London.

'Next, please,' I repeated louder. With difficulty the patient levered himself up from the wooden bench with the help of a stick. He

79

wore a battered stained trilby hat frayed at the brim and an old suit several sizes too small so that his belly bulged over the tight waistband of his trousers. He hobbled to the chair beside my desk with dramatic effort and handed me his blank hospital card. Carefully he lowered himself into the chair, exhaling a breath that carried the rancid smell of stale beer. He removed his hat with his right hand in which he was holding his walking stick, and it banged against the desk. I recoiled in mock horror at the studied histrionics but said nothing.

'It's me bleeding foot and me bleeding 'and, doc. Cor, stone the crows!'

Mr Grounds was clearly an avid reader of the *Sunday Express* in which a humorous columnist with the pseudonym of Beachcomber regularly introduced such catchy phrases as 'Cor, stone the crows'.

'Look, doc, look,' gasped Mr Grounds as he twisted round and gingerly lifted his left hand on to the desk above him. It was swollen, fiery red and obviously exquisitely painful.

I studied it. 'And what about your foot?'

He looked down at the home-made felt boot held in place with a safety pin.

'Blooming awful.'

Mr Grounds was led away by a nurse to one of the curtained cubicles built behind a partition at the end of the room. Two medical students approached.

'Can we sit in?' When they were not on a ward round or at a lecture, some of the keener students liked to drop in and see what was going on in Sorting Room.

'Something special here,' I said. 'Come and see.'

They examined Mr Grounds's hand and foot. I asked him some questions. 'Hear that?' I said. 'I learnt the other day that gout usually starts in the night or is present on waking in the morning. As you heard that happened here. He was woken in the night by the pain. It's a useful diagnostic tip. How d'you treat gout?'

'Colchicine,' said one of the students, but declined to be drawn further.

'Yes, colchicine. It's derived from the yellow crocus and I believe was first introduced into England from France during the Restoration. Charles II had gout and heard of this remedy from his relatives at the French Court.' History isn't one of my strong subjects but a good story, whether true or not, helps students to remember. 'So the king sent for the royal botanist and told him to grow crocuses and extract the colchicine from them. The botanist planted acres of crocuses in Essex and that is why Saffron Walden is called Saffron Walden – the yellow wood.'

'Unlikely story,' quietly suggested one of the students who was a late entry to medicine having previously taught English at Eton. 'Saffron Walden sounds more like a Saxon name to me, probably existed long before the Restoration.'

'As you like, Crawshaw. Perhaps you'll look it up in the library and tell us when you've found out.'

Mr Grounds returned a week later; his hand and foot were much improved. He was grateful.

''Ere you are, doc – a present.' From a wicker bag he drew two large crabs. 'Know 'ow to tell they're fresh?' he asked. 'You squeezes 'em, see? If water comes out, they're fresh – not all dried up, see?' I was delighted; such a delicacy in wartime was rare.

A few days later Johnson, the cheerful casualty porter who shepherded the patients into the men's Sorting Room, sidled up.

'Sir, I've heard they've got razor blades at Peter Jones' store in Sloane Square,' he said confidentially.

There was a perpetual shortage of razor blades in the war and often I had to make one last three or four increasingly painful weeks.

That afternoon things were quiet. I slipped out of the hospital and took the Underground to Sloane Square.

'One packet only,' said the girl behind the counter.

'I've got a lot of friends at the hospital,' I tried persuasively.

The girl eyed me, not knowing whether to believe this or not. 'All right, you can have three.'

As I left the shop on my way back to the Underground on the other side of Sloane Square, a man wearing spectacles with dark blue lenses was standing on the pavement outside. On his chest rested a small wooden tray held horizontal by a length of dirty tape strung round his neck. On the tray were boxes of Pride of England matches and hanging down from it a notice that read 'Totally Blind – Please Help'. As I hurried past there was something familiar about the man but I couldn't remember where I'd seen him before.

As instructed Mr Grounds reappeared in Sorting Room a week later, this time nearly cured of his gout. He produced another pair of crabs from his wicker bag.

'Know 'ow to tell a 'en from a cock?' he asked and proceeded to demonstrate.

Suddenly I remembered. 'I know you. You're the blind man outside Peter Jones. You rascal! You can see as well as I can.'

Mr Grounds didn't deny it. 'Well, guv...' he said glumly. 'Got to make a living some'ow, ain't I?' It didn't occur to me to ask why Mr Grounds had not been called up for military service. If it had occurred to me, I wouldn't have asked; it was none of my business.

Not until six years later, after I returned from India, did I see Mr Grounds again. I recognised him instantly, standing on the pavement just outside the Sloane Square Underground station tapping the curb with a white stick at the Belisha crossing into the Square. He was unmistakable with the same tray on his chest and the same grubby Pride of England matches, but now the notice read, 'Totally Blinded in the War'.

'Old rascal!' I thought as I went to talk to him.

'Hello, Mr Grounds. How are you? How's the gout?'

'Who are you?' the voice was querulous.

'Don't you remember – during the war – at St Thomas's? You taught me all about crabs.'

Mr Grounds brightened – of course he remembered. 'Cor, stone the crows! Fancy meeting you again, doc. 'Ere, give me a 'and across this bleeding road, will yer? It's a fair sod this crossing.'

I looked at him in surprise. 'Are you really blind?' I asked.

'Corse I'm blind.' Mr Grounds said without any self-pity. 'Copped it with a doodle-bug at the end of the war, didn't I? Was the bleeding glass that did it. Whole front of the house came in. Killed the missus. Look...' He lifted his tinted spectacles and I saw two grey, clouded, shrunken sightless eyes.

* * *

Gout is often portrayed as a fun disease. Certainly over the years magazines have printed humorous cartoons portraying irritable gouty gentlemen. It is a source of amusement because the condition is generally believed to afflict only the well-to-do, and particularly members of the aristocracy who drink too much port. To poke fun is considered legitimate because it is deemed a self-inflicted disease and never fatal. Neither happens to be true.

Doctors enjoy patients with gout because it is a disease for which there is effective treatment. Although sometimes difficult to diagnose in the first attack, this is usually easy if it is remembered that the pain nearly always wakes the patient in the small hours or is present on waking in the morning. The diagnosis can be confirmed by a number of laboratory tests. There is no shortage of effective drugs to relieve the severe pain of acute gout nor – and equally important – of drugs to prevent future recurrences. The disease is eight times more common in men than women, and usually presents in males between the ages of twenty-five and sixty-five, although I have seen an eighteen-year-old schoolboy with gouty arthritis of the ankle. In women it seldom occurs until after the menopause, as Hippocrates first pointed out. Often there is a family history.

The disorder is all to do with the elimination from the body of uric acid which is excreted by the kidneys. The well-known tendency of alcohol to precipitate acute gout is due to the metabolic products of the alcohol interfering with the renal excretion of uric acid. The bad reputation of port is in part related to its high alcohol content and in part to it being drunk in large quantities in the old days. Nowadays it is drunk in smaller amounts at the end of a meal, before and during which other alcoholic drinks are likely to have been consumed.

Patients certainly do not find gout amusing. In an acute attack the pain can be excruciating, and may occur at some socially inconvenient time – when the patient is about to go on holiday or is scheduled for an overseas business trip. Commonly the base of the big toe is the first site to be affected but, in decreasing order of frequency, the ankles, wrists, elbows and the small joints of the feet and hands may be involved.

If not recognised, or if inadequately treated, the chances of chronic gout develop after many years so that the affected joints become deformed. Crystals of uric acid may form stones in the kidneys; these can be extremely painful and the kidneys may be permanently damaged, leading eventually to death from renal failure.

In the emergency treatment of acute gout, cortisone or one of its modern equivalents can be very effective, although not necessarily more so than some newer drugs known as non-steroidal anti-inflammatory agents, NSAIDs for short. I recall an emergency that arose in an Irish bookmaker whose prosperous London business came from private telephone lines to many of the clubs in St

James's and Pall Mall. Three days before he was due to leave for a salmon fishing holiday in his native Connemara, he developed acute gout in his right wrist. It was redder than his rubicund face, extremely painful, and swollen 'almost beyond belief' as he put it. Little short of a modern therapeutic miracle was required if he were to hold a fishing rod and avoid losing the deposit he'd paid to fish in his homeland. I gave him some prednisolone to relieve the acute situation.

Six days later a fifteen-pound salmon in a wicker basket was delivered to my rooms – a tribute to the corticosteroid and to the bookmaker's skill with his rod.

8

III: Psychological Ill-health

Soon after qualifying and having to cope single-handed with patients, it became clear that many of them did not suffer from the diseases we'd read about in textbooks or had been taught about in outpatient clinics or on the wards. We were not so naive as to think that even if they did have a diagnosable illness it would conform closely to the orthodox description, and we soon appreciated that many patients had difficulty in giving a coherent history of what they had noticed to be wrong; often they were vague and sometimes contradictory.

Mrs Bertol provided an important lesson when she appeared one morning in Sorting Room. She was a little lady, sixty years old, neatly dressed in black. Carefully she placed her hospital notes, a thick wad of cards, on my tall old-fashioned desk and quietly said, 'Good morning,' as she sat down.

Perched above her I scanned the top card. Each month the date had been rubber-stamped in, and against each my predecessor had written 'Rep. Mist. 1/12' – meaning that the same mistura or mixture was to be repeated for a month. What was the mixture and for what was it being given? Thumbing through the earlier cards they all showed the same entry, month after month and year after year. Right at the back of the notes were some unreadable hieroglyphics.

'What's wrong with you, Mrs Bertol?' I asked.

She looked puzzled. 'I just want another bottle of medicine, please.'

'I understand that, but why?'

'I just want another bottle of medicine, thank you,' Mrs Bertol said primly.

'I know, but what symptoms have you got?' I thumbed through the notes again trying to discover what the mixture was, and eventually found it – a so-called tonic without any scientifically proven efficacy for anything.

'Mrs Bertol,' I said gently, 'I want to examine you, to take a proper look at you. Please go behind the curtains; nurse will look after you.'

Mrs Bertol gave a pained, an exasperated look – almost of disbelief – but went obediently.

I climbed down from the chair and entered the partitioned examination cubicles. Lying on the couch and covered with a thick calico sheet, a naked Mrs Bertol was still wearing her shabby black velvet hat with its floppy brim and a large yellow-headed pin stuck through it.

Questions about her weight, appetite, bowels and any pains revealed nothing unusual. Mrs Bertol said she had a little arthritis in her fingers from scrubbing floors. Otherwise everything was all right and when it came to examining her I was none the wiser as to what I was looking for. Her blood pressure was normal; everything was normal. Puzzled, I went back to the desk and recorded on the card that nothing abnormal had been found. Mrs Bertol emerged from behind the curtain. This time she did not sit down but stood, her face almost level with the top of the desk.

'I'd like my medicine now, please doctor,' she said in a determined quiet voice.

'Please sit down,' I invited but Mrs Bertol remained standing. 'Look, I've examined you from head to toe and I can't find anything wrong. I don't think you need any medicine. You're healthy.'

A brief look of concern crossed Mrs Bertol's face. She took a deep breath and pursed her lips to give added force to what she was going to say. 'Young man,' she began, 'I've been coming to this hospital every month since my hubby was killed in 1917. I like this hospital. I come on the third Monday of every month – always have done. I like to come and meet my friends here, and have a cup o' tea for a penny. That medicine, it does me good.' She paused and took another breath before her final outburst. 'And young man, it's going to take someone much older and much wiser than you to stop me coming, see?'

Yes! I saw, and smiled as I wrote 'Rep. Mistura 1/12' and handed her the wad of cards. 'Goodbye, I'll see you in a month's time.'

'Thank you,' Mrs Bertol did not smile as she left.

Over the months we became friends. I learnt a lot about Mrs Bertol and her deceased husband – now a shadowy figure – and her lonely childless life cleaning offices at night when everyone else had gone home. I also learnt that loneliness was a disease that had not yet reached the textbooks. A little useless tonic and the companionship of the hospital could bring relief certainly more cheaply and perhaps as effectively as counselling or psychotherapy.

At least twenty per cent of the patients in Sorting Room had no discernible physical disease. They suffered from anxieties, insomnia and bizarre aches and pains for which there was no apparent cause. Bemused by many of these patients whom we suspected of having psychosomatic illness, I sought help from a slender volume, *The Common Neuroses*, by Dr T.A. Ross, a psychiatrist at Guy's Hospital. From this it became clear that patients with emotional or psychological problems could suffer and truly experience aches, pains and other symptoms in almost any part of the body. This was a revelation but without any training in psychotherapy, which was the recommended method of treatment, I faced a therapeutic brick wall which years later was partially demolished by Dr Michael Balint's *The Doctor, His Patient and the Illness*. Thus began a lifelong interest in psychological medicine, some knowledge of which is essential to everyone practising in any branch of clinical medicine.

Psychotherapy or even psychoanalysis, in one or other of their several forms, plays an important role in the treatment of several psychiatric disorders – not serious because they aren't lethal but incapacitating because they cause a great deal of human suffering. Anxieties, phobias, disturbed interpersonal relationships and compulsive behaviour are conditions that respond poorly to such medication as tranquillisers and are best helped by some form of psychotherapy.

The term 'psychological medicine' has merit because the inclusion of the word 'medicine' is a reminder that such disorders are part of the generality of medicine and that psychological disturbances may be the consequence of some physical disorder far distant from the brain. An elderly male patient, when he had a urinary tract infection, used to greet me on the ward round with a cheerful 'And how is the Father, the Son and the Holy Ghost today?' When the infection was controlled, the cot sides on the bed could be taken down and I received the more conventional greeting, 'Good morning, doctor.' Many other physical diseases may lead to a serious mental upset that remits when the underlying disorder is cured. Belatedly it is increasingly appreciated today that mental ill-health may be the consequence of a disturbance of the numerous chemical substances, the neurotransmitters, that regulate the activity of the cells in the brain. Research into mental processes is not made easy by the brain being protected inside a rigid bony skull that makes it inaccessible to removal of a small piece of tissue for chemical or microscopical examination. Nor can the diagnosis of many mental illnesses be confirmed objectively by laboratory tests or X-rays; it depends solely on the clinical picture.

Regrettably the training in psychological medicine we received as students was woefully inadequate. It is painful to recall the ineptitude of our senior consultant psychiatrist who was just as incomprehensible to his patients as he was to us. His inability to establish any rapport with those who sought his help was uncomfortable to perceive, and after attending two or three of his clinics we simply absented ourselves – not that he appeared to notice.

Fortunately we learnt something about schizophrenia, which at that time was the most commonly recognised mental disorder. Once a week a bus took us to a Dickensian lunatic asylum in South London, still standing today, where a clever, if histrionic, medical superintendent resplendent in a short black coat and sponge-bag trousers gave us lecture-demonstrations. From him we learnt about the various forms of schizophrenia and his clinical demonstrations of individual patients, selected from more than a thousand in the hospital, were unforgettable.

Largely through the inventiveness of the pharmaceutical industry, much progress has been made in the treatment of schizophrenia. In 1952 there were nearly 160,000 schizophrenic patients in mental asylums in England. By 1988 there were only 60,000. However, this great reduction, which has further progressed, may mean that too many who are not really ready for an independent existence have been discharged into the care of the community. The ability of most of them to lead independent lives is due to the invention in 1953 of the drug chlorpromazine (Largactil). This compound is still used but has largely been replaced by related compounds which have a longer duration of action and fewer side-effects. By moderating the action of the neurotransmitters, the chemical substances that allow one cell in the brain to communicate with another, these pharmaceutical compounds have brought relief to many patients who suffer from delusions or hallucinations or are prone to aggressive behaviour.

Another important and common psychiatric disease is clinical depression for which successful medicinal treatment was first discovered in 1955. It is not a new disease and in the past was often called 'melancholia'. The term 'endogenous depression' may be applied when the cause is unrelated to external events whereas 'exogenous depression' or 'reactive depression' is the consequence of unfavourable outside events such as bereavement, loss of a job, marital disruption or financial worries. Since the 1939–45 war the number of patients with endogenous depression has increased – in Sweden, for example, doubling over a period of thirty years. No doubt the advent of effective treatment may have led doctors to diagnose the condition more readily, and led depressed patients to seek help. In the United Kingdom, six per cent of the population, some 3 million people, suffer from depression each year and 4000 of them commit suicide. The disease is twice as common in women than men, sometimes with a strong family history. The middle-aged or elderly are most often affected but adolescents and young adults are not exempt. The reasons for the increased incidence are unknown but changes in tradition and social structure, disruption of family ties and religious bonds, and isolation, may play a role.

For the patient, and for those who are close, clinical depression is a terrible disease. The misery it engenders is hard for anyone to comprehend unless they have experienced it. Nothing is more galling for a depressed woman to be told to pull herself together and 'snap out of it'. The sufferer lacks confidence; the future holds nothing, being devoid of hope. There is a pervasive loss of pleasure or enjoyment in life and a lack of interest, even in hobbies. The patient is devoid of self-esteem and is self-reproachful for being a failure. Everything has turned out badly and nothing has been accomplished. The patient ruminates on the futility of life. Tiredness is a common symptom and there is an inability to concentrate or make decisions. The pattern of sleep changes with the patient often waking at two or three o'clock in the morning although some patients, particularly younger ones, sleep excessively. The depression is worst on waking and during the morning, sometimes lessening later in the day and further improving with a drink of alcohol in the evening. Severely affected patients may be slowed down in their actions and thoughts; they lack drive and are apathetic, dejected and despondent. In others excitability, loquaciousness or violent behaviour may fluctuate with depression, a variant known as bipolar or manic depression. Without treatment the average duration of a depressive episode is about nine months, but many patients suffer for longer periods than this and relapses are common. Fear of the stigma of mental illness may deter the patient from seeking medical advice.

Some depressed patients have less obvious or prominent mental symptoms, and the clinical picture is dominated by physical symptoms which may take many forms, notably excessive tiredness and pains that often mimic some structural abdominal or intrathoracic disorder. The patient is anxious and fears some sinister occult disease. When after a consultation the diagnosis of the somatic symptoms remains uncertain, the doctor should ask themselves how *they* are feeling. In a curious way depression is 'infectious' and if the doctor is feeling depressed, it is likely that they have temporarily 'caught' the disease from the patient.

As they live longer, more and more people develop another mental disorder – dementia – manifested by progressive intellectual deterioration. Forgetfulness of somebody's name is so common in later life that we accept it as part of the normal ageing process, but patients with dementia are liable to forget not only people's names but who they are and what they do. Eventually the demented patient can't remember who he or she is, how to find their way home, fails to recognise their wife or husband or children and may develop bizarre irrational ideas. This distressing condition may be caused by vascular and other structural changes in the brain, which must be excluded, or by Alzheimer's disease which is being increasingly diagnosed.

* * *

I had waited in the lobby of the hotel in Mayfair just long enough to find out the room number of the patient when Dr Michael Kremer arrived.

'I gather we're doing a duet,' the eminent neurologist said. 'Might I suggest you conduct the consultation and I play second fiddle? When you've finished I may want to ask a few more questions and...'

90

'Of course, and you'll want to make your own neurological examination, I'm sure. Let's go up.'

The grey-haired lift-boy swished us silently to the second floor. 'On your left, gentlemen, at the end of the corridor,' he directed. I rang the doorbell outside the room.

A nurse in uniform opened the door. 'Good afternoon; good afternoon, sir. Mrs Venables is expecting you.'

We went into the bedroom with its two adjacent beds. Mrs Venables, wearing a pink ribboned satin bedjacket, was sitting up in the right-hand one; the counterpane on the other was undisturbed.

'Good afternoon.' I shook Mrs Venables's hand and introduced Michael Kremer. 'I'm sure your solicitor has explained why we've come to see you.'

'Dear Lord Bruford, such a nice man and such a kind friend. I know exactly why you're here, but he hasn't really told me – much too considerate of my feelings. You've come to see if I'm potty.'

'Oh! I wouldn't say that.' The word potty had certainly not been used by David Bruford, the eminent solicitor, an adviser to prime ministers and businessmen and the *confidante* of troubled ladies seeking divorce. Without allegiance to any political party he sat as a cross-bencher and sometimes negotiated on the government's behalf with foreign heads of state. He used everyday words but had the gift of stringing them together in a unique manner. When he'd instructed us, Lord Bruford explained that Mrs Venables was contemplating making a new, somewhat unusual, will; some of her family questioned her testamentary capacity.

'She's getting on in years,' he said. 'She always appears *compus mentis* on the rare occasions I go to Chesterfield to see her but I thought it prudent to have the opinion of two eminent medical men like yourselves. She can't get about much now and has nurses looking after her day and night.'

Thus Mrs Venables had come to London to be seen by us.

The next half-hour was spent enquiring about Mrs Venables's daily activities and how she felt. She admitted to no significant symptoms except for tiredness and the need to spend much of her time in bed. 'Is this so unusual at my age?' she asked. 'I am eighty-eight.'

When it came to examining her, I pushed the unoccupied bed to one side in order to be on the patient's right-hand side. On the carpet between the two beds lay a pile of grey fluff, a page torn

91

from the *Evening Standard*, a crumpled Mars bar wrapper, a black wizened banana skin and a cigarette butt. To avoid calling attention to this shortcoming on the part of the hotel staff, I gently pushed the debris with my foot under Mrs Venables's bed. The examination revealed nothing abnormal.

'Dr Kremer, over to you,' I said and gestured to the patient.

The neurologist asked Mrs Venables a string of questions which she answered impeccably. Who was the prime-minister? The foreign secretary? What were the dates of World War II? Then he fluently examined her nervous system with infinite care before pushing the empty bed back into position.

As we put together our papers and put them in our cases, the nurse fluffed up Mrs Venables's pillows and tidied the bed. She was sitting bolt upright, alert, with her hands resting on the smoothed linen sheet. When we came to say goodbye, Mrs Venables was preoccupied, peering intently out of the window. Suddenly she prodded the bedclothes with her right index finger. She moved her head a little and made another prod, this time with the middle finger of the other hand. Silently we watched. Mrs Venables moved to get a better view through the window, and again prodded the sheet.

'What's she doing?' I whispered to the nurse.

'Don't know – she often does it at home.'

'What are you doing?' Michael Kremer asked.

'Controlling the universe,' she replied intently. 'You see that pigeon? When I press this button, it flies away from that plane tree ... and when I press this one,' she spoke more quickly and made a sudden stab with a finger, 'it lands on the window-sill of the house opposite. Look...' another imaginary button was pressed. 'Now I've made it fly back to the tree again.' She continued with this task for several minutes before adding, 'I'm so busy running the world all day long, I suppose it's not surprising I get tired.'

Lord Bruford telephoned after receiving our reports. 'Most helpful,' he said. 'I am most grateful to you. In view of your reports, I shall advise Mrs Venables to leave her old will unchanged. Am I to take it that there's no treatment for dementia?'

'Not yet, I'm afraid.'

9

IV: Drugs

Today understandably many people equate the word 'drug' with a 'hard drug', such as morphia, heroin and cocaine, which conjure up a picture of Colombian drug barons or sleazy back-street dope peddlers. Such substances are so highly addictive that they often lead to criminal activities or prostitution simply to raise the money to buy them. Drug addiction is not a new phenomenon; the literature of the nineteenth century bears testimony to men addicted to the opium pipe and ladies to laudanum, another opium preparation. Only the magnitude of the problem is new; in 1990 more than 7,000 heroin addicts were notified to the Home Office and 45,000 drug-related offences were recorded by the police and customs officers. Drug addiction was rare in my youth although I remember as a child a pretty female socialite, whose photograph appeared in the newspapers, being convicted of cocaine sniffing. I encountered my first and last patient with a drug problem, not of course including alcohol, when I was a medical registrar.

* * *

A smartly-dressed middle-aged woman, wearing a hat and holding a neat handbag and gloves on her lap, sat beside the high desk in Sorting Room.

'Would you please renew my prescription?' she asked politely, and handed me her thick bundle of hospital prescription cards stapled together and then carefully, almost reverently, unfolded a letter from the Home Office. She was a registered morphine addict – Number 32 to be precise – and was authorised to receive daily three injections each of 30 mg (the usual single dose is about 10

93

mg); the prescription could only be valid for a period of five days. She looked normal enough but once aware of her problem I saw that she had the characteristic pinpoint pupils of a morphine addict. I wrote the prescription in the formal style required by law, writing out the dosage in words – not as numerals. I paused before signing my name – in full instead of the usual scribbled initials.

'What d'you do?' I asked. Reasonable inquisitiveness is neither a professional nor a social fault.

'I'm night superintendent at a children's hospital,' she said, and named a well-known London institution.

'How long have you been there?'

'Seven years.'

'You're in charge of the whole hospital at night, with about a hundred children and babies under your care and perhaps twenty nurses to supervise?' It was the impertinent question of youth.

'Twenty-five nurses,' she corrected. 'They know. There've been no problems – no complaints about my work.'

I assumed 'they' were the senior medical and nursing staff and probably the hospital's Board of Governors. 'How did this come about?' – I held up the Home Office letter, uncertain that my question was justified.

The night superintendent smiled sadly. 'When I was training as a probationer at *this* hospital,' she said, 'a friend and I were doing our first turn of night duty. We couldn't sleep during the day. The trams outside our bedroom made the most awful screeching noise every time they went round the sharp curve this side of Westminster Bridge. One morning early, before we went off duty, my friend and I stole some morphia from the drug cupboard on the ward. I had the most wonderful sleep in my life; so did my friend. She never used morphine again but I'm sorry to say I have ever since.'

'Haven't you been treated?'

'Yes, I've been an inpatient twice but they've never managed to wean me off completely. I'm an addict, I'm sorry to say, but it doesn't interfere with my work.'

'Has the dosage increased over the years?'

'I've been on the same dose for twenty years.'

I signed the prescription and did so every five days for many months until I changed my job. I wondered whether the dictum of one of my teachers had indeed been correct; he maintained that drug addicts were born and not made.

*   *   *

To doctors the word 'drug' is synonymous with any medicinal preparation – be it a capsule, a tablet or a liquid, taken by mouth or given by injection. The number of effective medicines has increased exponentially during the last fifty years. The first pharmacopoeia I had, published in 1933 jointly by the British Medical Association and the Pharmaceutical Society of Great Britain, contained some 300 drugs and of these, with scientific hindsight, only 100 had any proven therapeutic action. The remainder were tonics, 'pick-me-ups', useless cough medicines and coloured water that only helped patients by virtue of their placebo effect. One particularly unpleasant concoction made from asafoetida, the extract of a root garnered in Eastern Persia and Afghanistan, has a taste beyond description. It was prescribed for 'difficult' patients in the hope, often achieved, that once they had taken it they would never come back for more.

By contrast the 1994 edition of the *British National Formulary*, now purged of such absurdities, contains more than three times as many drugs as the edition more than half a century ago. Each of the 950 preparations has a proven pharmacological action and an acknowledged therapeutic use. Some will be discarded in time and will be replaced by newer preparations; others are 'me too' drugs which have a very similar action to others in the same class. Not included in this latest count are fifty different oral contraceptives, which have profoundly influenced social behaviour and enhanced human happiness.

The increased effectiveness of the new agents has inevitably brought an increased risk of adverse side effects but with drugs, as in life generally, you seldom get something for nothing. The media, sometimes but not always with justification, may mount a strident pogrom against a newly-developed drug because of its real or assumed adverse effects even though it has been scrutinised most thoroughly by the Commission for the Safety of Medicines. Certainly the use of any new drug calls for increased knowledge and continuing awareness on the part of the prescriber because almost any therapeutically effective agent given in the wrong dose or under the wrong circumstances may induce side-effects. Some people, as a result of their inherited make-up, metabolise and render a particular drug inactive more slowly than others, and older patients are liable to react more adversely than younger ones.

Before any new product is deemed effective and safe for the treatment of human beings a great deal of expensive testing in several species of animals and in man is necessary. To bring a new drug to the market today will take about ten years of research and cost $300–400 million before it is licensed for use in patients by the Food and Drug Administration in Washington, the Commission for the Safety of Medicines in London or the recently formed European Commission, also located in London. Despite this, long-established drugs may produce strange symptoms under exceptional circumstances.

* * *

A little group stood just inside the entrance to Casualty. For once Sister Beale was silent, listening intently. Johnson, the porter, his head slightly tilted to one side, was listening too – respectfully. I peered to see who the third member of the group was – the one who was doing the talking. All I could see was a stocky middle-aged woman. As I drew closer, I recognised Mrs Henriques from Paris Street, which ran at right angles off the other side of the main road outside the hospital. Paris Street was flanked by two rows of small terraced houses whose owners let rooms in which medical students stayed – some for a year or two and others, as I had, for a short period when on call for midwifery in the district. I walked over to hear what was going on.

'Doctor Bayliss!' Mrs Henriques's face beamed in recognition.

'Mrs Henriques says she's got a student staying with her who's gone mad,' Sister cut in.

'Mr Tredgold, Bunty they call 'im. He's gone all peculiar. Lying in bed with the curtains drawn, and as red as a beetroot 'e is. 'E won't talk and 'e keeps grabbing at the ceiling like this...' Mrs Henriques raised a hand above her head, made a fist, brought it down again and repeated the movement with her other hand.

'Can he walk over to Casualty?' I asked.

'Gor bless you, no.'

I looked through the glass panel in the entrance door to Casualty. It wasn't raining. 'Johnson, take a trolley and some blankets over to Paris Street and bring him back, would you? Put him in one of the rooms; I'll take a look at him.'

'Sir!' Johnson hurried away, no doubt reliving his Royal Army

96

Medical Corps days in the trenches in the 1914–18 war, going into the quagmire of no man's land to bring back some shot-to-pieces Tommy.

Half an hour later I saw the student. Sister Beale accompanied me and stayed, something so unusual that despite her great experience I guessed she was interested. Bunty Tredgold gave no sign of recognition; he kept grunting and uttering unintelligible words with his forearm across his forehead and eyes. He was certainly as red as a beetroot. I felt his forehead. 'His temperature, Sister?'

'A hundred and three degrees (39.4°C). Pulse a 120 – regular.'

I continued the examination. Bunty's body from the waist up was bright red; the redness faded temporarily when the skin was pressed. He was burning hot. I asked for a spatula and torch. With one hand Sister handed me a chipped enamel kidney bowl containing a flat heavy metal tongue depressor and with the other a battered tin torch. The tongue was dry, not a trace of saliva in his mouth. The throat was red but there was nothing else abnormal. I asked for a throat swab. Sister had read my mind and at just the right angle held the test-tube with the swab inside it. As I swabbed the throat, Bunty waved his arms about. He sat up and began to strike out. Sister Beale gently restrained him.

'It's all right, Bunty,' I reassured him; he lay back again, staring at the ceiling with unseeing eyes. It was then that I noticed how widely dilated his pupils were; they were enormous. I shone the torch into them; instead of constricting, the pupils remained dilated. I completed the examination but found nothing else abnormal. I hadn't the faintest idea what was wrong with him.

'Got to admit him, Sister,' I said. 'He'd better go into a side room off a ward, and tell them to barrier nurse him – he may be infectious.' I sat at the desk writing up the notes. At the bottom I wrote, 'Diagnosis:...' and paused to scratch my head before adding, 'GOK? Scarlet fever.'

* * *

Dr Evan Jones pushed clumsily through the double doors into Central Hall just before three o'clock. The group of students and house staff had been waiting since two o'clock but we hadn't wasted the time. We'd been discussing the new drug penicillin, and how tedious it was collecting all the urine a patient on this

97

treatment passed and then having to send it back to Oxford where the antibiotic was extracted and recycled. At that time the dosage was 4000 units every four or six hours whereas today the dose may be a million or more units and supplies are so plentiful that recovery from the urine has long since stopped.

Evan Jones emerged from the consultant's cloakroom, struggling into his over-starched white coat and pushing a bunch of unopened letters into one of the pockets.

'Hello, chaps! What's new?'

'We've got Bunty Tredgold in a side ward. I think you'd better see him first.'

'God, I know Bunty. What's up with him?'

'Admitted him through Casualty yesterday.' I described what had happened as Evan listened with total concentration.

'Amazing! Really amazing, don't you know!' Evan kept on saying.

Like a rugger scrum in pursuit of the ball we swept down the main corridor of the hospital and turned into City ward. Evan put his arm round Sister's waist and gave her a squeeze; she smiled. The door to the side room had a notice pinned to it – BARRIER NURSING – in large red letters. Outside was a coat-stand draped with white gowns. An enamel bowl full of white milky Dettol, with an old bristle nail-brush floating in it, stood in a chipped white metal stand. Beside it on a table was a box of clean white cotton masks and a pile of huckaback towels. Evan lifted the temperature chart from its hook on the wall beside the door. He glanced at it and handed it to the students.

'Look,' he said. 'A temperature of 103. Pulse a 110. Quite something.'

A student was reading my notes. 'What's this diagnosis of GOK, sir?' He asked.

'God only knows,' Evan said.

The student looked puzzled.

'That's what it means,' Evan explained. 'G-O-K,' he spelt the letters out, 'stands for God only knows. Got it?'

'Are you all going in?' Sister was worried about the number of gowns required.

'Oh, we must! The chaps must see this, Sister. Don't let's bother with gowns.' She looked surprised but didn't say anything.

We stood round the bed in the darkened room – Bunty unaware

of our presence. His eyes were fixed on the ceiling. His hairy arms, protruding from the short sleeves of his white gown, lay on top of the counterpane. Rhythmically he raised first one arm and then the other, reaching up to grasp something invisible in the air above him.

'Catching butterflies,' said Evan enigmatically. 'They always do that – catch imaginary butterflies. Sister, could we have a bit more light? Want to look at his rash.'

She pulled up the dark green roller-blind. Bunty put his hands over his eyes to protect them from the light. Evan demonstrated the rash that blanched when the skin was pressed. He talked to Bunty who did not comprehend and was talking rubbish.

'You see? God, he's hot. Feel him,' Evan instructed the students. 'Let's look at his eyes.' Sister handed him a torch and Evan shone the light first into one eye and then the other. 'Not a flicker. D'you know, not a flicker – amazing,' he repeated. 'Come on all of you. Look at these eyes.'

Back in the corridor I began to wash my hands in the Dettol solution.

'Don't bother, man; he's not infectious,' said Evan confidently. 'Amazing! What's he got?' he addressed the students and leant back against the wall. There was silence. 'What gives you unresponsive widely dilated pupils?'

Several suggestions were offered – a cerebral haemorrhage, a head injury, blindness in both eyes.

'He's blind in a sense because he can't focus, but didn't you notice he blinked when I poked my finger at his eyes? Obviously he doesn't like the light. No, he's not blind. What makes you "as hot as a hare, as blind as a bat, as dry as a bone and as mad as a hen"?' Evan laughed.

To my surprise I heard myself say, 'Atropine poisoning,' and added, 'fancy missing that!'

'You're right, man! Bloody good! Amazing! Atropine poisoning! Of course it is. How the hell has Bunty got atropine poisoning? He'll be all right, Sister. Tepid sponge him – all that stuff. You'd better measure his urine output. Make him drink and, if he doesn't, put up a drip.'

The problem of how Bunty Tredgold had got atropine poisoning remained unexplained for nearly a week. I happened to be walking past the ophthalmic department when I saw Mrs Henriques sitting on a bench outside.

'Hello!' I said.

'How's Mr Tredgold?' Mrs Henriques asked.

'Fine. He'll be coming out tomorrow. What are you doing here?'

'It's Doris, doctor. She's hurt her eye. They say she's got a foreign body in it but she don't know no foreigners. She 'as to come here every morning to have it seen to, and she doesn't 'alf carry on when I put them drops in her eyes.'

In the eye department I found Doris, a lanky sixteen-year-old, being seen by the ophthalmic registrar. She had had a foreign body in her eye, and was being treated with atropine drops.

I went back to Mrs Henriques. 'Tell me, how exactly d'you put Doris's eye drops in? Pretend I'm Doris and you're putting the drops in my eyes. How exactly do you do it?'

We acted it out with me sitting on the bench beside Mrs Henriques. 'What d'you do when the drops dribble down Doris's face?' I asked.

'Mop 'em up, like this...' She took a spotless handkerchief from her bag and held it to my cheek. 'Always use a nice piece of muslin, I do.'

'Muslin? D'you use the muslin for anything else?'

Mrs Henriques hesitated. 'Well, I strain the gentleman's coffee through it – every morning I do.'

'The same piece of muslin?'

'Oh, yes! Can't get muslin nowadays; on the clothes' rationing, it is.'

I put my hand on her shoulder. 'When Mr Tredgold comes out of hospital, would you do something for me? Would you boil, really boil, for five minutes, that piece of muslin in a saucepan of water? Then keep it just for straining Mr Tredgold's coffee – and for nothing else. I'll get you some pieces of gauze to mop Doris's cheek with. Throw each piece of gauze away after you've used it. Understand?'

Mrs Henriques understood. I hurried away to enlighten Bunty and tell Evan.

* * *

Atropine is an ancient drug. It used to be extracted from deadly nightshade whose bright red, attractive berries are very poisonous, especially to children. The botanical name is *Atropa belladonna* –

Atropa derived from Atropus, one of the Fates who cut the Thread of Life, and belladonna from the Spanish for beautiful woman because Spanish ladies used to put atropine in their eyes to enlarge their pupils. Nowadays atropine is obtained from an Australian plant, the narcotic properties of which were discovered by the Aboriginals.

Many people, often without knowing it, encounter atropine at some time in their life. In combination with morphine it is often used as a premedication before a general anaesthetic is given for a surgical operation. The morphia relieves anxiety and the immediate postoperative pain; the atropine dries up the saliva and the secretion of mucus from the windpipe and bronchial tubes, which could interfere with respiration during the period of unconsciousness. Atropine or belladonna by mouth is also used in the treatment of some intestinal diseases, and by topical application, in the form of drops or an ointment, in the treatment of many eye conditions.

10

V: Hypnosis

For more than two years it had been quiet in London and elsewhere on the home front, but on the clear night of 16 June 1944, ten days after the Allied landings in Normandy, I heard an unfamiliar noise followed by the sound of ack-ack guns and then total silence – seconds later came a loud explosion. Passing the deserted unused wards on the upper two floors, I climbed the stairs to the roof of St Thomas's and leant on the parapet, looking south.

Johnson, the Casualty porter, was there too. Across the sky came another plane, easily seen against the blackness of the night sky because of the flames emerging from its tail. The anti-aircraft guns fired furiously. The flames suddenly stopped; the plane dived silently to earth and then came a huge explosion.

'My God!' I said. 'The ack-ack have hit it – unbelievable! They've shot it down!'

'That, sir, is Hitler's secret weapon. One landed in Hackney marshes three nights ago.' Johnson shook his head in polite disagreement.

For months the Germans had boasted of their secret weapon and Lord Haw-Haw in his propaganda broadcasts from Hamburg had nightly spelt out the fate that awaited England.

'That, Johnson, is defeatist rubbish,' I said with youthful pomposity. 'I don't want to hear any more of that sort of talk.'

'Sir!' Johnson drew himself to attention; service in the RAMC had taught him how to deal with officers! Nothing more happened and we went back downstairs.

Next morning the newspapers carried banner headlines – 'Hitler's Secret Weapon Hits London'. I felt very small.

'I'm sorry about last night, Johnson,' I apologised. 'You were quite right.'

'Sir.' Johnson grinned in forgiveness.

We soon became aware of the devastating injuries wrought by doodle-bugs. One landed at nine o'clock in the morning in York Road, beside Waterloo station, blowing to smithereens two double-decker buses crowded with passengers on their way to the City. Within minutes more than a hundred had been admitted to Casualty. I was one of the team that decided their priority for treatment. This triage took half the morning and many of the wounded died before they could be admitted. Not only had they multiple wounds and fractures but some had been hurled by the blast across the street into a brick wall and pulped like a grape trodden under foot. Others were peppered with flying debris. It was hard to know where to begin and how to assess the extent of their often extensive multiple injuries.

One particular casualty was a middle-aged City gent whose thigh bone was sticking out through his trouser leg. He seemed surprising well – with little pain and no bleeding. Not until the afternoon did I accompany him to the operating theatre where Paddy Kelly, the surgical registrar, had been working all morning.

Paddy looked up from a table where he was just finishing an operation. He gave my patient a cursory glance. 'D'you think I'll have to take his leg off?' he asked.

I was puzzled that the patient was so well. He wasn't shocked and he chatted away happily. 'I'll get a portable X-ray done,' I said.

The X-ray showed that the patient's own femur was normal and intact; the piece of bone sticking out of his thigh through his trousers belonged to somebody else. Under anaesthesia Paddy removed the unknown person's piece of femur, the wound in the thigh was cleaned and powdered with a sulphonamide drug; the fortunate City gent limped out of hospital next day.

Rumour had it that V1 bombs – so-called by the Germans not because V stood for Victory but for *Vergeltungswaffe* (weapon of revenge) – were raining down on London at the rate of fifty a day. The force of their blast was much greater than that of the bombs in the Blitz. Within a fortnight 200,000 houses were destroyed or damaged. The hospital reverted to the state of tension that had prevailed during the Blitz but now the tension was continuous because the doodle-bugs came at any hour of the day or night. The sirens sounded ceaselessly and it was difficult to remember –

104

not that it mattered much – if the all-clear had sounded or not. Like everyone else I found myself straining to hear the characteristic noise of the propulsive rocket; if silence came there were twelve seconds in which to take cover and it was cold comfort to believe that the V1 you didn't hear was the one that got you.

Three months later, in September 1944, isolated unexplained explosions, which had a curious double bang, began to occur. Although strict censorship concealed the truth for nearly two months, we guessed quickly enough, particularly when the explosions began to occur three or four times a day and sounded close even though many were as far as ten miles away, that they were not caused by burst gas-mains as we were led to believe. The V2s were more unexpected and unacceptable than the flying bombs. They arrived unheralded, falling silently and invisibly from a height of sixty miles without the helpful warning of a doodle-bug that did give you time for evasive action and a better chance of self-preservation. During the Blitz camaraderie had been shared by all but the V-bombs brought only personal and solitary fear. Morale had fallen because people were tired after four years of working unacceptably long hours and eating a dreary monotonous diet. Trivial irritations became major ones and tempers were short. The allied advance from Normandy was slower than we had been to led to expect.

* * *

The explosion was too far away to take any notice of. Half an hour later Johnson sought me out. 'There's a casualty in, sir,' and he handed me the casualty officer's notes.

'What's it about?' I asked.

'A V2, sir. Landed on a housing estate. A lot of people killed, I'm told. We've only had one casualty so far.'

'Bad?'

'Don't think so, sir. She doesn't look too bad to me – no blood around.'

'Okay. I'll be down in a minute.'

The patient did not look too bad. Her face and hands were filthy dirty and her hair coated with thick grey dust, but her eyes were open and she did not look shocked or as though she were in pain.

'Hello,' I said, and turned to the casualty officer. 'Tell me.'

'This sixteen-year-old, Penny, lives with her parents and two younger brothers in a house on the edge of one of the Lambeth estates. This afternoon she left home to go to work – she's a clerk at Waterloo Station. She'd gone a few, a hundred yards down the road when a V2 landed behind her. Just before the blast blew her off her feet, she momentarily saw her home and the neighbouring flats disappear in a cloud of dust. She was knocked out for a few seconds and when she tried to get up her legs wouldn't work. She's paralysed from the waist down; she's paraplegic.'

'Admit her. Penny, what about your parents and your brothers?'

Penny hardly moved her mouth as she said in a flat toneless voice, 'Nobody seems to know.'

When later that afternoon we did know, the news was as bad as it could be. Penny had lost her mother and father, her two brothers, her home and all her belongings. When Sister broke the news, Penny showed no emotion; she barely nodded her head – no tears and no response as Sister squeezed her hand.

When I saw her later that evening she was in the first bed on the left in George ward. She had been given a blanket bath and her hair had been washed. She answered all my questions like an automaton. With apparent indifference she cooperated with the physical examination in which I tested her paralysed legs to discover if she could feel the gentle touch of a wisp of cotton-wool or the prick of a needle, whether she could distinguish between hot and cold, or feel the vibration of a tuning fork. The tendon reflexes were all normal. There were no visible external injuries and an X-ray of her spine showed nothing abnormal.

Proving a negative is never easy and the lack of any abnormal physical signs simply didn't add up. Reluctantly I came to the conclusion that the paralysis of Penny's legs had no physical basis – her paraplegia was hysterical.

As I wrote up her notes, one half of my brain was wondering how on earth to treat her. Hypnosis suddenly came to mind. I had attended several meetings of the Cambridge University Medical Society when demonstrations had been given by a professional hypnotist who annually appeared for a week at the music hall in St Andrew's Street. Such popular 'entertainment' became less common after 1952 when a Member of Parliament, concerned about the potentially damaging consequences, successfully introduced a private member's bill in the House of Commons that allowed local authorities, if they thought fit, to prohibit such stage performances. Perhaps I could hypnotise Penny. I put screens round her bed and told Sister not to disturb us. Penny was lying on top of the bed clothes. I persuaded her to tell me about the explosion, to talk about her dead family and about her future aspirations. She answered each question in the fewest possible words and did so in a flat unemotional voice.

'Now I want you to relax, Penny,' I said. 'Lie back on your pillow and fix your eyes on the end of my pencil.' To my surprise, in what must have been a very amateur way, I succeeded in hypnotising her. I told her that when she woke she would be able to walk.

'Now lift up your right leg.'

She did.

'Good! Let your right leg fall back on the bed. Good! Now lift up your left leg.'

Again success.

'Now Penny, sit up and swing your legs over the side of the bed. That's good. Now stand up.'

She did and I pushed aside one of the screens. 'Let's go for a little walk.'

I took her hand and to my astonishment, and relief, she walked barefooted into the centre of the ward, round Sister's table and back to her bed.

'Well done! You'll be all right now,' I told her. 'Get back into bed and I'll come and see you in the morning.'

We started the round next morning in George ward.

'This the patient you told me about last night?' Hec Johnstone, the Resident Assistant Physician, asked as we stood beside Penny's bed.

'Yes.' I concealed any ill-founded satisfaction.

'I'm very sorry to hear about yesterday, Penny,' Hec said. She ignored him. 'Very sad. I hear your legs are better. Would you waggle your feet, please.'

Nothing happened.

'Would you please lift up this leg.' Hec patted her right leg.

Penny continued to look straight in front of her.

'Penny, I want to see how you walk, please.' Hec raised his voice a little.

Penny moved her eyes to look at the Resident Assistant Physician.

'Come along, please. I want to see you walk, Penny.'

Penny cupped her hand to her ear. 'What did you say?' she asked in a flat voice. 'I can't hear you.'

'Oh, God! She's developed hysterical deafness,' I whispered.

Hec could barely conceal his uncharitable but understandable incredulity. 'That'll teach you,' he said quietly. 'Now what the hell are you going to do? How are you going to set about hypnotising a deaf patient, eh?'

After the ward round I shamefacedly sought Dr Shorvon, one of the junior consultant psychiatrists. 'That'll teach you to meddle in areas you know nothing about,' he said without rancour. 'You'll now understand that hypnosis doesn't cure this sort of thing. The patient, as in this case, will simply exchange one hysterical manifestation for another. This girl sounds as if she's "frozen"; she's still in a state of shock. You say she hasn't wept; she's shown no emotional reaction to the devastating loss of her whole family. Send her down to the department and I'll abreact her.'

Penny was given a small intravenous dose of an anaesthetic, pentothal, and in a semi-conscious state was made to relive the horror of seeing her family killed and her home demolished. This was a painful experience – she screamed and she wept; she railed against God; she pleaded for her own death. It was almost unbearable to watch her suffer, but after three abreactions she began to improve and a week later Penny left hospital physically well. She could now express her misery but only time would heal her deep emotional wounds.

*　*　*

The Story of San Michele influenced medical students of many generations. It was the fourth, last and most successful book written by Dr Axel Munthe (1857–1949). First published in April 1929, with an initial print-run of 7000 copies, five more impressions were called for that year and twenty-four the next. A cheaper hardback edition appeared in September 1932 and eight impressions of this were sold during the next five months. In 1950 a paperback edition was published and is still in print. Up to 1982 the total sales in the United Kingdom alone were 850,000. A new edition has recently been published by the Folio Society.

Axel Munthe was born in Sweden, educated at Uppsala University and studied medicine in Paris where he worked hard: 'no Mimi to mend my coat or wash my linen', he writes; 'no time for idle gossip in the cafés, to laugh, to live, to love'.

He practised first in Paris and later in Rome. He eventually retired to his beloved villa, San Michele in Anacapri, but died in Stockholm at the age of 91 having lived, as he explains, a charmed life escaping from the horrors of cholera in Naples, an earthquake in Messina, to say nothing of an avalanche on Mont Blanc and a bullet through his hat in a duel.

Written in the first person it is hard to believe that *The Story of San Michele* is not based on the author's life; Munthe tells us much about himself and about medicine as practised by a fashionable doctor during the last years of the nineteenth and the early ones of the twentieth centuries.

As a medical student in Paris, Munthe is puzzled that Death stalks the wards of the La Salpêtrière and Hôtel Dieu Hospitals 'to struggle so long with the life of a little child, while He suffered the life of the old to ebb away in peaceful sleep'. It seems inconceivable to us today that euthanasia, or more correctly assisted deaths, should have been performed by an unqualified and seemingly unsupervised medical student. 'Was it not my mission to help those to die I could not help to live?... Even sweet Soeur Philomène had looked at me disapprovingly when, alone among my comrades, I had come with my morphia syringe after the old padre had left the bed with his Last Sacrament'.

Munthe expresses guilt for 'dumping on suffering mankind expensive patent medicines and drugs', knowing that the 'number of efficacious drugs could be counted on the ends of our fingers'. Fee-splitting between consultants and general practitioners is a matter of course. Before operating half the surgeon's fee is paid in advance. Although today private hospitals may demand payment of the hospital charges before admission, it is doubtful that any patient is 'aroused from the chloroform and the operation postponed in order to verify the validity of a cheque'.

In 1886 Munthe goes to help in a cholera epidemic in Naples. On first reading his account of this, I seriously wondered if he'd ever seen a case of cholera. Not once is diarrhoea mentioned, and the disease often seems to run an unusually precipitous course. Puzzled by this I turned to his first book, *Letters from A Mourning City*, written while he was in Naples at the time and published in

1887. Here too there is no mention of diarrhoea: perhaps the omission is a matter of seemliness.

Throughout his stay in Naples Munthe is terrified of contracting the disease; he cannot sleep and spends his nights cowering in one of the numerous churches, fearful of the millions of rats 'quite bald with extraordinary long red tails, fierce blood-shot eyes and pointed black teeth' driven from the sewers when the Sanitary Commission starts 'its vain attempt at disinfection'. Understandably cholerophobia was common in the nineteenth century, even among the medical profession. Many doctors believed the disease was contagious and would put a handkerchief to their mouth, wear gloves to touch the patient and hold a scent bottle to their nose, staying with the patient as brief a time as possible, but Munthe was aware that the micro-organism that causes this water-borne disease had been identified in 1883.

The overall mortality was eighty per cent and Munthe makes little mention of treatment. He is unaware that fluid replacement by vein had first been tried, unsuccessfully, by some Scottish doctors in 1832 when the unsterile fluid was given in amounts too small and in the wrong concentration. Not until 1910 at the Medical College in Calcutta was intravenous fluid shown to be effective, but not until World War II was a simple method evolved to determine precisely how much fluid a particular patient needed. The two inventors of this technique from the Rockefeller Institute in New York showed that as much as a hundred litres (176 pints) might be necessary to make good the fluid lost from the bowel of a patient with cholera. This was in Cairo in 1944 and, when two years later in 1946 I was posted to Delhi, this technique was widely in use, which gives some idea of the speed with which important medical advances may be adopted.

During his years in Paris Munthe has contact with Charcot (1825–93), the great French nerve specialist. Apart from acknowledging him as an outstanding teacher, Munthe is not complimentary about the neurologist to whom 'patients from all over the world flocked, often waiting for weeks before being admitted to the inner sanctuary'. As a diagnostician Charcot with his 'sensitive cruel lips was uncanny in the way he went straight to the root of the evil, often apparently after only a rapid glance at the patient from his cold eagle eyes... He never admitted a mistake and woe to the man who ever dared to hint at his being in the wrong'. His voice 'was imperative, hard, often sarcastic; sharing the fate of all nerve specialists, he was surrounded by a bodyguard of neurotic ladies'. Charcot's hatred of fox-hunting is the reason given for his alleged dislike of the English.

Every Tuesday Charcot gave a stage performance of hypnotism – 'nothing but an absurd farce, a hopeless muddle of truth and cheating' – at La Salpêtrière Hospital attended by a public audience of 'authors, journalists, leading actors and actresses, fashionable *demi-mondaines*, all full of morbid curiosity'.

Munthe tries to extricate a young female patient from Charcot's clutches by instructing her under hypnosis how to leave the hospital and come to his house so that he could return her to her farming parents in Normandy who think their daughter is working in the hospital kitchens. He nearly succeeds but a nun catches the girl just as she is leaving the hospital and under hypnosis, we are told, Charcot reverses Munthe's instructions.

Far from dismissing the value of hypnotism Munthe uses it for treating drug addiction and sexual inversion (homosexuality), and for the relief of pain after surgical operations, in childbirth and on mortally injured soldiers in the 1914–18 war. Today we can hardly accept Munthe's claim that 'specialists in nervous and mental disorders can no more do without hypnotism than can surgeons without chloroform or ether'.

Munthe's description of Charcot is certainly inaccurate and his attitude towards him strongly biased. Other biographers show that Charcot did not dislike the English; he was a frequent visitor and addressed the British Medical Association on several occasions. He had many professional friends here. His daughter, Jeanne, married first an Englishman and, after he died, a Scot.

Charcot transformed the Salpêtrière from an asylum and prison for the detention and incarceration of beggars, insane women, prostitutes and perverted girls, and women convicted of adultery, theft or murder into the world's greatest centre for neurological research. He was a brilliant teacher and was respected worldwide for his research and knowledge. Nevertheless, it is probably true that he disliked criticism and was austere; he was known as 'Caesar' by his junior staff.

Many eminent contemporaries looked upon Charcot's interest in hypnosis as 'a slight failing', although he is given credit for proving that a subject could not be persuaded to do something against his conscience and would not perpetrate any crime, including rape, under hypnosis. On the other hand Charcot often failed to check the results of the research done by his assistants, and it is generally agreed that he personally never hypnotised a single patient. Munthe did in fact succeed in removing the hysterical girl from the hospital to his home. When Charcot learnt of this, he threatened Munthe with police action and Munthe was conducted by a Chief Assistant to the entrance of the Salpêtrière and refused future access to the hospital.

Although Munthe presents himself as a compassionate, cosmopolitan and cultured man, he is whimsical, introspective and sentimental. Clearly he has his dark side as shown by his constant concern with Death and his episodes of depression. The more often you read *The Story of San Michele* the more you realise it is not a true autobiography but a work of fiction. It has even been questioned whether Munthe was awarded the French *Legion d'Honneur* as he claimed. What he hoped to achieve by going to Naples in the cholera epidemic is a mystery; was he simply an observer?

Hypnosis still arouses suspicion. Despite the suggestion by the British Medical Association in 1955 that it should be taught in all medical schools, it receives little attention today, partly perhaps because it smacks of quackery, partly because its application has not been properly defined and partly because not everyone is hypnotisable. Certainly it is used successfully by dentists to eliminate pain and some surgeons, particularly in China, use it as an alternative to anaesthesia for such major operations as amputation of the leg.

11

An Ethical Dilemma: Euthanasia

Promotion to the post of Resident Assistant Physician at St Thomas's in 1944 was, at the time, the acme of all I sought to achieve. Certainly it was a mark of distinction but in a very parochial sphere. It brought new responsibilities and a very real improvement in accommodation – a sizeable sitting-room on the first floor of the hospital, an adjoining bedroom with a wash-hand basin and a nearby bathroom shared only with my opposite number, the Resident Assistant Surgeon. The sitting-room was unusual in that above the marble mantelshelf was a large sash window set in the chimney breast over the fireplace. You could stand warming your legs at the gas fire while resting your elbows on the mantelpiece and gazing at the splendid view down the River Thames.

The telephone rang.

'There's a Colonel Coxton at the lodge. He'd like to see you, sir,' said Johnson. 'He's ex-RAMC and the father of one of our old students.'

'Professionally?' I asked. Muted conversation took place.

'Not exactly, the colonel says,' was Johnson's ambiguous reply.

'Bring him up, will you?'

A few minutes later the door of the sitting room was thrown open and Johnson in his best military manner announced the visitor. I shook hands with a tall well-groomed man – a little older than my father – with greying hair and a neatly trimmed grey moustache.

'Let me take your coat, sir. Come and sit down.'

'No need, thank you,' Colonel Coxton said. 'Won't take a moment. I'm Johnny Coxton's father. Remember him?'

'Of course, we're contemporaries.'

'Exactly, he spoke of you. I'd like your opinion on these

113

X-rays.' He opened a large manilla envelope and handed me the films.

I held them up to the window over the fireplace. As I glanced at the first X-ray to see which way round to hold it, I saw the patient's name in the top right-hand corner. In silence I studied the films of a barium swallow and then turned to Colonel Coxton.

'Your films, I think?'

'Yes, my X-rays.'

'Of course. Well...' I hesitated; there seemed no alternative to speaking the truth. 'These show what I take to be a carcinoma at the lower end of the oesophagus, and it looks as though it's spread into the adjacent right lung.' I paused.

'Thank you – for your frankness.' Colonel Coxton stepped forward and took the films out of my hands. 'That's exactly what they told me at the Cambridge Hospital in Aldershot. Obviously it's inoperable – even I know that. I'm all right at the moment but when things get bad I'll come back. Then you can see me out but it's not to be a long lingering business. Understand? And don't tell my son. He's with the Corps in Italy. A damn'd sight more risky for him to fly home than to stay with his unit.'

I had almost forgotten Colonel Coxton when three months later a letter came. He could not eat solid food; it got stuck. He could barely swallow liquids. He was thirsty and there was some pain. His wife and daughter were fussing about him. He would like to come into hospital.

Forty-eight hours later Colonel Coxton was admitted to the side room off George ward. He had lost a lot of weight; gaunt with sunken cheeks, he was skin and bones.

The colonel was not best pleased when the house physician came to take his history and examine him. 'Damn'd waste of time,' he growled, and resented the barium swallow and meal that were done next morning.

I didn't look forward to the forthcoming interview on the ward round just after lunch. I stood on one side of the bed with Sister George, for once without a staff nurse in attendance, on the other. 'Colonel Coxton...' I began.

He was sitting almost bolt upright in the bed, as though at attention. 'Get on with it, man. No need to beat about the bush.'

'... You've got, as you know, cancer of the lower end of your oesophagus. It has spread to the lungs and downwards to involve

114

the front of your stomach – that's the lump we can feel in the upper part of your abdomen. I've shown your X-rays to the surgeons. They say it would be difficult to put a tube through your abdominal wall into your stomach to feed you.'

'Wouldn't dream of having a damn'd gastrotomy. What's the point? Waste of time. Be a good fellow – we've all had to do this sometime in our professional lives. You've got to fix me up. Sister, you agree, don't you?'

To my surprise Sister George slowly nodded her head in agreement. Her eyes were fixed on Colonel Coxton's as she squeezed his hand.

'I'll come back later on and we'll talk about it, sir.'

Outside in the corridor I looked at Sister George. To me she was a woman a little younger than my mother – wise, experienced, gentle, kind, a Christian and a strict disciplinarian. I turned to her for advice. 'I can make him comfortable and keep him going with a drip for a bit,' I said without enthusiasm. 'What do *you* think, Sister?'

'You must do what you think is right. It's pointless keeping him alive just to prolong his suffering. If you really want to ease his ... er ... passage, I see no harm in that. It seems perfectly ... humane ... right to me.'

I went back into the colonel's room, beckoning Sister to stay behind. 'Colonel Coxton, I think we understand each other. I'll come tomorrow evening and together we'll...' I was not allowed to finish.

'Tomorrow? But I said goodbye to my wife and daughter this morning. For God's sake let's get on with it – now.'

For a moment I stared at Colonel Coxton; there seemed nothing more to say. I nodded and left the room. 'Sister, I'm going to give Colonel Coxton an injection. I'll write it up on his treatment sheet.' We walked into the ward and Sister brought his drug sheet. I was going to do something that I'd never done before. Medical ethics were to me unknown, not discussed or taught in 1945, but mentally I'd often pondered over exactly this sort of situation and wondered what cocktail of drugs one would use. I wrote, Injection diamorphine 30 mg, and paused to consider what to add next.

'Here are three ampoules of heroin. What else do you need?' Sister was not overawing and content to allow me to take the responsibility.

'The heroin will ease his discomfort, calm his mind and make him drowsy.' I said. 'Now we want a quick-acting barbiturate to send him off to sleep and a longer-acting one to keep him asleep.' In succession Sister George produced from the drug cupboard the necessary ampoules of barbiturates and, without me asking, a vial of insulin.

After the intravenous injection Colonel Coxton shook hands with us formally. Sister George lowered the roller blind and settled him so that his head rested comfortably on the pillows. 'Thank you, my boy. Thank you, Sister,' he said and closed his eyes.

'Now just you go to sleep,' she said quietly, and lightly stroked his forehead.

On several occasions during the afternoon I crept on tip-toe into the darkened room. Colonel Coxton's breathing was shallow and irregular. There were long pauses when he did not breathe at all, usually a sign that the end is near. His pulse was weak.

At seven o'clock as I walked through Casualty on my way to meet Evan Jones and the others, I put my head round the glass-panelled door of the porters' lodge. 'I'm off to the Rodney.'

'One minute, sir,' cautioned Johnson. 'They've just telephoned from George ward; you're wanted there urgently.'

I turned on my heels. Sister George was in the corridor outside Colonel Coxton's room.

'He wants a word with you ... and he's hopping mad.'

I opened the door as quietly as possible and tiptoed into the darkened room.

'What the hell d'you think you're doing?' Colonel Coxton exploded as he switched on the light. 'I dreamt I was dead. I always leave my half-hunter on the locker beside my bed. I put my hand out to feel if the watch was still there; it wasn't. So I knew I was dead. At that moment the damn'd electric trolley with the ward dinners came thundering down the corridor making its usual bloody awful noise. What the hell d'you think you're up to, eh?'

'I'm awfully sorry, sir', was all I could think of saying.

Colonel Coxton was not as angry as he made out; the tone of his voice carried a hint of amused surprise.

'All right, then, all right. Now get on, and don't make a balls of it this time.' Colonel Coxton lay back on his pillow and closed his eyes.

He died peacefully two hours later.

116

*　*　*

It is against the law for a doctor or any one else to kill a patient deliberately or to assist a patient to commit suicide. What happened to Colonel Coxton should not happen today; nor would one expect it to. To plead ignorance or lack of experience is no excuse for what took place, but today, as a result of the pioneer work of Doctor Dame Cicely Saunders and others, we have, or should have, the knowledge and the skills to provide exemplary care for those at the end of their life. Everyone hopes for a quiet and easy death – for themselves and not least to spare their relatives and loved ones. There are individuals and teams of experts especially trained in the terminal care of the dying. Distressing symptoms can be relieved, and it is important that the public is made aware of this. Failure to make use of the expert advice available because of inexperience or ignorance may jeopardise a doctor as happened when the intense suffering of a patient with long-standing rheumatoid arthritis was terminated by the injection of a lethal substance of no therapeutic value. The doctor who gave the injection was convicted of attempted murder and sentenced to twelve months' imprisonment, the sentence being suspended for a year. When later he appeared before the General Medical Council, the President commented that it was a duty, rightly expected by the public, for doctors to make a patient's death bearable and dignified by easing pain and suffering. It was, he said, outside that duty to shorten life simply to relieve suffering.

This lesson has been widely learnt in the many hospices for the dying that have been opened throughout the British Isles in the last forty-five years, and is incorporated in the training of expert Macmillan nurses who care for patients dying of cancer at home. Allied to the pharmacological control of physical pain has come a better understanding of how to provide psychological relief of the emotional distress so that the patient dies with a peace of mind also shared by the relatives.

Regrettably there are hospital consultants, and their junior staff and nurses, who still need to learn how to care for a patient under their care who slips from their therapeutic grasp and no longer will respond to any curative treatment. Subconsciously this may be interpreted as a personal and professional failure. Under such circumstances the consultant fails in his responsibility if he fails

117

to institute palliative care or, if ignorant of this, does not invoke the help of colleagues versed in these matters.

It is not surprising that many people abhor the thought that when they become ill they may be kept uselessly alive. Patients have the right to accept or refuse any medical treatment offered them. The days of paternalism when the doctor made all the decisions have long passed. Patients expect to be informed, consulted and to chose for themselves. Doctors have an obligation to ensure that what they do is in accord with their patient's wishes. There may be circumstances in which 'heroic' treatment may be tentatively, or even persuasively, offered by a doctor, but in honesty he must warn that the treatment may not succeed or that any prolongation of life may not be of acceptable quality.

Some patients, long before they become seriously ill, make it clear in a living will that under certain circumstances they do not wish to have their life prolonged. This avoids ambiguity and absolves their children of the potentially painful responsibility of making a decision on their behalf. In the absence of a living will, and not always is it known to the relatives or the doctors that this exists, the position becomes even more difficult, particularly if the patient is unconscious or mentally incompetent. The doctor should ask the patient's family to decide because they are likely to know the patient's wishes better than anyone else. Their major concern will be to spare their parent physical pain, but there are other important but less imperative considerations such as the future dependency of the patient on others, the abdication of privacy and the loss of personal dignity. The process of dying may be prolonged by naso-gastric or intravenous feeding and by holding at bay with antibiotics that harbinger of death, pneumonia. There is also cardiopulmonary resuscitation (CPR).

When I was a student, a patient was deemed dead when breathing and the heart had stopped. Today CPR may bring such a patient back to life. This dramatic intervention may save life but, when applied to patients in hospital, the success rate is not high; about sixty per cent do not respond and of those who do only twelve per cent survive for another month. The intention to give or not give CPR, should the need arise, is now routinely taken in most hospitals by the medical team in concert with the nursing staff after discussion with the patient and/or the patient's relatives. Patients at risk must be asked to express their wish in the event

118

that something goes wrong. This delicate subject can be broached when the diagnosis and treatment are being discussed between the doctor and the patient. During their illness patients may change their mind and the doctor may change his advice if, for example, an inoperable cancer is revealed at an exploratory operation.

A major problem arises when a patient is in a persistent vegetative state. If the brain is totally deprived of oxygen for five minutes or longer, cerebral function is irreparably destroyed. Thereafter for weeks, months or years the lungs may continue to breathe, with or without the help of a respirator, and the heart may continue to beat, but never again will the patient be capable of an independent life, to speak, to comprehend, to feed or control his bodily functions. In other instances brain death may be less complete; spontaneous respiration and consciousness may be sustained without the patient having sufficient cerebral function for a sentient existence. To provide water and food through a naso-gastric tube and impeccable nursing care may be all that are required to keep the patient 'alive'. For how long should this be continued? Who is to decide when to take the positive step of withdrawing the naso-gastric tube, switching off the respirator if one is being used, or to take the less immediately lethal step of withholding antibiotics if the patient develops pneumonia?

This problem came before the British courts in the case of a young man who had suffered irreparable brain damage. Three years after the accident he did not respond to questions or commands; his eyes did not move towards a light or a voice; he could not swallow. Despite assiduous physiotherapy his limbs were wasted and barely moved in response to a painful stimulus. Daily visiting by his parents and exposure to music had failed to stimulate his brain; he remained a vegetable. He continued to live in this senseless state only because food and water were being given through a naso-gastric tube and antibiotics added when he developed an infection. It could be argued that to stop naso-gastric feeding would cause discomfort by inducing thirst, but this can be circumvented by oral hygiene, slivers of ice, sedatives and pain-killing drugs. The parents of the young man believed they were expressing his wishes when they asked for the feeding tube to be removed. The doctor in charge asked the coroner what would be the legal consequences if he withdrew the tube and, to his surprise, was told that he might find himself facing a charge of murder. The hospital on the doctor's behalf appealed for a judicial ruling. The High Court, the Court of Appeal and finally the House of Lords decreed that tube feeding did constitute medical treatment, and it could be discontinued if there was no prospect of the patient improving. The tube was withdrawn and the young man died.

The pressing, worrying, problem that today keeps the question of euthanasia in the forefront of people's minds is the increasing age of the population and their own fear of infirmity and senility. Whenever Her Majesty the Queen learns that one of her subjects has reached the age of a hundred she sends a telegram; ninety per cent of the recipients are women who live so much longer than men. In 1952 she sent 200 telegrams and in 1992, forty years later, she sent 3500. Government figures confirm that during this time there has been a sixteen-fold increase in the number of centenarians. Whereas in 1985 there were 3 million people aged seventy-five or over in the British Isles, there will be 4 million in 2006 and 5 million in the year 2025. This steep increase in the elderly causes medical, social and economic problems because many are incapable of leading an independent life. In the past they were looked after by their children. Today this is less common because the children may be past middle-age and not in good health themselves; they may live far from their surviving parent; they may have children of their own to look after; they may have a house of a size or configuration only suitable for themselves and their offspring. More and more people towards the end of their life are cared for in residential homes, nursing homes or hospitals for geriatric patients. There, in the fullness of time, they develop their terminal illness; the process of dying may be as protracted and distressing to their children as it is to the aged parent.

As we grow older, we all fear senility. The elderly patient is more likely to be a woman. No longer can she care for herself. She survives only because others do almost everything for her. She cannot walk but sits all day in a chair until she is put to bed at six o'clock, with cot-sides for fear she falls out, and is taken out again at eight o'clock next morning. The nurses have given up asking what she would like to eat; they just put the plate of food in front of her, and may have to feed her tediously – spoonful by spoonful. In her final months she may become demented. She does not know her children to whom she has become a sad caricature of her former self. She stares vacantly out of the window or around the dowdy sitting-room with its chairs ranged along the walls like tombstones on the periphery of a graveyard. She does not watch the permanently blaring television set, nor speak except to say in a flat toneless voice, 'I'm sorry.' She shows little other emotion – either pleasure or sadness, except on brief occasions when she screams. Some sections of society advocate a peaceful release for such a person, but even with a living will no doctor would countenance action beyond keeping the old lady as comfortable, mentally and physically, as he can. Certainly sedatives to quieten her and analgesics to relieve pain are given but not in amounts that will deliberately hasten her death, although in practice the duration of the process of dying may thereby be shortened.

It is not surprising that legalisation of euthanasia, which may be of two types, is often discussed. In the first, assisted suicide, which is open only to patients who have mental competence, the physician provides the wherewithal so that, when the patient wishes, he or she can commit suicide, the ultimate responsibility being more in the patient's than the doctor's hands. In the second, voluntary euthanasia, the physician not only makes the means available but at the request of the patient performs the final act. This carries a greater risk of error, coercion or abuse than physician-assisted suicide, but the need for either form is an admission of medical failure to provide the adequate pharmacological and psychological support that should be available in a terminal illness, but regrettably is not always instituted.

If assisted suicide or voluntary euthanasia were ever made legal, stringent safeguards would be required because the manner of operating the law and the mechanics of delivering death raise major bureaucratic and practical problems. After confirming the correctness of the diagnosis in consultation with specialist colleagues, whether he likes it or not the doctor would have to adopt the role of executioner. I doubt that many doctors would wish to do this. Legalisation of voluntary euthanasia might destroy a patient's trust. Imagine working as a doctor in an old people's home, in a hospice or in a hospital where legalised voluntary euthanasia is overtly practised. How would the other patients, particularly the many who are already fearful of what goes on in any institution, feel?

Already hospital doctors make the decision not to resuscitate, not to embark on emergency surgery, not to initiate or continue intensive care, or not to persist with useless therapeutic endeavours because in their judgement the patient can no longer benefit from such treatment. Without doubt hospital and family doctors, within the privacy of the patient's home, have made the passing into the next world of those they care for easier and will continue to do so.

12

Indian Bugs and Other Micro-organisms

The war in Europe had been over two months when I walked up the gang-plank to embark the *Empress of Scotland* at Liverpool. Out of the corner of my eye I caught sight of Bill Trethowan climbing a gang-plank further down the ship's side, carrying in each hand a black leather case. We met in the main lounge.

'Good to see you!' I put my hand on Bill's shoulder; to shake hands was impossible because he was still holding his trumpets. We hadn't seen each other since we'd joined the army together and spent two weeks at the RAMC depot in Crookham, where we did some desultory square bashing and had courses in map-reading and military law. Most of us had been in the Officers' Training Corps at school and were quite proficient at forming fours and presenting arms. On the last night we had a hilarious treasure-hunt driving round the countryside, going from one map reference point to another, and ending finally in a friendly country pub. There followed a week at the School of Hygiene in Mytchett where we learnt about gas and chemical warfare, the control of malaria, and the many different types of latrines that the army can provide in the field depending on the terrain and the number of troops who will use them.

'You're posted to India too?' I asked

'Yes, I'm a graded specialist in psychiatry. I've just seen two other medics who were up at Cambridge with us.'

The Merchant Navy purser, who in peacetime was accustomed to meeting the requests of his passengers, arranged for six of us, all contemporaries at Cambridge, to share a tiny cabin well below decks with an unopenable porthole.

The liner carried a cross-section of military personnel. Some were rejoining their units in India after their first home leave in five years. Others from British regiments were on their way to join the Fourteenth Army fighting the Japanese in Burma. There were Queen Alexandra's nurses, a dozen members of the Voluntary Air Detachment (VADs) and officers' wives joining their husbands whom they hadn't seen since the war started.

Nearly everyone was seasick in the Bay of Biscay. Those who ventured on deck wore a fixed artificial smile on their green faces. We wondered why hyoscine tablets were not issued; a double-blind trial in the *Queen Mary* on repeated Atlantic runs with US troops had shown it to be very effective, but perhaps this was considered too trivial a matter and the prophylactic tablets would have cost money.

Once through the Straits of Gibraltar morale rose. Daily PT on deck for the other ranks was organised by their NCOs and company commanders, and a few officers did exercises on their own before breakfast but, as one might expect, the medical fraternity took little interest in keeping fit. Officers from the Indian Army gave Urdu lessons which were poorly attended. Housey-housey was organised for the other ranks by the purser – bingo being the only form of gambling officially allowed.

The senior RAMC officer on board was Colonel (later Lord) Max Rosenheim, who one day was to become Professor of Medicine at University College Hospital in London and President of the Royal College of Physicians; he organised twice weekly seminars and lectures for the medical personnel. He told us about the health problems that he'd encountered in the North African and Italian campaigns. When he learnt that I had been on the two-weeks course in tropical medicine at the Royal Army Medical College in Millbank, he made me give two talks on diseases more specific to India.

This Millbank course was the best I've ever attended. It was run by an Australian, Robert Drew, who later became a major-general in charge of the Army Medical Services. Each forty-five-minute lecture was followed by a two-hour practical organised by a highly-trained sergeant and corporal technicians with access to a remarkable collection of slides and specimens. Under the microscope we saw worms, intestinal parasites, their eggs and cysts as never before. We learnt to identify the different species of malarial parasite. A remarkable number of tropical diseases were covered – from kala-azar to cholera, smallpox to elephantiasis, rabies to amoebic dysentery. It was a *tour de force* and convinced me that, with the right materials and good instructors, it was possible to teach a technical subject in a surprisingly short time although, of course, only clinical exposure would bring the wisdom of experience.

The six of us in the cabin started a poker school. The stakes were minimal and the lack of skill so evenly distributed that by the time we reached Bombay nobody had lost more than a few pence. Otherwise I buried myself in a two-volume American tome on tropical medicine and Margaret Steen's long and engrossing novel, *The Sun is My Undoing* – escaping into a world of slave ships trading out of Bristol and torrid passions and intrigue in the West Indies.

The five-weeks sea voyage were less tedious and uncomfortable than we had expected, but our restlessness increased as the ship approached Bombay. Flying fish were seen in greater numbers and other ships using adjacent sea lanes in the Indian Ocean left wisps of black smoke hanging motionless on the horizon. The Deccan Mountains were our first sight of land. We crowded on deck and, as the ship drew closer, we saw that the arid brown mountains dotted with scrub were hemmed at their base with green *ghats*, the foothills rising from the sea. The first identifiable building in Bombay was the Gateway to India, a neoclassical monument built to welcome Queen Victoria on her only visit to this jewel in her crown.

The ship docked, and a score of military and civilian officials climbed the gang-planks. On board it was strangely still without the thudding rumble of the ship's engines. From the shore came the ceaseless noise of cranes, shunting railway engines and the iron-clad wheels of carts, transcended by the shouts of coolies carrying loads on their head as they weaved like ants over the quayside.

By evening it was my turn to be interviewed by an RAMC officer who sat with a *babu* clerk at a table in one corner of the officers' lounge.

'Ah, yes, Mr Bayliss,' the captain shuffled his papers, 'you're posted to Number 121 Combined Military Hospital. I've no idea where that unit is – no idea at all. Might be anywhere.' He smiled blandly. 'I see that on arrival you are to be the medical specialist with the rank of major.' He sniffed in disapproval and after a long pause, said, 'they should know at the Medical Directorate in Delhi where the hospital is, so I'll post you to the British Military Hospital in Delhi Cantonment; they'll look after you for a day or two while you find out. A military train leaves for Delhi tonight. Report to the Transport Officer at Bombay Station for your rail pass. A truck will leave here at twenty hundred hours. Collect your baggage on the quay when it's been offloaded.'

The interview was over. Posted to a hospital that was lost – what a start to life in India! I rose to leave.

'Your mail, sahib.' The *babu* handed me a package of letters tied together with a piece of coarse wispy string. I went down to the cabin to read them in peace. As I opened the door Bill Trethowan exploded.

'Typical, bloody typical! They've had five weeks while we've been at sea to decide what to do with us and all they can do is send me to Deolali Transit Camp outside Bombay where I suppose I'll kick my heels for another five weeks.'

'I'm posted to a CMH but nobody seems to know where it is; so I'm going to Delhi to find out,' I said.

'Why can't they ring up and ask?' suggested Bill. 'And what is a CMH anyway?'

'A Combined Military Hospital,' I offered. 'It's a hospital that takes both British and Indian troops and officers as patients, and has a mixed British and Indian medical staff. Presumably this one is mobile – under canvas, and nobody knows where it's gone.'

* * *

The next evening I sat listening quietly at the dining table during my first meal in the Officers' Mess at the British Military Hospital in Delhi Cantonment, feeling like a new boy at school. An officer arrived late, apologised to the commanding officer, and sat down beside me.

'I'm Headington, the psychiatrist here,' he introduced himself. 'What a day ... thank God I'm going home next week – done nearly three years.' He sipped some soup and addressed the mess in general. 'I've got a remarkable patient in the padded cell – mad as a hatter. Every time Sergeant Scroggy takes in a bowl of water for him to wash with, he goes *doolali* – throws his arms around, pants in the most extraordinary way, shouts and then chucks the water all over poor Scroggy.'

126

Nobody said anything until in a quiet voice – and one of my many faults is facetiousness – I muttered, 'sounds like a nasty case of hydrophobia.'

Total silence; everyone stopped eating.

'Hydrophobia? D'you mean rabies?' Headington stared at me in horror.

'Well, yes ... I suppose I do. Fear of water *is* a symptom.'

An hour later I saw my first case of rabies. Not unexpectedly the poor patient died. A very frightened Sergeant Scroggy was given a large number of painful injections of rabies antiserum into his abdominal wall for two weeks and happily didn't contract the disease.

Not until many years later did I see another case. One evening Professor Lord Rosenheim telephoned me at home in London. 'You're the only person I know who's seen a case of rabies. Would you mind coming to University College Hospital – right away?'

In a side ward was a young RAMC lieutenant who six weeks before had been bitten by a dog in Palestine. He too had rabies and, alas, he also died. Had he reported the bite at the time and been actively immunised with rabies vaccine and protected with human rabies immune globulin, which was then available, his life would have been saved.

After jungle training and six months with the Fourteenth Army in Assam and North Burma before the Japanese capitulated, I returned to Delhi Cantonment and took charge of the medical division at the British Military Hospital.

*   *   *

'Sit, boy, sit!' In a more conversational tone I added, 'Now be a good dog, Barney, and wait here.'

Barney sat in the shade of the verandah with his back against the wall. The product of a smooth-haired Dachshund and a Corgi he had a svelte black coat except for two white front paws. He always ran behind me as I cycled round the scattered wards in the hospital compound. The original hospital had consisted of only a central brick building, two storeys high with wide verandahs as a screen against the heat; tacked on at the back was a single-storey outpatient department surrounding three sides of a square. The newly-built wards were freestanding and widely dispersed to prevent infection spreading from one to another. In one corner was the smallpox ward, surprisingly often used because some officers and other ranks refused vaccination at home, usually claiming on religious grounds to be conscientious objectors to the procedure. Why they were ever posted to India was a mystery; there was a high risk of them contracting smallpox and, even if they did not die of the disease, they were off duty for many weeks. There was a ward for patients with cholera which was seldom used, a ward for those with typhoid fever, and a busier ward for those with dysentery or more mundane types of diarrhoea.

I glanced back to be sure Barney was not following and opened the door to the commanding officer's outer office which was crammed with desks bearing ancient imperial typewriters that looked like dogs sitting up to beg. A sergeant stood to acknowledge my arrival.

'Is Colonel Escritt free?' I asked.

'I'll see, sir.' The sergeant opened the door to the inner office a few inches and peered round the corner.

'Major Bayliss,' he announced and pushed the door open.

'Hello, Dick, come and sit down.'

I saluted, removed my cap and sat on a chair opposite Colonel Frederick Escritt, universally known as Fred.

'We've got a bit of an outbreak of diarrhoea in the Officers' Mess,' I began. 'Nine officers in the last three days. They're quite bad; it's impossible to look after them in their quarters.'

'I'm not sure you aren't going to have another one. I've got terrible collywobbles. Been on the thunder-box four times already this morning. What's the cause?'

'Don't know, I'm afraid. The lab hasn't grown anything exciting so far. It's not *Sonne* or *Shigella* or one of the *Salmonellas*.'

'You've ruled out bacillary dysentery then?' Fred stopped to think. 'The incidence is disproportionately high among officers.' He scanned the lists of recent hospital admissions. 'Only three cases of diarrhoea from the Sergeants' Mess and none amongst the private soldiers. What about other units in the area?'

'Quite a few officers from the Rajputana Rifles' depot in the cantonment.'

'Any from headquarters in Delhi?' Fred asked.

'None from GHQ.'

'What about the QAs?'

128

'Two nursing sisters are in the female officers' ward. I've notified the Assistant Director of Medical Services.'

'Fat lot of good that'll do. He's worse than useless – spends most of his time in the Gymkhana Club in Delhi.' Fred was seldom so outwardly critical. He doubled up in his chair.

'Excuse me a minute,' he said and hurriedly left the office. Five minutes later he was back.

'Any blood?' I asked.

'No, but I think I'd better come in. Fix it, would you? I'll go to my bungalow and get my kit. See you on the ward.'

I collected Barney and walked along the verandah to Matron's office. It was only courteous to warn her that the CO was being admitted. Then I went to the officers' ward on the first floor. Without prompting Barney went straight to Sister's office and lay down under her desk; he knew better than to follow me into the ward.

'Sister, I'm admitting the CO. He's got diarrhoea like the others. Can you juggle about with the beds? Major Smith is in the side room; ask him if he'd mind joining the junior officers in the main ward.'

When Fred Escritt arrived with his bearer carrying his bag, he gently admonished Sister Judy Dickson. 'I'd have been perfectly all right with the others in the ward, Sister. No need to put me in a side room.'

We smiled at this characteristic remark. Universally Fred Escritt was considered the best of commanding officers. He had been a medical student at Guy's during the 1914–18 war and served as a dresser in a hospital ship during the Gallipoli campaign. He returned to finish his studies at Guy's and then joined the RAMC. He served in Kurdistan in 1923 where he promoted for the first time the evacuation of casualties by air. People loved Fred and would do anything for him. It was said that one day, when he was in Kurdistan, he had to fly to Kabul in Afghanistan. On arrival at the airfield only a two-seater plane was available. His faithful servant, Hamid, would have to be left behind. Hamid persuaded the pilot to tie him to one wing and to lash two cases of beer, equal to his weight, on the opposite one. Fred was a tall, lean, highly intelligent man with an irreverent sense of humour, particularly regarding unnecessarily restrictive army regulations. His always twinkling eyes were accentuated by his

129

sharply pointed pixie ears that stood out from his head at right angles. His quiet unobtrusive brand of discipline enhanced the efficiency and orderliness of the hospital; it contributed to the happiness of the patients and staff; and it increased our regard and respect for him.

After I'd examined him, Fred said with a laugh, 'Never been examined so thoroughly in my life before. Thank you. Now look, I know you've enough to do but would you look into this diarrhoea for me? Be an epidemiologist, a detective, for a few days.'

'Certainly, of course I will.'

The afternoon and evening were spent questioning all the diarrhoea patients. It took a long time; people were hopeless at remembering whether they had dined in their mess or in Delhi and what exactly they'd eaten or drunk before the illness began. After dinner, naked to the waist because of the heat, I sat in my bungalow at a bare trestle table trying to make some sense of the data. The medical officers, sisters and sergeants each had a separate mess. It was unlikely that one particular food was used by all three. Suddenly the common denominator became obvious. People with diarrhoea drank whisky and *soda*, or gin and *tonic*; those who drank whisky and water or pink gin did not have the condition.

Next morning after breakfast I asked the mess steward for two bottles of soda and tonic water. 'Put them on my mess bill,' I told the puzzled *khitmagar.*

With Barney running behind, I cycled to the path lab. 'I may be barking up the wrong tree but would you mind looking at these – bacteriologically?' Major Hermann Lehmann, the pathologist, had been my supervisor in biochemistry at Cambridge and was destined to become a distinguished haematologist after the war.

Then I hurried to the outpatient clinic. The benches on the verandah were already crammed with patients. In the consulting room the orderly, an RAMC corporal, exhibited concern because two Indian general duties medical officers from the hospital had jumped the queue and were sitting beside my desk.

'Don't tell me you two have both got the trots?'

'Yes, sir,' they said in unison.

'What d'you drink in the mess before dinner?'

The Sikh grinned. 'Scotch and soda'.

'And you?' I asked.

The other lieutenant hesitated.

130

'You may be a Muslim, Aziz, but I know damn'd well you drink.'

'Gin and tonic, sir.' Aziz smiled.

In the officers' mess everyone – British, Anglo-Indian, Indian, Christian, Hindu or Muslim – was treated the same but for one religious concession. When a pork or beef dish was served, there was always an alternative vegetable or egg curry.

After finishing outpatients, I cycled back to the path lab to be greeted by a serious faced Hermann.

'Know what you've given me?' he asked. 'Sewage, pure sewage. Both the soda and the tonic water are full of organic matter and teaming with bacteria that look like *E. Coli* but I shan't know for certain until the cultures are through tomorrow.'

Together we bicycled to the mess for lunch. Captain Roger Hershaw, the hospital's quartermaster, was sitting on a high stool at the bar sipping a glass of Murree beer. He was a regular soldier who had risen from the ranks. Everyone accepted that quartermasters were given a cut of the profitable deals they made with the Indian contractors who supplied the hospital with produce. It was common knowledge that Hershaw's ancient but well-kept Chevrolet was loaned to him by one of his important local suppliers.

'Roger, where do our soft drinks come from? Soda water and tonic water – that sort of thing?' I asked.

'A contractor here in the Cantonment. He supplies all the units in the area – has done for years. Nice feller. Anything wrong?'

'Not sure. Could you give him a ring after lunch and say I want to come and see him? Don't give him too much notice. I'd like to be at his place within fifteen minutes of you telephoning. Would you mind driving me there?'

* * *

The fat Punjabi had heard the car coming. To increase his stature he stood on the top of the two chipped whitewashed concrete steps leading to his office.

'Sahib, sahib.' He bowed, his chubby face lit in a broad smile, his hands positioned in greeting – the fingertips touching, the palms together. If the prospective visit had caused him any concern, the fifteen minutes' notice had apparently been enough for Mr Naipal to put his house in order because he was confidently at ease.

131

The quartermaster effected the introductions.

'I'm honoured, Major Sahib. I'm honoured, Captain Sahib.' Again Chandra Naipal put his hands together and bowed.

'I'd like to look round your bottling plant, Mr Naipal,' I said.

'A great pleasure, Major Sahib. Very modern bottling plant, very clean, everything very *thhik hai.*' Chandra Naipal led the way and, as he strode across the dusty earth, his baggy *dhoti* trousers rose up his legs to expose hairy ankles and dirty brown *chapplis.*

The plant was larger than one might have expected, and surprisingly clean, with white tiled walls. The returned empty bottles were soaking in huge tanks of chlorinated water, the old labels being removed as they floated to the surface by a coolie with a fishing net on a long pole. The bottles were then put on a moving track and rinsed with water before the insides were sterilised with a powerful jet of steam. The correct amount of water was put automatically into each bottle before it moved down the track for an injection of carbon dioxide after which the top was sealed with a crimped metal cap. On a parallel line bottles of tonic water were being filled with quinine cordial and water followed by an injection of carbon dioxide.

'Where does the water come from?' I asked.

'Royal Engineers, sahib. All water in Cantonment comes from Royal Engineers. Very deep holes in ground, sahib. Very clean, very good *pani.*' Naipal smiled with confident self-satisfaction.

'And where exactly does the water come in?'

Chandra Naipal ordered a coolie to lift the metal cover off a manhole. Below was the pipe with a water meter and a stopcock.

'And where does the water go from here?' I persisted.

'Into roof, sahib.' The Punjabi pointed to the terracotta tiles covering the bottling plant.

'I'd like to look.'

Naipal explained that the only way into the roof was through a trapdoor in the ceiling of the factory. A ladder would be needed. It was not the sort of place a Major Sahib should go.

Five minutes later a workman was the first to climb the primitive ladder with its irregularly spaced rungs tied to the side poles with hemp and bits of old twine. He raised the trapdoor and reached down to take the lighted paraffin lamp that Chandra Naipal was holding. I followed him through the opening.

In the roof space were three large galvanised tanks, their sides discoloured with patches of rust. The rough wooden floor of the loft was thick with dust, bird droppings and feathers. I put my hand over the rim of the nearest tank. It had no cover. In the dim light I reached down to feel the surface of the water.

'Give me that *butti*.' I took the paraffin lamp from the coolie and lowered it inside the tank. 'Oh, my God! Roger just look at this!'

A thick scum of rotting leaves and feathers covered the surface of the water; floating on it were the decaying bodies of long-dead birds, drowned rats and a larger object that looked like the remains of a cat.

Sewage, I thought as I climbed carefully down the ladder. 'Sewage is just about the right word,' I said aloud as I reached the floor.

* * *

Bacteria are so small that they are of course invisible to the naked eye. They were first observed by a Dutchman, Anthony van Leeuwenhock (1632–1723), a naturalist who developed the microscope. Louis Pasteur in Paris and Robert Koch in Berlin were the founders of modern bacteriology, and it is a science that grows daily. New micro-organisms are still being discovered and sometimes prove responsible for a disease of previously unknown cause that had been given an eponymous name, such as that of the physician who first described it or the location in which patients first contracted it.

Many thousands of different types of bacteria live in close proximity with animals and man, but relatively few cause disease. In the vegetable world, bacteria are essential for many natural biological processes. In a teaspoonful of fertile soil it is said there may be as many micro-organisms as there are people on the earth. The process of fermentation that produces alcohol in wine is bacterially dependent as is the manufacture of cheeses. Bacteria destroy various types of waste, and for many years have been used in domestic septic tanks and in larger municipal sewage plants. Several species of bacteria dissolve fat and grease. Whereas plumbers were constantly having to unblock the drains of short-order restaurants where many hamburgers are cooked daily, nowadays the drains are less expensively kept patent by pouring these micro-organisms in powder form down the kitchen sinks.

Several 'new' diseases caused by micro-organisms have been

133

recognised in recent years, although undoubtedly they occurred in the past. In 1976 an outbreak of pneumonia occurred in a group of Americans attending a convention at an hotel in Philadelphia. One hundred and eighty-two legionnaires developed the disease and 29 died. The cause of the pneumonia was not one of the usual micro-organisms and for a time the pathogen remained unknown. Eventually the cause was identified and appropriately named *Legionella pneumophilia.* It was not really new because studies in many countries of former patients, who had had pneumonia without the causative organism ever being identified, were found by retrospective blood tests to have had legionnaires' disease. *Legionella pneumophilia* is an aquatic organism which multiples rapidly in water at 30–38°C. Most epidemics are caused by the inhalation of droplets of water blown from the cooling towers of improperly serviced air-conditioning plants located on the roofs of buildings. Such occurred some years ago from the roof of Broadcasting House in Portland Place, London, and led to an outbreak of ninety-three cases with three deaths. Isolated cases may arise from the inhalation of droplets of water from a shower head, a Jacussi or, if the taps are infected, even the mist that rises from a hot bath or a wash-hand basin. The disease is now more common because of the increased use of air-conditioning, but fortunately the organism is not robust and proper regular maintenance of the hot water and cooling systems will destroy it.

Another 'new' disorder is Lyme disease which was first described in the mid-1970s after the investigation of outbreaks of a curious form of arthritis that developed in children and adults living in the vicinity of the township of Lyme in Connecticut, USA. Subsequent cases have been diagnosed in other parts of the US and throughout Europe. A great deal of research was needed to discover the cause and how the disease was transmitted. The micro-organism was first identified by an American, Dr Burgdorfer, and named after him. *Borrelia burgdorferi* is spread by a tick which lives mainly on deer and mice. Sometimes dogs, which themselves may also suffer from Lyme disease, transmit the tick to their owners. One particular dog, which had got wet hunting in the woods on a rainy day in an island off the coast of Massachusetts, came into a sitting-room and shook himself. The people in the room were sprayed with water and also, unbeknown to them, with ticks. Many of them subsequently developed Lyme disease.

The micro-organisms enter the skin when the tick bites. After a few days a painful rash may appear at the site of the bite and the micro-organisms are disseminated throughout the body. The patient experiences malaise, chills, fatigue and a fever with aching muscles and joints. There may be nausea and vomiting, backache or a sore throat. Later, meningitis with headache and pain and stiffness in the neck, or involvement of the facial nerve (Bell's palsy) may develop. The heart may be affected. Within weeks or as late as two years after the onset, arthritis may develop with swelling, pain and hotness of the joints, particularly the knees. Antibiotics are usually effective. Lyme disease is not uncommon in rural England, particularly where there are deer. Ticks carrying the micro-organism are present on the deer in Richmond Park near London and may cause arthritis in dogs taken there for exercise as well as in their owners.

Food poisoning remains an ever-present problem but the great reduction during the last half century in the number of cases of typhoid fever in Great Britain is the consequence of several public health measures. The quality of water has improved; the standards of sanitation and sewage are higher; stricter hygiene is imposed in the food chain; patients who develop typhoid fever are treated vigorously and on recovery are unlikely to become chronic carriers of the organism; travellers to areas where hygiene is unreliable are vaccinated against the disease. Today people seldom contract typhoid in England unlike in the days of Queen Victoria whose husband tragically died of it at the age of forty-two. Nor should we forget that Prince Albert was a great protagonist of the flushing water closet which was first widely promoted at the Great Exhibition of 1851 held in Hyde Park, London.

Nevertheless outbreaks of typhoid fever do occasionally occur in Britain. Some years ago there was an outbreak in Bournemouth. As in other epidemics, the initial patients developed a mysterious febrile illness which at first was difficult to diagnose but after appropriate investigations proved to be typhoid. The local medical officer of health, responsible for determining the origin of any epidemic in his region, stuck into a plan of the town red pins at the place where each patient lived. All were in an area that was supplied by one dairy which in turn got its milk from one farm. When the farm was inspected it was found that the milk churns were washed in a stream running down one side of the farmyard.

Bacteriological cultures from inside the milk churns and from the stream grew *Salmonella typhi.* The next question was how the typhoid bacilli had got into the stream.

An ordinance survey map showed a country mansion upstream from the farm. This was owned by a retired governor of one of our smaller colonies who was a cricket enthusiast and had his own cricket pitch. Each July he invited a dozen friends and their wives to stay for a week during which a series of matches were played against visiting teams. The house had its own septic tank but the capacity of this was overwhelmed by so many guests, and the effluent seeped into the stream. It was laboriously established that one of the recent guests, for many years an Indian civil servant, was a chronic carrier of the typhoid organism.

Sometimes an outbreak of typhoid fever may be first diagnosed a long way from its origin. Early in March 1963 a young lady was admitted with an undiagnosed fever to a side room in Westminster Hospital, London. It took a few days to establish that her pyrexia of unknown origin, or PUO as it is called, was due to typhoid fever. In a London teaching hospital typhoid is a rarity, and other less well-staffed establishments might have transferred the patient to the local fever hospital; but we had the resources to look after Judy, who would not constitute a danger to other patients or to the staff if everyone obeyed the strict rules of barrier nursing. The patient was also important for teaching medical students and the house officers. She was notified to the local Medical Officer of Health who wanted to know where she'd contracted the disease. We couldn't be sure but thought it significant that in February she'd been to Zermatt for a fortnight's skiing. The incubation period is eight to 14 days, and it seemed likely that she'd picked it up in Switzerland.

A few days later we admitted another patient with PUO. Naomi was aged twenty-eight and also proved to have typhoid fever. She too had been to Zermatt but had stayed in a chalet whereas Judy had been in a hotel. A doctor from the Department of Health telephoned to find out exactly where the two patients had stayed. On the wall of his office at the Elephant and Castle was a plan of Zermatt and already nine pins were stuck in it; all the patients had stayed in the lower part of the town. The British government was the first to alert the Swiss government of the outbreak of typhoid fever in one of their top ski resorts.

Earth subsidence had caused one of the main sewers in Zermatt to fracture and the contents were contaminating the drinking water carried in an adjacent pipe which had also been cracked. Only people staying in the lower part of the town were exposed to the polluted drinking water. After painstaking investigations an assistant chef, who had once worked in the Far East and cooked in a hotel upstream of the severed sewer and cracked water pipe, was found to be a chronic carrier of *Salmonella typhi.*

Antibiotics and good nursing cured our two patients, and a year later Judy and Naomi enjoyed a week's free skiing in Zermatt as guests of the town council.

Another member of the salmonella family, *Salmonella typhimurium,* is today a more common cause of food poisoning. This micro-organism was introduced into British poultry and turkey farms by contaminated animal foodstuff imported from abroad and has become widely disseminated. It is now endemic in the industry and difficult to eradicate. Salmonellosis is not peculiar to Britain. Boiled eggs disappeared from the breakfast tables of many ski resorts in Austria during the 1992–93 season when an outbreak of food poisoning caused by infected eggs led to the temporary closure of two hotels in the Oetztaler Alps at the height of the season. Eggs may take longer to boil at 6000 feet than at sea level, but every breakfast egg in the hotel we go to in Lech is so hard boiled that no salmonella could possibly survive.

What may prove a significant advance in our understanding of the cause and the treatment of peptic ulceration is the finding of a micro-organism, *Helicobacter pylori,* in the stomach of patients with a gastric or duodenal ulcer. In 1983 in Australia this hitherto unknown organism was isolated as the result of a fortunate oversight on the part of a bacteriologist who forgot to throw away what appeared to be a culture plate without anything growing on it when he went home for the weekend. To his surprise on his return to the laboratory on Monday morning he found a previously unknown organism growing. The association of *Helicobacter pylori* with peptic ulceration has now been convincingly demonstrated. The micro-organism is seldom found in the stomach until adolescence and thereafter its prevalence increases with age. Although the symptoms of a peptic ulcer can be effectively relieved with antacids and drugs that reduce the secretion of acid in the stomach, there is a liability to repeated recurrences unless the *H. pylori* is eradicated with antibiotics and bismuth. It is not yet clear what the precise role of the micro-organism is in causing ulcers because in some communities a large proportion of the people harbour *H. pylori* without any having ulcer symptoms.

Virus diseases are another story. The current worldwide epidemic of autoimmune deficiency disease is too much part of contemporary history to be discussed here. However it would appear that the virulence of the organism is already changing so that the mortality from this infection is not as speedy or as inevitable as was at first the case.

13

Malaria

The first light of dawn shone faintly through the skimped unlined orange curtains as I freed the bottom edge of the mosquito-net tucked under the mattress and patted the palm of my hand across the top of the bedside table. I couldn't find my watch. With concern I sat up in bed and felt more carefully. No watch, no wallet, no Parker pen, no money – only a bunch of keys, my spectacles and the bedside light. I put my glasses on and stuck my head under the mosquito netting. The room was in chaos – my clothes scattered over the floor with the drawers in the cupboard half-open and the desk rifled.

'Barney,' I said quietly.

Barney slept in a basket lined with an old army blanket immediately underneath my *charpoy* to avoid the draught created by the electric fan that turned laboriously with a faint squeak in the ceiling above. Ordinarily he anticipated my waking and would stand, his tail wagging, beside the bed ready to lick my hand as it emerged from under the mosquito-netting.

'Barney!' This time I shouted.

A faint half-bark half-grunt came from afar. Naked, I jumped out of bed. The French windows leading to the verandah were open. I went outside. The grunting noise was louder. I walked along the verandah to a door that led into an empty storeroom beyond which was the bathroom. The storeroom was lined with built-in cupboards and Barney was standing in front of one, his eyes fixed on a door that was ajar.

'What is it, boy?' I whispered and crept forward. Gently I opened the cupboard. Inside was a naked Indian, his skin glistening from the grease smeared over his body to make apprehension more difficult. Hanging over his forearms were some of my clothes and in his hands he held my watch and wallet. I closed and locked the cupboard.

'Good boy. Stay, Barney, stay.' I went back to the bedroom, quickly pulled on a pair of trousers and a bush shirt, pushed my feet into a pair of *chapplis*, grabbed my cap and ran down the path, across the road to the guardroom at the entrance to the hospital compound.

A sleepy sepoy saluted.

'Turn out the guard,' I shouted. 'Loose-*wallah*, loose-*wallah*, there's a burglar in my bungalow. Hurry, *juldi, juldi.*'

I went back to keep guard with Barney. Ten minutes later a corporal and three men arrived. They grabbed the loose-*walhah*. Half an hour later the military police took him away.

'What about my things?' I asked. 'My wallet, my watch, my pen?'

'Sorry Major sahib – evidence,' the Indian policeman said. 'You can't have anything back until after the hearing in the magistrates' court – we must have evidence.'

After breakfast I cycled to the hospital kitchens and asked the head *khansama* for a bone to reward Barney with. We waited outside until the chef returned – with the thigh bone of an ox that was bigger and heavier than Barney.

'I'm afraid that's a bit too large. Haven't you anything smaller?' I pointed to my forearm.

A month later I got my valuables back.

* * *

I had tried to delay my visit to Meerut until the monsoon came which would make the journey more tolerable, but the monsoon hadn't come. In the intense dry heat, the ancient fifteen-hundred-weight truck edged its way slowly along the road, which at this point had deteriorated into corrugated baked earth, and a cloud of brown dust thrown up by the rear wheels was blown forward by the ceaseless wind so that the driver and I were engulfed in our own self-generated suffocating sandstorm. With a thump the wheels went over a bump and the truck was back on a tarmacadam surface. The cloud of dust retreated as the driver accelerated. I bent forward to stroke Barney, lying asleep at my feet on the metal floor.

As the medical specialist, I was responsible for the patients in six military hospitals within a 200-mile radius of Delhi. Each hospital had to be visited once a fortnight. The smallest one in Meerut, some 70 miles away, was a particular favourite. It was sufficiently close to be visited in a day, and the building dated back to the Indian Mutiny of 1857 where the sepoys had first mutinied against the British who succeeded in holding the town. The graves of the few who were killed lay in the immaculately kept cemetery beside the church. Most of the gravestones, however, bore witness to deaths from natural causes that nowadays would be avoided by improved public health, antibiotics and advances in medical management. The British who governed India in Victorian times seldom stayed on long enough to die there so the cemetery contained mainly young people – some of them very young. A surprisingly large number of women in their twenties had died in childbirth. When I first viewed their headstones I clenched my hands at the horror of the primitive obstetrical practices of those days and the ravages of puerperal sepsis. There were also the small graves of infants and young children whose cause of death was not revealed; they had probably died of diarrhoea or from one of the infectious diseases – deaths that would not happen today. Equally tragic were the graves of young subalterns, aged nineteen or twenty, who had died, it said on the tombstones, of typhoid fever.

I was not happy; I'd had enough of India. I despised myself for developing the characteristics so unlikeable in those who had not had home leave for several years. I too was in danger of becoming lazy, and my professional standards were beginning to slip. Attention to detail was too much trouble. Oh God! when would the monsoon break? After months of relentless heat I longed to stand naked on the parched brown lawn outside my bungalow and let the deluging rain pour over me, soaking my hair. For the second successive year I had prickly heat. I itched all over – my skin peppered with tiny pustules. Some fool dermatologist had advised less bathing and not to use soap – and smell like a badger no doubt. I stroked Barney's ear with envy. The only difference the hot weather seemed to make to him was that he slept more and breathed faster. Clearly dogs had superior homeostatic mechanisms for regulating their body temperature than human beings. 'Why can't I just exhale my heat like a dog?' I thought, and scratched Barney's back rather than my own.

141

'Good morning, sir.' Lieutenant Masood Khan smiled broadly as he stood on the whitewashed step outside the front door of the hospital and saluted. I returned his greeting and, pushing back the door with its shiny brass handle, walked into the shaded hall with its gleaming polished parquet floor smelling of beeswax. Barney and Lieutenant Khan followed, the Indian rubbing his hands in evident delight. These fortnightly visits were clearly an occasion of great joy to him. Without anyone to relieve him, the general duties officer was on continuous call looking after some thirty medical patients. My visits were the only time he was taught anything or had someone to talk medicine with.

'How are they?' I pulled down the front of my crumpled bush shirt and straightened my belt.

'All right,' Masood Khan answered, 'except Balwant Singh's no better.'

I remembered this patient well having seen him on two previous occasions. On the first Masood Khan told me that Balwant Singh, who had just been admitted, had malaria. I had done little more than ask the sepoy whether he'd taken his mepacrine tablets regularly. It was a stupid question because the answer was invariably, 'Yes'. I had felt the patient's left upper abdomen and confirmed that he had an enlarged spleen. The man did not look particularly ill. Khan said that the blood slides were positive for benign tertian malaria and he would treat Balwant Singh with paludrine, a new drug made by ICI in England which had been flown out to India in recent weeks.

A fortnight later, on my second visit to the patient, he was much the same. Balwant Singh had a fever every night, not every other night as often occurs in benign tertian malaria.

'What's going on? This man's had paludrine for the last two weeks?'

'He has, sir,' Khan had confirmed. 'And the blood slides are still positive for BT malaria.' He held out the laboratory reports.

I had talked with Balwant Singh and this time examined him from head to toe. Apart from the enlarged spleen there had been nothing to find. He looked a little thinner but that was no bad thing in this overweight Sikh.

'Interesting. We've treated about twenty patients with paludrine at the British Military Hospital in Delhi and they've all responded very well. I wonder why this man – I suppose I should say this man's parasites – are resistant to the drug? No point in going on with it; you'd better give him quinine,' I said.

And now on my third visit Balwant Singh was no better after a month's treatment.

'He's had quinine for the last fortnight? Let's go and look.'

As we entered the dimly lit ward Barney made his own way to Sister's office and lay quietly under her desk. Sister Connie Best, a Queen Alexandra's nurse, greeted us – all smiles. She wore an immaculately ironed white short-sleeved uniform with a wide white belt at the waist and a red epaulette with gold pips on the left shoulder. A white veil, set well back from her forehead, framed her pretty face and hung down behind to shoulder length. Beside her was a trolley with the patients' notes, a blood pressure measuring machine and all the necessities for examining a patient – from a spatula to a kneejerk hammer.

As if on parade all the patients lay in bed at attention. Nothing moved in the ward and there was silence except for the ceaseless dripping of water. The verandahs on either side of the ward were hung with screens of *khas-khas tatti* made of rushes, straw and long grass which dripped from the buckets of water thrown over them by the *malis* who, until the rains came, could not do any serious gardening in the hard-baked fissured red earth. In the absence of air conditioning, the *khas-khas tatties* effectively kept the temperature down and the searing heat and light out.

Sister Best held out the temperature chart. Apart from the expected random irregularities, the fever had not varied for four weeks, and the paludrine and the quinine hadn't made one iota of difference.

'Masood, I simply don't believe this chap's got malaria.'

Masood never disagreed with anything I said. 'I thought that too, Major sahib, but the blood films are all positive.' He proffered a handful of recent laboratory reports.

They all read the same: 'BT Malaria Positive + + +' and were signed by someone called Prabhu.

'Who's Prabhu?' I asked.

'Our pathologist, a Jemadar-sahib – a warrant officer. He's not medically qualified, but he was trained in Poona and my goodness what experience – he's been everywhere.'

'Let's go and see him. We'll be back in a minute or two, Sister. Lead the way, Masood.'

At the end of the ward we pushed aside the *khas-khas tatti* smelling of rotting vegetation and stood on the verandah where the heat hit us with what seemed a physical blow. We screwed up our eyes against the light and walked across the dusty compound to a Nissen hut. Masood opened the door to the air-conditioned laboratory where we were greeted by a lean sprightly Indian aged about forty.

'Jemadar-sahib, we're interested in the blood films of a patient called Balwant Singh. He's not responded to treatment with either paludrine or quinine and his blood films continue to show benign tertian malarial parasites. Could we look at his most recent slides, please?'

'Ah! sahib,' the Jemadar-Sahib's face assumed an expression of grave concern, 'since six months my microscope it has been broken. It is in Poona, sahib, being repaired.'

'So?'

'Sahib, I am thinking it safest if all blood films for suspected malaria are reported as BT – benign tertian – positive three plusses. Then they will be treated. If they have malaria, they get better; if not malaria they are no worse off, sahib.' He held out his hands, palms up, to emphasise the hopelessness of his position and the logic of his thinking.

I pondered. Yes, under the circumstances the Jemadar-sahib had done the right thing short of telling the truth. I laughed as I leant forward and squeezed the pathologist's arm. 'You're absolutely right, Jemadar-sahib. As soon as I get back to Delhi, I'll raise merry hell at GHQ until you have a new microscope.'

In due course sepoy Balwant Singh recovered from a quite different tropical disease – kala-azar.

* * *

Every year 2 million people in the world suffer from malaria and surprisingly and disturbingly 1 million, mostly children, die. Another cause for concern is that the incidence of malaria and the mortality from it are increasing.

Travellers to malarious areas of the world usually follow their travel agent's advice and take antimalarial drugs. No prophylaxis, however, is totally effective and the traveller may not take the drug conscientiously. In 1991 some 2300 travellers developed malaria on their return to the United Kingdom and of these 13 died, including a fifty-seven-year-old man who sadly had contracted the disease on his honeymoon in Kenya. Very seldom today is malaria actually contracted in the British Isles, but not so long ago a mosquito infected with the malarial parasite travelled in an aeroplane from West Africa to Gatwick and one summer's evening escaped into the Sussex countryside. The landlord of a public house not far from the aerodrome and a district nurse, cycling past the inn where she paused to rest, were bitten and both developed malaria.

The spread of malaria depends upon two factors: the presence of the plasmodial parasite, which causes the disease, in the blood of members of the community and the presence of mosquitos that transmit the parasites from one person to another. The control of malaria requires manipulation of both factors, and at high cost eradication has been successfully achieved in some parts of the world, notably Europe and the USA. Elsewhere success has been only partial, as in India where for a time the incidence was reduced 500-fold. In other areas eradication has been less successful, or not even attempted, because of the lack of money or commitment aggravated by the malarial parasite becoming resistant to therapeutic drugs.

Several methods are used to prevent mosquitos from transmitting malaria. For the individual, insect repellents, wearing clothes in the evening that cover as much of the exposed parts of the body as practical, fitting screens on windows and doors and a mosquito-net over the bed at night are all essential measures. Spraying long-lasting insecticides on the walls of buildings kills mosquitos. DDT is one of the best known and was widely used but some strains of mosquito have become resistant, and concern about the effect of DDT on the environment and fear of its toxicity have led to its avoidance, at least out of doors, in favour of other compounds that are more biologically degradable and usually more expensive.

Interfering with the mosquitos' breeding will control malaria. The larvae of the insect develop just beneath the surface of stagnant water, and various strategies can be used to interrupt this stage in their life cycle. Marshland can be drained and irrigation channels allowed to dry out temporarily so that the larvae perish. The surface of stagnant water can be sprayed with a film of diesel oil with or without an insecticide. The oil prevents the larvae from breathing; this measure must be repeated every week or two.

Several different drugs are used to treat patients with malaria.

Some suppress the parasite after it has entered the patient's bloodstream and prevent it from multiplying so that the patient does not have an attack of malaria. Others kill the parasite when it is in the bloodstream during an attack of malaria and so relieve the patient's symptoms. Yet others may eliminate the parasite when it is lurking in the patient's liver but does not cause any symptoms.

The oldest antimalarial drug is quinine. Derived from the bark of the cinchona tree, it was first described by an Augustinian monk in Peru in a book published in Spain in 1639. He wrote, 'A tree grows which they call the fever tree, whose bark, the colour of cinnamon, is made into powder amounting to the weight of two silver coins and given as a beverage, cures the fevers'. For three centuries quinine was the only effective remedy, and its lack was severely felt during the 1914–18 war when the German U-boat blockade largely prevented cinchona bark being imported from South America. After World War I, the search for man-made alternatives was hindered by the lack of any readily available laboratory animal that could be infected with the same malarial parasites that affect human beings. This search was accelerated during World War II when, with the outbreak of hostilities in the Far East, the mortality amongst the troops was likely to be as high or higher from malaria than from enemy action.

At the onset of World War II a drug invented in the early thirties had largely displaced quinine as a preventive and a treatment. This was called mepacrine in the British army and atabrine by the Americans. It had relatively few side-effects although it turned people's skin yellow. This did not lead to confusion with jaundice caused by infective hepatitis, which was also widespread, because mepacrine did not turn the whites of the eyes yellow whereas jaundice did.

Inevitably the troops believed that a tablet, which had to be taken compulsorily, was intended to suppress their libido and, given time, would render them impotent. In Burma, where there was malignant malaria, the disease was so virulent that it was a court martial offence not to attend the early morning parade at which the tablets were dispensed under an officer's supervision. No matter how ill a soldier felt he had to attend this early morning parade; if he remained in his quarters and was suffering from malignant malaria, he was likely to be dead by the time a medical orderly came to see him later in the day.

146

That mepacrine has no adverse effect on libido was apparent when in and around the town of Gauhati in Assam there was a sudden increase in the incidence of gonorrhoea in the soldiers from many nations who were preparing to drive the Japanese out of Burma. The source was a brothel that had been opened in a large house on the outskirts of the town. Putting the house out of bounds had not the slightest effect, so a platoon of Gurkhas was ordered to mount a twenty-four-hour guard; but the ladies were so persuasive that by the end of the first week ten of the Gurkhas had been admitted with gonorrhoea to the Combined Military Hospital housed in what had been an American-funded college of higher education. To me it seemed more practical to treat the source. Twelve charming *petite* Chinese ladies, giggling with shyness and shading their faces from the noonday sun with umbrellas, minced their way in high-heeled shoes along the dusty road to the hospital where they were admitted to a ward set aside for their week's special treatment. Only then did the hospital's quartermaster point out that he had to account for all the rations they ate. Had they been British soldiers he would have sent their name, rank and number to the Paymaster General in Blackpool who would have docked their pay; the ladies had no such identification particulars. The quartermaster was persuaded to invent fictitious personal details in the hope that, by the time Blackpool realised they were bogus, we would all be a thousand miles away or the war would be over.

During World War II a major research project in the USA led to the development of chloroquine, although afterwards it was found that this antimalarial had been synthesised by the Germans as early as 1934. Another new compound, proguanil or paludrine, was developed in Great Britain. Since the war other new compounds have been developed. Unfortunately in Central and South America, in India, Southeast Asia and Oceania, and in sub-Saharan Africa the malarial parasite is nowadays often, partially or wholly, resistant to treatment with chloroquine and paludrine. Despite less commercial interest in the western world in producing new drugs for a disease that primarily affects poor people in the developing world who have not the money to pay for it, research continues to develop a vaccine that will either cure the disease or prevent people from contracting it. The use of the active ingredient of a Chinese herbal remedy is also proving of great value.

14

Friends as Patients

The orderly handed me the telephone.

'Brigadier Lipscomb would like a word with you, sir.' The voice of the girl in the Medical Directorate in Delhi had the sing-song Welsh intonation of an Anglo-Indian.

'Lipscomb here. Are you alone?'

'No, but I can be in a second.' I made signs for the orderly to remove himself and the patient from the consulting room in the outpatient department of the British Military Hospital in Delhi Cantonment. Brigadier Martin Lipscomb, Consultant in Medicine to the army in India, incited general admiration. He kept in touch with clinical medicine by coming on ward rounds at the hospital and would drive out from Delhi in his 1922 Rolls-Royce open tourer, a present from a grateful maharajah patient. With his round clean-shaven face, laughing bright-blue eyes and well-brushed white hair, he never pulled rank and professionally was much respected.

'All clear, sir.'

'I wonder if you could manage to come to Delhi this afternoon or this evening and see a patient? For several reasons I don't want to do this myself. She's the wife of a brigadier in intelligence here at GHQ. Her husband tells me she's insane. He wants her sent home by hospital ship, rather than stay on here and be repatriated with him later on. Bill Trethowan, the specialist in psychiatry, is away up country. I can't get hold of him, so thought you'd be the best person to handle this. I've known both of them socially for so long that none of us would be comfortable in a professional relationship. The patient says she's got nothing wrong but psychiatric patients often do, don't they?' He paused.

'What exactly is the problem?'

'Something about her smashing their best dinner service over her husband's head. Also she took some monkeys on a military train. Be a good fellow and go and see what it's all about. I've left the psychiatric forms for you in an envelope at their bungalow. When can you go?'

'About four o'clock this afternoon, if that's all right, sir.' Goodbye to my game of tennis. 'What's the patient's name?'

'Mrs Holford, wife of Brigadier Holford.'

'Oh, I know him. We sometimes play tennis together.'

'D'you know him well?' Lipscomb asked hesitantly.

'Not well. I've never been to his bungalow and we're not on Christian name terms.'

'Well, that's all right then. I'll tell them to expect you about teatime. Here's the address.' Brigadier Lipscomb dictated. 'Send the papers, marked "Private", direct to me at the Medical Directorate, would you?'

I was driven to the bungalow in the only transport the quartermaster had available. The old army truck did scant justice to the impeccably pressed green bush shirt and trousers that the *dhobi* had ironed and my bearer, Rugbeir Singh, had laid out. I walked up the gravel path bordered on both sides by a row of whitewashed stones flanked by a single file of drooping orange-yellow zinnias set with military precision. Brigadier Holford stood waiting on the verandah.

'Afternoon.' He greeted me with a smile.

I saluted. The brigadier was typical of his *genre* – tall, slender, hair greying at the temples, aged about fifty. He ushered me into the bungalow and introduced me to his wife.

'How d'you do? Please sit down.' Mrs Holford had an Irish accent, and beckoned me to a chair beside a low, round, embossed brass table laid for afternoon tea and covered with a white lace cloth fraying at the edges. She tinkled a small hand-bell to summon the *khitmagar.* Not until later did I notice that the cups and plates were of assorted sizes and patterns. Mrs Holford was about the same age as her husband but plump and rather untidy. Her pale red hair was straggly and her hands distinctly grubby with unkempt nails.

During tea we talked pleasantries – about the consequences of partitioning the country into India and Pakistan, the comings and goings of Nehru and Jinnah, when exactly the British forces would withdraw, when I would be demobbed. Mrs Holford seemed perfectly normal.

'My husband will retire when we've finished handing over,' she said. 'We're going to live in Ireland.'

'In due course, in due course.' The brigadier was conciliatory. 'There may be one or two things to tidy up here before I can get away. The Indian army will need British advisers for a while.'

I must get on with this job, I thought. I was procrastinating because I felt distinctly uneasy; my training in psychiatry was so inadequate. I knew quite a lot about the psychological problems induced by physical illness but had little experience of psychiatric diseases *per se*.

'I believe you have some papers for me?' I asked. The brigadier handed me an envelope. 'Mrs Holford, shall we talk privately in your bedroom?'

It was dark in there; the curtains drawn to keep out the heat. I sat on the edge of the double bed while she sat on the stool beside her dressing table, at ease and relaxed.

'What have you noticed wrong, Mrs Holford?'

'Me? There's nothing wrong with me. I'm fine, thank you.' My eyes were adapting to the darkness. Mrs Holford sounded friendly and was not defensive. She was spontaneous but thoughtful in her answers to the many routine questions I asked. Half an hour later I was little the wiser. Mrs Holford seemed perfectly normal. She had, it appeared, a talent for watercolour painting which she had learnt at her convent school in Galway and then at St Martin's in London before she had married. Three children were in school 'at home'.

While she undressed to lie in her dressing-gown on the bed, I waited outside in the corridor reading the documents from the Medical Directorate. *History of Present Psychiatric Disorder...* *Details of Current Abnormal Behaviour...*, *Recommended Treatment and Disposal...* How was I going to answer these?

Mrs Holford called that she was ready. I examined her, tested her short- and long-term memory, and made her do mental arithmetic. She knew the names of the members of the Cabinet; she could take seven from a hundred correctly, and seven from ninety-three and seven from eighty-six. There was no hint of dementia, no history of hearing voices, no neurotic traits of significance.

When Mrs Holford had dressed again, I took the bull gently by the horns. 'Mrs Holford, I've heard something about you breaking china.'

'Yes, I have on several occasions,' she admitted. 'I'm Irish, you see. I can get very angry with my husband. He lies to me, I'm afraid. Yes, once or twice – maybe a few more times – I've hit him over the head with a dinner plate or thrown a saucer or two at him.'

'And why should you do that?' The Irish phrasing was infectious.

'Why? Because he's unfaithful. Nine months ago I was at home on leave – on my own. When it was time to come back, my husband did everything he could to stop me. Myself I had to go to the War Office in London and make them give me a passage. I guessed my husband was being . . .' she hesitated, '. . . being unfaithful.'

'I see. Go on. What happened?'

'I arrived unexpectedly. I found him and his secretary in . . . in . . .'

'In bed – *in flagrante delicto?*'

'Not actually in bed but near enough to make no difference. I knew what they were up to.'

'And what's this about you and some monkeys on a train?'

'Poor things!' Mrs Holford sounded more cheerful. 'Friends of ours in Aundh, near Poona, were going home and they had some pet monkeys. *Somebody* had to look after the poor dears; they couldn't just be left.'

'So?'

'I went down and brought them back here.'

'And?'

'They were fine in their wicker baskets on the train, the *Deccan Queen*, as far as Bombay; it's only a short journey from Poona. But it seemed unkind to keep them locked up all the way from Bombay to Delhi, so I let them run around in the compartment. The terrible thing is that one of them escaped. When I got out somewhere to have lunch at a station restaurant, the little darling slipped out with me and ran away.'

'What did you do?'

'I asked the officer in charge of the train if some of the troops could help me look for him. They scoured the restaurant and the trees behind but couldn't find him. You see there were lots of ordinary monkeys there too. I expect he'll be all right,' Mrs Holford added brightly, 'but sometimes tame animals don't get on well with wild ones, do they? Nature can be very cruel.'

'Is there anything else you'd like to tell me?'

'I'd like to show you my watercolours, if you're interested.'

Some of the paintings were of Indian villages with brown earth, mud huts, primitive wells, rusting oil drums, a pile of carefully shaped cow-pats to burn under the mud ovens, the outline of children playing on a dirt road. Others were of Ireland with green fields and trees, rickety stone cottages, grey-black clouds fast blown across a blue sky.

I went to find the brigadier. 'Shall we go into the compound? We can talk privately there,' I suggested.

At the back of the bungalow three monkeys swung on a trapeze in a cage, picking their feet or nibbling nuts. 'Bloody monkeys,' the brigadier said as we strolled passed. 'D'you know my wife held up the military train for two hours at Kishangarh – for two hours! She had all the troops turned off the train to look for a bloody monkey. As though you can tell one monkey from another.' He turned towards me, his face serious. 'She's not right in the mind. It's been coming on for some time. One day she'll really hurt somebody – or herself. Did she tell you about smashing our Crown Derby?'

'No.'

'She went berserk – *doolalli*. After dinner we were sitting at the table and suddenly without warning she smashed a plate over my head. Damn'd lucky it didn't cut me. Then she started throwing the side-plates at me – extraordinary.'

'What provoked this?'

'Nothing – out of the blue. Not only once either. Another evening when the *khitmagar* was out on an errand, I went to the kitchen to get some ice. Millicent just screamed at me. She picked some plates – our best china – off the kitchen table and started hurling them at me.'

Mrs Holford's behaviour did seem a little beyond the bounds of Irish idiosyncrasy but was the brigadier telling the whole truth? We strolled on round the compound. When out of earshot of the *mali*, who was spraying the grass with water, I looked Brigadier Holford straight in the eye.

'Your wife says you are having an affair with your secretary, sir.'

The brigadier stopped in his tracks and drew himself to attention. 'I can tell you as an officer and a gentleman there's not a word of truth in that – not a word. That too is part of her madness.'

153

Back in my bungalow in the Cantonment I started filling up the psychiatric questionnaire. It was easy enough to describe the patient's abnormal behaviour; it was less easy to give a diagnosis. What should be the treatment and disposal of the patient? Sooner or later Mrs Holford would have to go home, so why not by hospital ship? It would be safer. Martin Lipscomb would have to countersign the report so if he didn't agree with my views...

A few days later Martin drove to the Cantonment to come on a ward round. 'Not much doubt about the diagnosis, surely?' he said. 'I've recommended repatriation by hospital ship. She's not certifiable but she'll be more comfortable going home that way. She might go berserk and that would upset everyone in a crowded troopship.'

A week later I received a formal invitation to dine with the Commander-in-Chief and his sister in Delhi. The twenty guests were arranged round the table so that those with the highest rank sat to the right and left of the host and hostess. I felt somewhat ill at ease, certainly being the youngest but not the lowest in rank. Four courses were served – unheard of during the war – and not for several years had I drunk Château Margaux. The ladies retired when the port was served, but the field marshall did not linger. As we walked down the hall from the dining room Auchinleck took my arm.

'I'd like a quick word with you, young man. Come into my study for a moment.'

My heart sank as the C-in-C steered me away from the others and shut the study door.

'Just wanted to thank you for all your help with the Holfords,' Auch said. 'You did a good job, if I may say so. Martin Lipscomb was most grateful too. Sad business. Holford's been having an affair with that ghastly secretary of his for years – silly fool.'

Barney barked as I let myself into the bungalow. Jackals were wailing round the dustbins in the *godown* at the back of the compound. As I undressed, I said aloud, 'An officer and a gentleman indeed!' and began to scratch. It really was time I went home.

Sir William Osler (1849–1919) was a distinguished physician who was born in Canada and qualified in medicine in 1872 in Montreal. He was successively professor of medicine at McGill University in Montreal, at Pennsylvania University in Philadelphia and at the Johns Hopkins Hospital in Baltimore. At Johns Hopkins he wrote single-handed a textbook of medicine that ran to many editions and persisted for several years after his death. In 1904 Osler was invited to become Regius Professor of Medicine at Oxford University, an appointment he held with great distinction. He was certainly the most brilliant and influential teacher of medicine in his day. Despite being an academic, Osler was very much a practising physician and he had a sizeable private practice. It was at Oxford that he advised his colleagues, 'never make friends with your patients'. This is sound advice, although a few doctors manage to become close friends with some of their patients without apparent detriment to the quality of the medical care provided. Nevertheless the possibility that objective assessment of a medical problem may become distorted if they become too friendly made Osler offer his aphorism.

In medical school I was advised by one of my teachers to follow Osler's advice and over the years I have tried to do so. His advice is not always easy to follow if, for example, the patient is a colleague or the spouse of a colleague, or *force majeure* is already a friend rather than a stranger or acquaintance. To spare a patient-friend discomfort, inconvenience or expense the doctor may misguidedly feel constrained to cut corners or forego an investigation which may range from something simple but fundamental and unpleasant, such as a rectal examination, to a more expensive procedure. It is also an established but unexplained fact that all too often one's colleagues fail to have a common-or-garden condition. Quite rightly we are brought up to believe that the commonest things are the most common, and medical students are constantly reminded that a bird on the lawn is likely to be a sparrow or a robin and is seldom a kiwi or an ostrich. This truism does not seem to hold when dealing with a friend, especially if that friend is a doctor or worse still a doctor's wife. In such a patient no disease ever runs true to form; inevitably there are unusual complications, or the treatment induces some previously undescribed side-effect.

Doctors should beware of the colleague who seeks medical advice as together they travel in a crowded hospital lift, surrounded by staff and patients, or when they meet on a Saturday morning wheeling their trolleys across the parking-lot of a supermarket. Nor should a consultation be allowed to take place over a casual cup of coffee in a noisy hospital canteen.

Some doctor-patients get quite cross if you ask them what *they* think is wrong. Admittedly by asking this you open yourself to the possibility of, 'I wouldn't be here if I knew, would I?' But many doctors or their spouses, like all patients, often have ill-founded fears as to what is wrong, and once these have been brought into the open they can be discussed and usually discarded to the patient's evident relief. It is also a mistake to treat a colleague or a colleague's spouse as if either knew anything about medicine. Their knowledge may not have been updated since they were students. Some gynaecologists, for example, have the weirdest ideas about coronary artery disease, as surprisingly often do their wives about the menopause. Because of this possible ignorance, everything must be carefully explained. Never should a doctor ask a colleague to arrange for his own, or his wife's, investigations to be done. Nor should colleagues be asked or allowed to prescribe for themselves; and remember they are no more likely to be compliant about taking medication than any other patient. It is wise to give them clearly written instructions. It is sometimes necessary to remember that, except for very trivial matters, it is unwise for doctors to treat members of their immediate family, nor does the General Medical Council approve of a doctor prescribing for his wife; one or two have been murdered in this way. In dealing with one's own family, of course, one difficulty is knowing, without becoming too involved, what is trivial and what is not. During the last major epidemic of poliomyelitis in Great Britain my eldest daughter, then aged eight, developed a severe headache. The next day she disliked the light. Fearing the worst and not wishing to become involved I asked one of my old chiefs, who had quoted Osler's aphorism to me many years before, if he would come and see her. Dr Forrest-Smith was a hawkish, somewhat conceited but kind man who always called his senior colleagues 'Laddie' and his junior ones 'Boy'. Despite being a know-all, he was a very good doctor. When I was Resident Assistant Physician at St Thomas's, he had telephoned one morning to ask if I could find a bed for 'the most important girl in the world'. I thought he meant Princess Elizabeth but was smartly told, 'Don't be silly, boy – for Beatle, my daughter.'

He advised that my daughter should be admitted to St Thomas's under his care. The great man simply observed, noted her normal temperature and after four days discharged her without a diagnosis beyond saying she had not got polio. Not until Caroline and I discussed the matter years later did she laughingly say, 'Poor Daddy, you were so worried – and I simply didn't want to go back to school!'

15

Fraud in Medical Research

'You have two options,' Brigadier Lipscomb explained as I sat in his office at GHQ in Delhi. 'Either you go home on a troopship as an ordinary passenger and revert to your substantive rank of captain the moment you leave Delhi with the inevitable drop in pay, or you go home working on a hospital ship and keep your rank,' he paused before adding, 'and the pay of a half-colonel.'

Being a lieutenant-colonel was a relatively new event. The quartermaster at the British Military Hospital in Delhi who usually knew his King's Regulations backwards had, rather belatedly we thought, discovered that if we consistently had 750 or more patients in the hospital at midnight on a Friday, when the bed occupancy was recorded for GHQ, many of us would be promoted – including him. The number of inpatients always fluctuated around the 750-mark and by not discharging patients until Saturday morning the bed occupancy could be maintained at this critical level.

The *El Nil* had once been the private yacht of the dethroned King Farouk of Egypt but, annexed by the British government, had been converted into a hospital ship. It arrived in Bombay half filled with 'forgotten' patients from Singapore who were suffering from severe psychiatric disorders. It took three days to load our patients being repatriated from India, and during this time local merchants selling everything from jewellery to Persian rugs swarmed over the ship. The carpet-*wallahs* were the most popular and, having had some experience of Persian rugs during my four years in India, I was asked to advise members of the ship's company which to buy and how much to pay. Many deals were struck and the carpet-*wallahs* considerately offered to pack the carpets in hessian bags for safe storage in the ship's hold during the voyage; they also submitted receipted bills for less than had been paid in the belief that this would reduce the import duty likely to be charged by the customs in England.

It proved a mistake to choose to go home by hospital ship, but I was not to know that the cruising speed of the *El Nil* was only eight knots or that we would pick up more patients in Karachi, Aden, Port Said, Haifa, Cyprus, Crete, Malta and Gibraltar – a voyage that took a very long time when we were all anxious to get home. It was a heinous offence, leading to a court martial of the medical officer responsible, if one of his patients committed suicide at sea by jumping overboard. This rare occurrence led to the unfortunate patients being locked below decks in the ill-ventilated, stiflingly hot wards and allowed no outdoor exercise or fresh air as we chugged painfully slowly across the Indian Ocean, through the Suez Canal and along the length of the Mediterranean.

It took three tedious days to unload our patients at Southampton. Nor when the ship's company were eventually allowed to disembark were the custom officers to be hurried. They intended to inspect every rug, and their disdainful dismissal of the receipted bills suggested that they knew the recorded prices were spurious. The first hessian roll was cut open; inside there was only straw and old newspapers – no Shiraz, Bukarra or Kerman rug. As each successive roll was opened, the full horror of the deceit became evident; all of them were stuffed with rubbish. Understandably the general dismay and anger were further enhanced when my three rolls were opened and revealed the rugs that had travelled with me from one posting in India to another.

Equipped with a grey herring-bone suit, which fitted surprisingly well, a pair of ugly and uncomfortable shoes and a raincoat with sleeves too short, provided by the government from a warehouse near Aldershot, I was demobilised. For four years I'd had to make no decisions about what work I did and had gone wherever I was posted; but now I faced unemployment. It was an uncomfortable experience, but the government was funding special supernumerary posts in the new NHS for demobilised doctors. That medicine had undergone a scientific revolution during the four years I'd been in India was obvious from the contents of the two medical journals – the *British Medical Journal* and *The Lancet* – that had faithfully arrived in India each week by airmail together with *The Times* printed on fine India paper and flown out in a pale-blue wrapper.

The Professor of Medicine at the Postgraduate Medical School at Hammersmith Hospital responded quickly to a letter seeking an interview. Two days later I met one of the great men of British medicine. Professor John McMichael, it seemed, would be pleased to give me a job; I would be paid as a supernumerary senior medical registrar, but would I mind being one of his research assistants with the title of Tutor in Medicine? A week later in 1948 I started work at an institution widely known simply as 'The Hammersmith'.

The consultant staff were mostly aged between thirty-five and forty-five – talented, idiosyncratic, charismatic individuals who queried the established doctrine that was accepted without question by most doctors. New specialties of rheumatology and hepatology were being developed. Endocrinology was advancing in leaps and bounds as new techniques of investigation were devised. The understanding of many cardiac conditions progressed, and respiratory diseases such as chronic bronchitis and emphysema, previously dismissed as untreatable and not worthy of further study, came under scrutiny. Pathology underwent a major change: necropsies became a detailed scientific discipline; the chemical estimation of many substances in a blood sample was automated and became a routine investigation of every patient. Radiology, which had stood still for fifty years, emerged as a dynamic subject leavened by many technological advances. The proponents of these advances might not have been so successful had there not been the guiding hand of John McMichael who, self-effacingly and in the minimum of words, steered everybody's hand. From this simmering cauldron of knowledge, research and scientific endeavour, many of the future professors of medicine throughout the British Isles, the Common-wealth and America were subsequently recruited. By head and shoulders the Hammersmith had the most progressive departments of medicine, radiology and pathology in the country. Postgraduate students from Britain, the Commonwealth and the USA eagerly sought instruction there, the best being taken on afterwards to do research; lifelong friendships and plans for cooperative research across the world were initiated.

Hammersmith Hospital had been built originally to serve an expanding local community, not as a teaching institution. Its Victorian ward blocks, three storeys high, are connected on the ground floor by a wide corridor. Fortunately between the ward blocks was

161

sufficient space to build lecture theatres and laboratories. Not until the late fifties were new buildings constructed by funds raised by supporters in the Commonwealth, and from the Wolfson Foundation, to house what are now the main lecture theatres and refectories. The Hammersmith is a clear example of how the best research work and high quality patient care depend on gifted people – and not just on bricks and mortar.

* * *

He was known at the Hammersmith simply as Ahmed – without any 'Doctor' in front of it. 'Ahmed' was all that was printed on the name-tag safety-pinned to the lapel of his white coat. Nobody knew whether it was his family name or his first name. Nor did anybody bother to ask where exactly he'd been trained – somewhere in India was all we assumed.

He was tall, lean, and good-looking with aquiline Persian features and impeccable manners. Soon after his arrival early in 1949, it was clear that lack of self-confidence was not a problem. He was eager to learn and had a photographic memory. If challenged over some statement, he would say with a smile, quick as a flash, 'It is correct, I am thinking. You will find it on pages 215 and 384 in Price's *Textbook of Medicine*', and invariably he was right.

One morning over coffee in the refectory Guy Scadding, the senior consultant in respiratory medicine, commented that there were about nine conditions that showed on a chest X-ray as miliary mottling. Without hesitation Ahmed with his usual smile interjected, 'I am thinking, sir, there are thirty-four', and without more ado recited all the many diseases that he believed could cause tiny shadows, the size of a millet seed, on an X-ray of the lungs.

After the NHS came into force in July 1948, all medicines were dispensed free of charge. Most of the doctors working at the Hammersmith obtained any medications they needed for themselves or their family from the hospital pharmacy. The head pharmacist made the medical staff write their prescriptions in a large leather-bound volume kept on the counter fixed to the door of the pharmacy.

I was about to start a ward round when the head pharmacist phoned.

'I'm sorry to bother you,' she said, 'but one of the postgraduate students has just written fourteen prescriptions for himself.'

162

'What's the matter with him?' I asked.

'The junior pharmacist didn't ask,' she replied.

'Then what sort of drugs are they?'

'Analgesics – pain-killers of one sort or another.'

'No controlled, dangerous drugs like morphine?'

'No.'

'Fourteen you said? Have they been dispensed? What's his name?'

'Not yet. Ahmed said he'd call back for them after he'd been on your ward round.'

'Okay, I'll have a word with him.'

On the ward round Ahmed was a little less talkative than usual. When we'd finished, I said, 'I want a word with you, Ahmed.' We walked slowly down the wide main corridor in the direction of the pharmacy.

'The pharmacist says you've written a lot of prescriptions this morning,' I began.

Ahmed's smile did not change. 'Oh, I did, sir.'

'Would you mind telling me what the problem is?'

'Oh! yes. I've got very bad toothache.'

We had reached the pharmacy and in the ledger were written Ahmed's fourteen prescriptions ranging from oil of cloves to pain-killing tablets containing aspirin, codeine and phenacetin.

'But why so many prescriptions, all aiming to do the same thing?' I asked.

'My textbook of therapeutics gives fourteen preparations for the treatment of toothache,' Ahmed replied.

'But you don't need all of them at once, surely?'

'It's what the textbook says.'

'What you really need is a good dentist. Won't aspirin with codeine and phenacetin, and oil of cloves to apply locally – not that it'll do much good – be enough for the moment?'

Ahmed did not seem upset at having his shopping list reduced to two items.

Six months later Ahmed took time off to sit the examination for the higher degree of Membership of the Royal College of Physicians. He passed, and nobody was surprised from the way he regaled us about the patients he'd been shown. He asked if he could stay on to finish the thesis for his MD degree in India. The subject was miliary mottling of the lungs but he needed more cases. Could he please use any patients with lung mottling that he saw in the

163

hospital? In his spare time he would like to be an unpaid clinical assistant on our firm, help in our research work, take blood samples and run errands. 'Goodness gracious, I shall make myself jolly useful,' he said.

And jolly useful he was. When there was nothing for him to do in the laboratory or on the wards, he went to lectures or ward rounds and attended the grand staff round every Wednesday morning. We surmised that he had private means, and learnt that his father had once been a qualified pharmacist in Bombay but was now a businessman.

Then suddenly Ahmed disappeared. A few weeks later came a letter from India full of gratitude for what the Hammersmith had done for him, and enclosing a present for me – an old, delicately painted, small picture of a young Mogul girl with red slippers, sitting on the grass and leaning back against a tree beside a lake, her head cupped in her hand with her elbow resting on her knee. 'Thank you for all your kindness', Ahmed wrote in his clear copperplate handwriting. 'My father is ill and I am applying for the Chair of Medicine here.' There was no address.

A few months later a copy of Ahmed's MD thesis appeared on my desk with a note, 'Thank you for your encouragement – Ahmed'. It was bound in leather and was nearly two inches thick.

'How did this get here?' I asked Jeanette Perkis, my young technical assistant.

'I don't know, I'm afraid. It was here on your desk when I came in this morning.'

I browsed through it. Between the introductory preamble and the discussion there were detailed case histories of numerous patients with miliary mottling of the lungs and dozens of photographic reproductions of their chest X-rays. Ahmed had been meticulous; all the case histories began with the patients' initials, their hospital number and the name of the consultant they'd been under. Several of the patients had apparently been under my care, but I couldn't remember any of them.

'Jeanette, when you've got a spare moment, would you ask records to get out the notes of these patients whose hospital numbers I've put on this bit of paper?'

In due course Jeanette brought the notes but although some had been under my care none had any pulmonary problem. On looking at the thesis again, the photographic reproductions of the chest

164

X-ray of these patients were all exactly the same. After further browsing, I made notes of the hospital numbers of more patients who allegedly had been in the Hammersmith. Apart from one, whose X-ray showed miliary mottling, all the others had unrelated diseases. Reluctantly I came to the conclusion that most of the Hammersmith patients were of Ahmed's invention. I gave a deep sigh, and was not sure if it was right to hope that his examiners in India would fail to spot that many of his case reports were fictitious.

Four years later pictures of Ahmed appeared in the London newspapers. He had been committed by magistrates for trial. Ahmed, it appeared, was a highly regarded and popular medical officer in our Royal Air Force. That he was an impostor might never have been discovered had he not been involved in a medical mishap which in fact hadn't been his fault. A court of enquiry had discovered that Ahmed had no medical qualifications – in India or elsewhere. His claim to membership of the Royal College of Physicians was fictitious; the records showed he'd never sat the exam. Further investigations revealed that his considerable medical knowledge had been gleaned from the textbooks of an older brother who had qualified in medicine at Edinburgh University, returned to India and shortly afterwards died. The money spent on this older brother's expensive education could not be wasted, so Ahmed had taught himself from his brother's notes and books and taken on his persona and medical certificates. Even Ahmed was not his name, but his brother's.

* * *

Deception in medical research is a grave matter. Such misconduct is rare but undoubtedly many instances never come to light and others are discovered only years after they have occurred. Every few years some fraudulent research is exposed, particularly in the USA – not because medical scientists are more dishonest there but because America has the largest medical scientific community pursuing medical research and fraud there attracts widespread attention from the media.

The deception may take several forms which, in increasing degree of contumely, can be listed as piracy, plagiarism, economic manipulation and fraud.

Piracy occurs when a research worker deliberately steals the ideas of another. This is not an easy charge to substantiate, because the concept behind many research projects is seldom totally original and often the idea has been culled from the published work of other researchers or from listening and talking to them at a medical meeting. That piracy has taken place is likely to become apparent only when two papers reporting the results of experiments carried out using very similar techniques are published in close temporal proximity. Even then piracy is difficult to prove, because it is not unusual for two people or for two groups to be thinking along similar lines.

Plagiarism involves copying verbatim, or nearly so, the written results of other research workers. In minor degree it is probably quite common but passes unnoticed or is difficult to prove unless carried to excess. A research worker, usually young, may steal a paper from some obscure journal; after rewriting the text and changing the data he submits it as his own work to another journal which accepts and publishes it. An example of this occurred in 1978 when a doctor from Poona in India was awarded a Fellowship to Yale in the USA. In November of that year his supervisor, the professor of medicine, was sent a paper by the editor of the *New England Journal of Medicine* to assess its suitability for publication. The paper had been written by a female Brazilian research worker in Washington, DC. For good reasons the professor of medicine advised the editor that the paper should be rejected for publication, although in fact it was later printed. Before returning the paper the professor invited his Indian colleague, who was working in much the same field, to read it out of interest. The Indian doctor made a copy and amended the data, changed some of the text and a month later submitted a paper to the *American Journal of Medicine*. By chance the editor of that journal sent the paper for peer review to the boss of the Brazilian researcher in Washington who, aware of her interest in the subject, invited her to look at it. She was astonished to see in front of her the essence of *her* paper, even with some of her sentences reproduced verbatim. When subsequently the Indian doctor's past and present research work was scrutinised, it was found that many of the experiments he reported had never been performed.

A medical scientist, conducting a clinical trial with a new drug that is proving successful, may gain financial reward by trading in

166

the shares of the pharmaceutical company that make the drug. Under such circumstances to buy shares would constitute insider dealing, and to disclose the promising results of the trial to a third party could amount to criminal liability. Furthermore a clinical research worker who holds shares in the pharmaceutical company whose drug he is investigating may be accused of having a conflict of interests. So seriously is this viewed in the USA that some fund-giving organisations have forbidden investigators (and their spouses and dependants) to buy, sell or hold stock in the company supplying the drug they are testing. Such restrictions seem draconian, and I personally would reject this implied conflict of interests.

The most heinous offence is for a research worker deliberately to falsify the results of his or her experiments or simply invent them. It is important to distinguish this type of fraud from a silly mistake, from carelessness, from bias or the ambiguities that inevitably arise in the interpretation of scientific data. Most research workers at some time in their careers have probably been tempted to 'cook' their results by omitting an apparently rogue finding. I well remember, when working with Sir John McMichael, looking at some aberrant results we'd obtained in one particular patient. With a laugh McMichael said, 'This is what I call an extreme example of human biological variation! These results are totally at loggerheads with those in the other patients we've studied. If you agree, I suggest we omit this patient.' His suggestion seemed sensible and right, but my conscience felt better when later I discovered that our technician had failed to put an essential reagent into the test-tubes that contained the blood samples from this 'deviant' patient and the results were indeed invalid.

Some workers simply fudge their results to get the answers they want; others record the outcome of experiments or tests that subsequent scrutiny of their laboratory notes shows they never performed. The acme for this sort of activity must go to an investigator who started falsifying his results when a medical student. When eventually exposed, after working at two highly regarded universities in the USA, he had published forty-five articles and more than a hundred abstracts, most of which were fictitious.

Fraud may involve innocent but naively uncritical collaborators. An eager young research worker may persuade his or her supervisor, perhaps the head of the department, to append their name to a paper. The head of the department, too busy to supervise closely all their research fellows, may have scant knowledge of the details of the work and may unwisely add their name to the paper, not wishing to appear superior or unfriendly. Exposure of this uncritical role may have serious consequences involving the resignation of the departmental head or the cessation of their future funding by external sources.

Pharmaceutical companies often enlist hospital consultants and general practitioners to partake in the clinical assessment of a new drug. Hospital physicians are usually involved at an early stage to assess whether the new drug is effective and/or induces any obvious side-effects. General practitioners participate later in post-marketing surveillance when the drug is given to a much larger number of patients so that its general utility can be assessed and infrequent side-effects detected. For this work the GP is remunerated either with a lump sum on the undertaking to admit a stated number of patients to the trial or on a *per capitum* basis for each patient enrolled. If busy, the GP may fail to enlist the contracted number of patients or may study them perfunctorily. When the deadline for reporting the outcome approaches, the GP may submit fictitious or incomplete results. Such deviations, often revealed by the results being too perfect, are usually detected by the medical director of the pharmaceutical company who is funding the trial or by an official in the governmental department who scrutinises them. In Britain cases of proven deceit are usually reported to the General Medical Council, and a number of GPs have been struck off the register for this offence. In the USA the Food and Drug Administration may ban a doctor from ever taking part in such trials again.

The extent and the frequency of deception in trials of this sort are unknown but when the work of nearly 1000 investigators in America was audited, it was found that the research of some 50 showed serious deficiencies but in only a quarter of these were the records inaccurate or unavailable, suggesting that only one and a half per cent of investigators could be deemed guilty of fraud.

The cause of these different types of deception varies from one doctor to another. 'Publish or be damned' is certainly true in academic medicine. The prestige of a department and its financial support from governmental or charitable bodies depends in part on the number of papers it publishes each year. Like others, doctors are not immune to vanity. They like their colleagues to see how clever and busy they are. They like being invited to give lectures, to speak at foreign medical meetings and to write reviews in a prestigious journal. Financial greed can seldom be a motive because the economic rewards are not significant. Rarely a more laudable motive is claimed as when an Australian research worker, who had produced valuable information in the early days of the contraceptive pill, explained that in later work he had fudged his data 'in the long-term interests of humanity'.

16

A Fat Lady in New York

The research work with Professor (later Sir) John McMichael at Hammersmith Hospital went well. After two years we had a better understanding of the mechanisms by which certain long-established drugs influenced for the better the function of the heart in cardiac failure. But now I wanted to study something different – to find out why patients with heart failure retained salt and water and developed swelling of their ankles and feet. It was realised that this oedema was due to changes in the functioning of the kidneys, but the precise mechanism was quite unknown. It was probably related to the action of an unidentified hormone circulating in the bloodstream. I believed it should be possible to use a new technique, paper chromatography, to identify and quantify this unknown substance when it was excreted in the urine. To undertake this project I would have to obtain a financial grant for the materials and apparatus and it would be sensible to do the work at a centre already orientated to such research which at the time the Hammersmith wasn't.

The handling of salt and water by the kidneys had been a subject studied for many years by Professor Robert Loeb of Columbia University at the College of Physicians and Surgeons in the Presbyterian Medical Center in New York City. Contemporaries, who had worked in the USA at the Mayo Clinic, the Massachusetts General or Brigham Hospitals in Boston, the Johns Hopkins in Baltimore or one of the three great medical schools in New York City were free with their advice. I applied to the Medical Research Council in London and was awarded a Rockefeller Travelling Fellowship. The US embassy issued me with an immigrant's visa which did not imply that I was deserting England but would allow me to accept legally a fee in the unlikely event that I was ever invited to give a lecture over there.

John McMichael, who was variously known as Mac, John or Jack depending upon how well you knew him, was one of my referees and was delighted when my application was successful.

'This sorts out the men from the boys!' he said, 'Bob Loeb's a great man; give him my regards. Of course your job here remains open and mind you come back. Too many people are tempted to stay in America – by the better facilities and better pay, I suppose.'

'Not by the salary I'm going to get.' The stipend was $5000 a year which proved rather less than the wages of the overweight elderly Polish immigrant who was to clean the laboratory and help wash up my glassware in New York City.

In 1950 relatively few people crossed the Atlantic by air. Most, especially if visiting North America for any length of time and taking with them clothes for all seasons, travelled in one of the great liners. The *Queen Mary* lay proudly in her berth at Southampton. She was a three-class ship and my three companions, all Rockefeller Fellows, and I travelled second class.

The hoots from the liner's siren brought everyone on deck. The four of us leant against the taffrail and watched the steel hawsers being winched aboard as two tugs towed the bows clear of the narrow berth. In the late afternoon we stood under the overcast September sky to watch as the *Queen Mary* moved majestically, gathering speed, down Southampton Water into the Solent. When we returned to our cabin, a formal invitation from the ship's doctor asked us to join him for cocktails at half past seven before the second sitting for dinner at eight-thirty.

Everyone enjoyed the five-day crossing. The *Queen Mary* was another world in which the passengers became more friendly, even uninhibited. Strangers introduced themselves to each other, passionate romances erupted overnight, and lifelong friendships were sworn that evaporated as soon as the liner docked in New York. The chatty cabin steward explained how to evade the guards who prohibited access to the Verandah Grill in first class or to the ballroom in the tourist class where there were younger more lively girls and the band was better – or so the steward said. For the first two days we ate our way through the elegantly printed menu, and marvelled at the twenty-four different cheeses on offer. Meat rationing, still in force at home, was forgotten. On the last day we

172

rose early to see the Statue of Liberty and watch the Manhattan skyline unfold. The *Queen Mary* docked, almost unassisted, at a peer beside Twelfth Avenue.

'We've now got the awful business of tipping,' said Andrew Kay, a future distinguished professor of surgery. 'I've no idea how much we should give our cabin and dining-room stewards.'

'Ring the ship's doctor and ask him,' someone suggested. The problem was solved.

Before breakfast, immigration officials came aboard followed by customs officers who were equally perfunctory. By nine o'clock I'd loaded my suitcases into a yellow cab to take them to Bard Hall, the ten-storey students' residence dwarfed beside the towering blocks of the Presbyterian Hospital on 168th Street in Upper Manhattan.

The atmosphere in the hospital – its scientific approach to medical problems, its search for constant improvements in the standards of patient care, the dedication and the quality of its staff – had a profound influence on me, exceeded only by that of Professor Robert Loeb himself. Like other great men Loeb turned his weaknesses, which sometimes he seemed calculatedly to foster, into strengths. Aged fifty-six he had a lean Jewish patrician face with bright sparkling eyes. Under no circumstances would he tolerate being called 'Professor', a word which in his view smacked of Teutonic authoritarianism. He was rated one of the three leading and most influential professors of medicine in the USA. It helped that he was a staunch Anglophile and had an almost naive conviction of the brilliance and integrity of young visiting British medical scientists. He was self-effacing, a shy, intensely thoughtful man, who shunned the limelight and had for twenty years declined to give a formal lecture or make a speech in public. He held strong convictions about what medical students should be taught and how medicine could best serve society. Seldom did he show any strong emotions but sloppy thinking, lack of attention to important detail and the drawing of unjustifiable conclusions from inadequate data made him visibly tetchy, and – rarely – overtly angry. He had a quiet abiding interest in, and unfailing memory of, people whether they were patients or junior colleagues. He was humble, yet quietly proud. He was gentle and kind, but the few who fell from his grace were never forgiven.

The hospital day started with a meeting in Bob Loeb's office at half past seven. The resident staff had long since christened this 'The Prayer Meeting'; its main function was to discuss those patients who had been admitted to the medical wards since six o'clock the previous evening. All the interns and residents were present, a smattering of medical students, particularly those involved with the patients concerned, some of the visiting fellows and a few of the consultants who were on ward service at the time and responsible for the inpatients. Apart from the new patients and those of longer-standing who posed particular problems, we also discussed the medical advances recently reported in the literature and the symphony concert given the previous evening in the Lewisham Stadium or at Carnegie Hall.

At my first Prayer Meeting Dr Loeb went out of his way to introduce me, to give from memory a short resumé of my *curriculum vitae* and the direction of my intended research. At the end of the meeting he introduced me to Dr Henry Aranow, a young attending physician two years my senior.

'Henry, would you take our friend down the stem and show him his lab in Room 814? Introduce him to the other people down there and ask them to take him under their wing.' He turned to me. 'I'll be down later in the morning. You can then fill me in on the details of your project.'

Henry Aranow was welcoming and helpful. He stayed half the morning chatting and telling me about the ins and outs of the Presbyterian Hospital. At eleven o'clock Dr Loeb arrived, perched himself on a laboratory stool and asked me – surprised to be addressed so soon by my Christian name – to tell him what I was going to do.

I explained my suspicions about the currently unknown hormone and how I wanted to look for it in the urine of normal people and of patients with heart failure and oedema. Also, how I was going to use paper chromatography for isolating it from the other hormones and then measuring its amount.

'No problem collecting urine from ward patients with heart failure. We can fix that with the head nurse. Tell me more about paper chromatography, a British invention I believe.'

I explained that the many known hormones and the unknown one could be extracted from twenty-four-hour urine collections. The extract would be dried and transferred to the top of a piece of filter paper about a foot wide and three feet long. By allowing

174

chemical solvents to flow down the length of the paper, the hormones would, according to their different chemical structure, move at different speeds down the paper and this would allow separation of one from another.

'I'll cut the filter paper into horizontal strips, extract the unknown hormone from the paper at that level, measure the amount of it and, when I've got enough, find out what its molecular structure is.'

'How long will it take you to analyse each urine sample, d'you think?' Bob Loeb asked.

'Three or four days, I expect.'

* * *

Two months later, to avoid the queue and save time, I was eating an early lunch in the immaculately clean staff cafeteria with its stainless-steel self-service counters.

Dr Loeb paused at my table. 'I'm leaving this afternoon for Washington. I hate to ask but would you mind taking the Prayer Meeting tomorrow morning?'

I half rose from my chair.

'Of course, I'd be delighted, Bob.' It had taken some weeks to comply with Dr Loeb's injunction to call him by his first name.

Bob moved to another table carrying his frugal meal on a plastic tray. To be asked to chair the seven-thirty Prayer Meeting was indeed a mark of approval.

If the interns, residents and students were surprised to find me sitting in the professor's chair early next morning, they did not show it. The boss-resident had greeted me a few minutes before the set time, so presumably he'd been forewarned. It was tempting to try to emulate Dr Loeb's particularly relaxed style of conducting the proceedings.

'Good morning everyone. Who'd like to begin?'

There was a momentary silence before the chief resident nodded imperceptibly to a woman sitting towards the front of the room.

'We admitted a sixty-year-old woman just before midnight.' Miss Burwood was a senior student – tall, attractive, with long glistening raven-black hair tied in a snood, and slanting brown eyes that suggested she had Oriental ancestry. Margie Burwood gave the patient's history in the prescribed meticulous way the students were trained to do and continued, '...Mrs Charka complained of extreme dyspnoea...'

I had to interrupt.

'Excuse me, but I'm sure she didn't complain of dyspnoea, my dear girl. Didn't she say she was short of breath?'

'I'm not your dear girl,' Miss Burwood almost spat the words.

I shifted uneasily in the chair at my *faux pas* and grunted.

'The patient complained of extreme shortness of breath,' Miss Burwood corrected herself. 'She couldn't lie flat but had to sit upright. For six months she's had swelling of both legs from the knees down. She's known to have had late-onset diabetes for six years.' The student went on to relate the patient's increasing and extreme somnolence, her liability to fall asleep at any time of the day – even when eating – and her exhaustion.

'On examination,' she continued, 'Mrs Charka was in distress; she was blue – cyanosed. She weighed 108 kilograms.'

'How much?' I asked in surprise, and scribbled on the pad of yellow paper on the desk. '108 kilos? That's more than ... it's 238 pounds ... nearly seventeen stone. Good heavens! Please go on.'

Miss Burwood described the rest of the physical findings and the results of the extensive investigations carried out in the early hours of the morning.

'What diagnosis or diagnoses did you make?'

'The patient is suffering from high blood pressure, congestive cardiac failure, respiratory failure, late-onset diabetes mellitus and morbid obesity. She's got the Pickwickian syndrome, I think.' Miss Burwood ended with a note of triumph in her voice.

'Excellent, dear...' I checked myself just in time. 'And why's it called the Pickwickian syndrome?'

'After Pickwick,' she shot back.

'And who was Pickwick?'

'A ... er ... British physician?' Miss Burwood was hesitant.

'I'm afraid not.'

'An American physician?'

The usually well-behaved house-staff tittered.

I didn't wish to make the girl (I must not be patronising and use *that* word, I reminded myself) more uncomfortable. 'You've done excellently. Might I suggest, if you can find the time, that you go to the library – not the one here in the Medical Center but the proper library down at Columbia University – and find out about Pickwick? He was a character in a book written by a famous British novelist of the last century who, I'm sorry to say, wrote a book rather critical of the United States.'

Next morning I arrived early to tell Dr Loeb about the task Miss Burwood had been set.

'Well done!' Bob chuckled.

Judging by the dark shadows under her eyes Miss Burwood had been up half the night. She gave a quick smile and sat on the floor at the back of the crowded room.

'Miss Burwood, I believe you've something to tell us,' invited Dr Loeb.

'Well, I was up very late…' she laughed, 'reading Charles Dickens's *Pickwick Papers*. It's fascinating, but it wasn't Mr Pickwick who had morbid obesity although he was overweight. It was the fat Boy Joe who kept dropping off to sleep at inappropriate times – in the middle of a conversation, even in the middle of a meal. Like the woman we admitted the night before last, he would probably have eventually suffocated in the cuirass of fat that encircled and compressed his chest wall. A British physician called Osler, who was Regius Professor of Medicine at Oxford University, first called it the Pickwickian syndrome.'

'Well done! But Osler – British?' Loeb sounded quite upset. 'Osler was born in Canada, was professor of medicine in Montreal and later at Johns Hopkins – long before he went to England. What do you think is the cause of the Pickwickian syndrome, Miss Burwood?'

'Morbid obesity?' she ventured.

'Just so. On Saturday morning we have a guest lecturer coming from Tulane University, New Orleans, to talk about obesity. He's done some interesting research in this field. I hope you'll all come and hear him.'

It was an unnecessary invitation. The eighth floor amphitheatre was always packed at ten o'clock on Saturday mornings.

*　*　*

Obesity is as much a disease as anorexia nervosa and some look upon it as the opposite side of the same coin. Whether you are the correct weight for your height is best decided by calculating

177

your body mass index (BMI), which is your weight in kilograms divided by the square of your height in metres. The normal BMI is twenty to twenty-five; anyone with a BMI between twenty-five and thirty is defined as being overweight, and anyone with a BMI between thirty and forty as obese; those with an index over forty are morbidly obese. In the United Kingdom in 1995, thirty-seven per cent of men and twenty-four per cent of women were overweight, and eight per cent of men and twelve per cent of women obese. Although there may be several different underlying causes, the fundamental reason for obesity is that the patient consumes more calories in food and drink than he or she expends as energy. With increasing fatness the patient becomes less active and energy expenditure is further reduced.

Fat patients find it hard to believe, indeed they may vehemently deny, they eat too much, and in public may not appear to have large meals. They won't believe the hard truth, which they say cannot possibly apply to them, that 'there were no fat people in Belsen'. Without consciously being aware of it, many eat snacks with a high calorie content. On their own, sugar tastes too sweet and fats too greasy, but together the fat reduces the sweetness of the sugar and the sugar reduces the greasiness of the fat, making a very palatable and delicious combination as in chocolates, ice-cream, pastries and biscuits.

Yet when admitted to hospital and a calorie-controlled diet is given under supervision weight loss invariably occurs. Patients do not lie deliberately but they report inaccurately the amount of food and physical activity they have taken. Sensitive modern analytical techniques allow accurate assessment in the free-living state of what energy is absorbed and what energy is expended in the form of fidgeting, walking and other physical activity. These methods have shown conclusively a serious misperception on the part of the patients of what they think they have actually eaten or done physically. On average the intake of food and the amount of exercise are under- and over-reported respectively by about fifty per cent. Not only are the food intake and energy expenditure inaccurately recorded on paper but they are also incorrectly registered in the patient's mind.

Why people should eat more than they expend in energy, and hence more than they require, is not clear. The appetite and the sense of satiety are controlled by the hypothalamus, a small organ inside the skull linked to the brain and the pituitary gland. Like the microchip in a computer the hypothalamus controls many different functions over which the individual has no conscious control. The centre for satiety may be set at too high a point so that the patient does not feel satisfied until more is eaten than is necessary. Rarely the appetite centre is physically damaged after a head injury; more often its level of activity appears to be maladjusted as a result of some inherited trait, overfeeding in infancy or childhood, or some psychological influence.

Being overweight or obese increases the likelihood of developing high blood pressure, coronary artery disease leading to a potentially fatal heart attack, diabetes, degenerative arthritis of the hips and knees, and gall-bladder disease. Morbid obesity by its sheer bulk, as in the Pickwickian syndrome, may be life-threatening.

Patients often fail to seek help because they are ashamed of their shape; others because they have tried in the past, often repeatedly, to diet without success. A few are proud and flamboyantly equate obesity with being successful, wealthy and influential. A forty-year-old Arab field marshal, who weighed thirty stone (420 lb or 190 kg) and had severe coronary artery disease, told me that to lose weight would diminish the respect of his ruler and of the army he commanded. In some cultures obesity in women is a criterion of beauty.

The weight of any obese patient can be reduced by a controlled diet that lowers energy consumption. If the previous habitual daily food intake is reduced by about a quarter, which in most patients amounts to a reduction of some 500 kilocalories a day, the patient will lose approximately one kilogram (nearly two and a half pounds) every two weeks on a diet of 800 to 1000 kilocalories. This can be slightly enhanced by supervised daily exercise which increases energy expenditure and induces a sense of well-being.

More rapid weight loss can be achieved by more stringent very low-calorie diets that provide 400 or 500 kilocalories a day, and which in recent years have become popular. Provided these liquid diets contain high quality proteins and adequate vitamins and minerals they do no harm over a limited period of time. Substantial weight loss of seven kilograms (15 lb) may be achieved in the first week or two and two and a half kilograms (five and a half pounds) in subsequent weeks.

Various drugs have been used to influence the hypothalamus.

Some, which suppress the appetite, are addictive and may make the patient excitable and mentally overactive. Others enhance the feeling of satiety and hence reduce the amount of food eaten. None are reliable and if used at all should be given for only a short time. A possible development in the future is a drug that impedes the absorption of fats from the intestines but proof of its safety and evidence that it does not damage the lining of the gut or impair the absorption of essential vitamins and minerals will require many years of study.

Some patients are simply unable to adhere to a reducing diet. This is not due to lack of willpower because the hypothalamus is sending strong signals to make them eat more. For them various procedures have been used as a last resort, mainly in those with morbid obesity. The teeth of the upper and lower jaws can be wired together, and the patient takes a low-calorie fluid diet through a straw. A balloon may be placed in the stomach so that a feeling of satiety is reached after only a small amount is eaten. Various surgical operations on the stomach have been devised, the most popular being to staple the stomach which reduces its size and accelerates the feeling of satiety. One simple, innocuous method of constantly reminding the patient, who has lost weight, not to regain it is to tie an unstretchable nylon cord around the waist.

Any underlying cause for the obesity, usually a psychological problem, must be addressed. Some patients benefit from behavioural therapy, which can be obtained by attending meetings run by such organisations as Weight Watchers, where group therapy and dietary control often bring success.

17

Medical Research

The first three weeks at the Presbyterian Medical Center were spent collecting the necessary laboratory equipment and reagents. Thereafter extracts made from twenty-four-hour urine collections from normal people were run on the three-foot long pieces of filter paper. The technique seemed to work: the many different steroid hormones excreted were well separated from each other and all but one of them I could identify, by various techniques, as known compounds. Urine samples collected from hospital patients with heart failure and oedema showed much the same pattern but the unidentified hormone was present in larger amounts and this was a consistent finding.

Bob Loeb was interested and quietly confident. After six months' work, on one of his irregular visits to the laboratory, he was positively enthusiastic.

'You're getting there,' he said late one afternoon. 'You're consistently getting this unknown hormone on your chromatograms and what's more the amount seems to correlate with the severity of the patient's oedema. Am I right? The hormone is present in much smaller amounts in normal people. You're on the right track. All you've got to do now is find out the molecular structure, the chemical formula, of this unknown.'

'But I'm no steroid chemist, Bob.'

'I know,' said Bob. 'This is so promising that you'd better get some outside help. Time's running out. There's nobody in our department or upstairs in biochemistry who can advise you.'

He arranged for me to visit an organic chemist at the Merck Institute, the research department of the great pharmaceutical company in Rahway, New Jersey, where the steroid hormone, cortisone, had first been synthesised on a commercial scale.

David Tennant, very helpful and intellectually generous, was about my age.

'Your compound moves fast down the paper,' he said looking at one of the chromatograms I'd brought. 'Faster than the hormones up here that we know about. It must have an unusual molecular structure. If you'll let me have some, I'll try and find out exactly what it is.'

'How much d'you want?'

'Only a milligram or two.'

'No problem. I've collected as much as I can from the chromatograms. It's quite pure.'

'It had better be,' David laughed.

'I'll bring it on Monday morning.'

In a widely used refrigerator, which stood in the hallway outside my laboratory, was a small conical glass flask containing about two teaspoonfuls of precious powder. This was the total amount, much more than David Tennant needed, of the unknown hormone that had been so painstakingly extracted from litres and litres of urine from patients with heart failure and oedema, separated from the other hormones on dozens of paper chromatograms and then eluted from the paper. The end was in sight. With Tennant's help there was a good chance that its chemical structure would be unravelled before it was time to return to Hammersmith.

* * *

On the Sunday morning I slept late. Although New York would one day be called the Big Apple, we had christened it the Champagne City because, without ever feeling tired, you could work all day and play all night. I'd gone to bed at two o'clock in the morning after my friends, the Aranows, had given a dance the previous night at their home in Hastings-on-Hudson – an old-fashioned dance with men wearing black ties, girls in pretty dresses and a real live four-piece band. Even the plainest American girls, and they are in a minority, instinctively knew how to make the best of themselves. All were elegantly dressed, sparklingly groomed and friendly. I had helped Doris Aranow carve the Virginia ham that she had cooked with a coating of cloves and a sprinkling of brown sugar. After the buffet dinner we'd danced to familiar foot-tapping tunes with little time to sit around drinking Jack Daniels.

182

On the following Sunday morning at ten o'clock the refectory in the basement of Bard Hall, the students' residence, was gloomy and deserted except for a few students disconsolately drinking Coca-Cola and desultorily thumbing their way through the 120 pages of the multisectional Sunday newspapers. I was hungry and decided to go to Joe's short-order café opposite the hospital. It was spotlessly clean and for ninety cents you could have the best of breakfasts.

'Hi, Joe.'

'Hi, doc. What's it to be?'

'Orange juice, bacon and two sunny-side up, please.'

A glass of fresh orange juice appeared on the counter. Joe turned to paint some butter on the bright stainless-steel hot-plate. Four rashers of bacon, spread with tongs, sizzled fiercely and were turned over. The toast popped up as Joe deftly decanted the eggs from their shells on to the hotplate. The coffee with a small plastic cup of cream, the toast, and the bacon and eggs arrived simultaneously on the counter. Joe pushed the glass sugar dispenser into place beside the cup of coffee.

'Heard the explosion, I s'pose?' he asked.

'Explosion? No.'

'Didn't see the fire-truck outside the hospital? Big bang but no fire, I think.' Joe moved down the counter to serve another customer.

I ate joyfully, wiped my mouth with a paper napkin and sucked at a fragment of bacon lodged between two teeth. 'Bye, Joe. Thanks. Be seeing you.' I put a dollar bill under the edge of the plate.

The entrance hall of the hospital was deserted except for a security guard gently massaging the leather holster that held his revolver as he strolled backwards and forwards in front of the doors to the elevators. I pressed an 'up' button and for once did not have long to wait for a lift. On weekdays the elevator lobby was always crowded and some statistically-minded intern had calculated that if two more elevators were added to the existing bank of eight the programme for training residents could be shortened by a month because so much time was wasted moving from one floor to another.

Dr Loeb, for once not wearing a white coat, was standing outside his office on the eighth floor surrounded by some residents, a hospital security guard and two firemen.

'You never put ether in a refrigerator, do you?' He asked in a quiet voice.

183

'Never.' It was a heinous offence. 'Why?'

'There's been an explosion. You'd better go and look for yourself. I'm afraid...'

I walked down the hallway and turned into the corridor that led to the laboratories. The brown linoleum floor was awash with water, a few drops still dripping from the sprinklers in the ceiling. Fragments of glass crunched under foot. Halfway down the corridor was the exploded refrigerator – its twin doors blasted off, its sides bulging outward. The force of the explosion had blown in the metal door to the laboratory opposite mine, taking the frame and breeze-block wall with it. The corridor was scorched black. I unlocked the door to my laboratory; it was jammed. I gave the door a kick – to no avail. I threw my weight against it with my shoulder, and it flew open. The lab inside was all right.

Only then did I realise the enormity of what had happened. Back in the corridor I looked carefully inside the shattered refrigerator. Everything had been totally destroyed.

'Oh my God,' I said and went back down the corridor. Any emotional display must be avoided at all costs, I thought, as I fought back tears. All Bob Loeb was allowed to see, as he grasped my shoulders, was an ashen drawn face.

'All gone?' Bob asked.

'All gone – every single milligram of the stuff.' The corners of my mouth twitched.

'Some god-damn fool. Every single refrigerator in the department has a big enough red notice on the outside – *Fire Hazard. No Ether Must Be Put In This Refrigerator.* What more can you do? People don't realise how volatile it is, whether it's in a stoppered vessel or not. The vapour spreads everywhere and one spark from the refrigerator motor... Thank God it was a Sunday and no one was hurt. I'm sorry, very sorry. I'm afraid we've let you down...' Bob Loeb turned and walked into his office shutting the door behind him.

* * *

I returned to England in the *Carinthia*, a pretty ship painted pale apple-green that matched my mood. I'd fallen in love with the United States, with its intellectual freedom – a freedom not so much political as of ideas – and perhaps it also brought relief from the constraints of my upbringing. In America financial support for research, always difficult and sometimes unobtainable in England, was more readily available. I had been tempted to stay. Jobs had been offered but would the warmth of the initial welcome be the same if I became an American citizen? Visiting scientists and doctors were spared the ruthless competitiveness in United States academia.

Back in London work was the only anodyne. John McMichael was warmly welcoming.

'Nice to have you back. Had a good time? Thanks for your letters. How's Bob Loeb? A great man.' Without time for me to answer, he continued, 'You haven't seen the latest issue of *Nature*, I suppose? Some people at the Middlesex Hospital seem to have identified the hormone you've been looking for.'

'Oh!' I could hardly believe my ears. 'Have you got a copy?' I glanced at his desk.

'Yes, here you are.'

I turned the pages of *Nature* until I found the article. It was written by a husband and wife team, Sylvia and Jim Tait, and was almost identical to what Dave Tennant and I might have reported.

'Good for them,' I said quietly.

In a later paper the Taits called the new hormone electrocortin because of its effect on the electrolytes, sodium and potassium, but shortly afterwards, because of its unusual chemical configuration, they suggested the name Aldosterone which remains to this day.

*   *   *

Medicine can advance only through research which takes many forms and pursues many objectives. Broadly it can be divided into research of a fundamental nature involving bioscientific experimental work in animals as well as in man and clinical research that is more immediately related to the care of patients.

Basic research attracts those with special aptitudes and often exceptional ability. Their studies are directed at unravelling the workings of biological systems. Every year new substances that act as controllers or messengers, either locally within a cell or at a distance within the body, are discovered; their activity is elucidated and their chemical structure defined. This increases our knowledge of how the body works and may explain at a molecular level what goes wrong in a particular disease. For example, the biological differences between normal and cancerous cells is being slowly unravelled. The genetic abnormalities responsible for such inherited diseases as cystic fibrosis and sickle-cell anaemia have been defined with the prospect that it may be possible one day to correct the underlying genetic defect.

Clinical research takes many forms. It may involve finding out whether a new drug is effective and if so whether it is more effective than previous ones. It takes about ten years and costs $200–400 million to develop a new drug and test its efficacy; even then careful post-marketing surveillance is necessary lest some infrequent or unusual adverse effect emerges when a large population of patients is given this new treatment. Research is badly needed to show whether one form of treatment or surgical technique is better than another. Until recently little attempt was made to monitor the effectiveness of any treatment given to patients in NHS hospitals because in official statistics the outcome was shown only as whether the patient had died or had been discharged; nor was it stated, if discharged, whether the patient's condition was cured, unchanged or worse. This lack of essential information has been blamed on the Ministry of Health as the monopoly employer, but it is the medical profession which must audit the success or otherwise of what it does. For example more than fifty different types of prosthesis were used to replace a damaged hip but no one knew whether one was superior to another in terms of the patient's subsequent mobility and freedom from pain, the incidence of perioperative complications and the durability of the artificial hip before it too wore out. To answer this question took fifteen years of careful study at great cost. When the answer was eventually obtained it was largely out of date because new prostheses made from different materials were by then available.

Good research workers are born, seldom made. Few young people embark on a medical career with the expressed intention of doing research, because early in their lives they have little idea of what it involves. Even with a penchant for research nobody can know that it is their *métier* until they've worked under the guidance of a skilled and wise supervisor. Nevertheless some exposure to clinical research with personal hands-on experience is deemed desirable at some stage in every doctor's training. Such experience certainly sharpens the intellect and heightens scientific critique so that the doctor is better equipped to assess the validity and significance of new discoveries and it unquestionably leads to improved standards of patient care.

To give every young doctor research experience would be impractical because of the cost, the lack of good ideas and facilities, and the paucity of suitable supervisors to provide the training. Some of the research done today is ill-planned and has little merit. About a third of proposed research projects are never started or are abandoned at an early stage through lack of financial support largely because the studies are ill-conceived, the methods to be used are inappropriate or the outcome would not have been amenable to statistical verification on account of an insufficient number of suitable patients. Of those that are completed the outcome in only half is of sufficient quality to be accepted by the medical press for publication. This does not necessarily mean that those which do not see the light of day are a total waste of time and money; as a result of their experience the young clinical investigators may be more critical and knowledgeable despite this experience being expensive and less well conceived and supervised than it should be.

Even when a young doctor finds he has the aptitude for research, it may not be easy for him to combine this with clinical work unless he finds employment in an academic department funded by a university. Even in this environment, after a few years he may find his commitment to research conflicts with the time needed for the clinical care of patients plus, today, increasing managerial or administrative responsibilities.

* * *

On my return from America the Postgraduate Medical School was buzzing with activity – and has continued to do so ever since. It is not possible to assess quantitatively the knowledge and advances that this institution has contributed to medical science and clinical progress over the years in the same way that a commercial company can be assessed by its profits and the market value of its shares. Peer review by acknowledged leaders in the world's scientific community and by the Higher Education Funding Council for England gives the highest marks to the Postgraduate Medical School whose contributions are continually rated amongst the best in the country and to be of international calibre. Not surprisingly the hospital is costly to run because it does much more than provide patient care to the highest standards; it is actively engaged in wide-ranging research in many fields of medicine and has programmes for postgraduate education and training in most aspects of medicine, surgery, radiology and pathology.

As a lecturer at the Postgraduate Medical School I had my own laboratory and a technician, and as a physician to its associated hospital I was in charge of twelve beds. A number of research fellows joined me and together we evolved a method for measuring one of the most important hormones, essential to life, secreted by the adrenal glands. We studied its level in normal people, including pregnant women, and in patients with a variety of diseases. As we were the only people in the country capable of measuring this hormone in 1946, colleagues in other hospitals sent us samples of blood from many patients with diseases of the adrenal glands which were presumed to be secreting too much or too little of this essential substance.

Inevitably not everything in the garden was rosy. One problem was that, although there was no time limit, after five years a lecturer reached the top of the salary scale; thereafter you could stay on but without any advancement in pay. There were no vacancies for a senior lecturer's post and John McMichael's policy was to encourage his disciples to go out into the world. Also there comes a time in the life of many doctors when they want to be their own boss and take full responsibility for what they do.

Another problem, but perhaps surprisingly not a pressing one at the time, was related to ethics. One morning at the start of a ward round I found that ten of my twelve patients were lying flat in bed without a pillow.

'What's going on, Sister?' I asked.

'They've been lumbar punctured.' Sister explained.

'Lumbar punctured? For heaven's sake why?'

'It's been found that the blood ammonia level is raised in cirrhosis of the liver,' the house physician explained. 'People with cirrhosis may develop curious mental symptoms and it's been suggested that the ammonia level in the cerebro-spinal fluid surrounding the brain might correlate with this hepatic encephalopathy. The liver people want to know what the ammonia level is in the cerebro-spinal fluid of normal people who haven't got cirrhosis, so they came and lumbar punctured your patients.'

I was surprised. A lumbar puncture is never pleasant and may be a painful procedure and rarely is followed by a protracted and severe headache. To do it on *my* patients without so much as a by your leave... The patients had in fact been asked whether they minded being lumbar punctured, but it is not always easy to refuse an investigation even when it is totally irrelevant to your own immediate medical care.

18

A Consultant at Last and a Thyroid Problem

The unexpected death of a previously healthy forty-five-year-old cardiologist, who collapsed and died of a heart attack whilst visiting his wife recovering from an operation in another hospital, created a vacancy for a consultant physician at the Westminster Hospital in London. Here at last was the possible opening I had been waiting for – a senior post in a London teaching hospital that would occupy me, I thought, for the rest of my professional life. The chief disadvantage of the appointment was that it was not full-time. In the new NHS the working week was divided into eleven half days or sessions – two sessions each day on Mondays to Fridays and one on a Saturday morning. The advertised post was for only seven sessions and the Governors of Westminster Hospital were unwilling, and financially unable, to remunerate the remaining four sessions during which I hoped to do laboratory-based research work. The prospect of doing private practice in addition to NHS work did not initially enter my mind. Firstly because I had been influenced by John McMichael's philosophy at Hammersmith; he was quietly but staunchly opposed to private practice which he said would deflect his disciples from continuing their research work and because it was in conflict with the ethos of the NHS with its free-for-all tenet. Secondly I thought that private practice would become something of the past if we fulfilled our commitment to the NHS and it worked as well as we thought it would. The Board of Governors at Westminster were persuaded with difficulty to convert a small room near my wards into a laboratory for my use but without any promise of financial support. A consultant physician, not a member of an academic professorial university department, was not expected to be interested in research and at the time, short-sightedly,

191

Westminster Hospital was the only teaching hospital in the country without any professorial units. I applied for the job; at least I would be my own master and it was up to me to find the financial support for research.

The mid-fifties and sixties were the halcyon, although still imperfect, days of the NHS. Problems of its paternity had been resolved; there had been several threatened miscarriages but, after a protracted delivery, the early gestational pains were over. The emphasis was on a consultant-led hospital service which was until the mid-sixties to undervalue and give less attention to the primary care provided by GPs. Nationwide the hospital coverage was fragmented, of uneven and often indifferent quality, and was in need of fundamental reorganisation. The voluntary and municipal hospitals were nationalised; scores of eager young doctors were properly trained as skilled specialists and within a decade the quality of care in many provincial hospitals equalled that of the metropolitan teaching hospitals. The voluntary London teaching hospitals, following tradition, were still run by Boards of unpaid Governors – public-spirited men or women prominent in the legal profession, industry, the financial world, politics or academia. At Westminster Hospital Lord Nathan, a distinguished solicitor and respected supporter of the Labour Party, was chairman; the other twenty or so members of the Board included Lord Fleck, chairman of ICI, Dr Holroyd, the financial director of that company, Lady Clitheroe, the community-conscious wife of the former Conservative MP Ralph Assheton, by then elevated to the House of Lords, Brian Salmon of the family who ran the successful Lyons catering enterprises, and other notables from the Church and commercial world including a Labour trade-union leader.

In the fifties the hospital's management was in the hands of the Board of Governors and the funding came direct from the Ministry. This was not an arrangement to the taste of Whitehall's civil servants because Lord Nathan did not hesitate to bypass them and lobby the Minister direct when any directives were not to his liking or finance for new drugs or apparatus was inadequate for the hospital's current or projected clinical needs.

The hospital staff did not feel they were employees of the NHS. They worked *in*, rather than *for*, the NHS, to which they were proud to belong, but their commitment was to their patients and their loyalty to the hospital. In our clinical work we were under no obvious financial constraints and anything needed to improve patient care was somehow provided by the House Governor. We worked hard. Apart from busy outpatient clinics and full wards to look after, there were junior staff to train, lectures to give, medical students to teach, nurses to train and numerous committees to attend. We were on call round the clock, including weekends, at a time when answerphones had not reached the British Isles. Not surprisingly in a consultant staff close on a hundred there was the rare black sheep who arrived late for his clinics or ward rounds but most of us happily worked many hours longer than we were contracted for as, according to the office of Manpower Economics, is still the case, with seniors uncomplainingly working on average fourteen hours a week more than they are paid for.

*　　*　　*

The concept of a health service available to everyone in the United Kingdom had its origins in 1911 when Lloyd George, then Chancellor of the Exchequer, introduced his National Insurance Act which for the first time provided free medical care for wage-earners, but not for their wives or children. From such early beginnings politicians and doctors foresaw a more comprehensive service. In 1919 the Ministry of Health was established and planning proceeded in a gradual crescendo for the next quarter of a century. A major forward step came early in the 1939–45 war when the Minister of Health set up the Emergency Medical Service (EMS) to provide treatment for the many air-raid casualties that were anticipated. Such casualties would be drawn from all levels of society and thus the Ministry would become directly involved with the health of the nation as a whole and not with just the insured working-class minority. The EMS also brought the Ministry of Health into direct administrative and financial involvement with the day-to-day working of hospitals.

Before the second war there were two main types of hospital – the voluntary and the municipal. The voluntary hospitals were not financially supported by the state and depended for their income upon endowments, the philanthropy of the local well-to-do, subscriptions from individuals, groups and local companies, and funds raised on flag days. Those voluntary hospitals that were involved in teaching medical students received some indirect financial support from the government through the University Grants Committee.

The municipal hospitals with a much larger number of beds were funded and run by local authorities who were responsible for the non-voluntary acute hospitals, workhouses and residential homes for the chronically ill or elderly, mental asylums, and isolation hospitals for those with infectious diseases. Improved collaboration between the voluntary and municipal hospitals evolved when arrangements were made for the evacuation of air-raid casualties from the cities and also for the ordinary sick of London who were moved from the capital through geographic segments radiating into the home counties and outward to the shires.

In addition to the government other organisations were planning a comprehensive health service. In 1940 the British Medical Association set up a Medical Planning Commission, which included consultant representatives from the Royal Colleges of Physicians, Surgeons and Obstetricians, and proposed a system that would cover all but the wealthiest ten per cent of the population. The Trades Union Council united with the BMA in their quest and their schemes evoked widespread public support, the matter being one of the burning issues of the day.

A White Paper outlining the proposed government scheme was presented to Parliament in 1944, and the National Health Service Bill became law in 1946. The Act came into operation in 1948 and had much wider scope than anything before because virtually everyone in the country, not just the working-class wage-earner with the exclusion of his wife and children, would be required to contribute to the NHS and would be eligible for treatment without cost from the doctor with whom they were registered. This applied also to the disabled, the elderly and the unemployed.

The service extended beyond GP care. Access to properly trained specialists and treatment in hospital would be included despite the fact that whole counties were without a single consultant surgeon, physician or obstetrician. In his maiden speech to the House of Lords on 1 June 1943 Lord Moran, president of the Royal College of Physicians, said, 'You may be surprised to hear that there are great areas of England, towns with a population of 100,000, where the major surgery and everything else is done by general practitioners... All this must end; it is one of the greatest evils of our time in the medical world.' Hospitals would be nationalised and the calibre of the staff improved. The state would take over the voluntary hospitals, leaving those with endowments and other sources of income to use as they saw fit. The specialist consultants at these hospitals, who previously had given their services free, would become salaried and paid by the Ministry of Health. Likewise the municipal hospitals would be centrally funded and run from Whitehall. Medicines would be supplied without cost to patients; eyes would be tested without charge and spectacles provided free.

*   *   *

Dr A.J. Cronin's novel, *The Citadel*, was published in 1937. Some people believe that it was as much responsible for promoting the social revolution that led to Britain's NHS as any other contributing factor including the masterly governmental report by Sir William (later Lord) Beveridge that appeared in 1942.

Cronin was born in 1896. He qualified at Glasgow University in 1919 after his medical studies had been interrupted in 1916 by service in the Royal Naval Volunteer Reserve as an unqualified surgeon sub-lieutenant. After qualifying Cronin started medical practice in a mining town in Wales. While there he obtained a Diploma in Public Health in 1923, a higher medical degree (Membership of the Royal College of Physicians) in 1924 and his MD degree from Glasgow University in 1925 – remarkable achievements for anyone, let alone for someone working in general practice. Between 1926 and 1930 he practised in London. He then returned to the Highlands and in 1931 published his first novel, *Hatter's Castle*, which was such a success that he gave up medical practice and became a full-time writer.

The Citadel was widely read and even more widely discussed. Launched with a brilliant publicity campaign mounted by its publisher, the eminent left-wing Polish immigrant Victor Gollancz, the demand for the 30,000 copies available on the first day of publication, 19 July 1937, was so great that the printing of another 10,000 was put in hand that afternoon. By the end of the month four more impressions were needed; in the first twelve days the total sales were 80,000 copies – remarkable even at a time when there was no competing television. Between August 1937 and the end of the year another 85,000 copies were sold. In the pre-war years everyone knew about *The Citadel*. A film of the book was made with breathless haste and appeared a year after the book was published. It starred Robert Donat with Ralph Richardson, Emlyn

Williams and Rex Harrison in supporting roles. Even if Victor Gollancz foresaw how Cronin's book might influence the public's view of doctors and medical care, it seems unlikely that the author intended it as a weapon of propaganda. Essentially it is a great story, a sentimental romantic novel, which relates too many different medical events to have the flavour of a political broadsheet. A hardcover edition remained in print until 1990 and a paperback edition dating from 1965 is still available.

What was it in this appropriately topical book that so intrigued the public and was so critical of the medical profession and the standards of medical care?

The hero is young Dr Andrew Manson whose father was killed in the last year of the 1914–18 war and whose mother dies of pulmonary tuberculosis. Alone in the world, he is an idealistic graduate of St Andrew's University where he has had a scholarship of £40 a year and a charitable loan, repayable after he qualifies, of £50 a year for five years. His professional life begins in 1924 as an assistant to a bed-ridden GP, Dr Page, who has suffered a stroke, in a Welsh mining town where 'there's no hospital, no ambulance, no X-rays, no anything' and his annual salary is £250 (in those days house officers in teaching hospitals were usually paid nothing but had free keep, or in municipal hospitals £75–100 per annum). While Dr Page's 'skin-flint, plump, pert, gushing' wife eats a lunch of hot beef steak and onions washed down with a pint of oatmeal stout, she feeds Andrew stringy cold boiled brisket and gives him water to drink. Fortunately the water does him no harm; it might have done because Andrew is living in the middle of a typhoid epidemic. An assistant in a neighbouring practice also has a number of cases of typhoid fever and discovers that the outbreak is due to the main sewer leaking into the town's water supply. The epidemic is contained by boiling the drinking water, but in the absence of any help from the district Medical Officer of Health, who is described as 'a lazy, evasive, incompetent pious swine', the two young doctors blow up the sewer in the middle of the night with dynamite stolen from a local coal mine.

Andrew delivers a miner's wife, who has been infertile for eighteen ears, and manages to staunch her life-threatening postpartum haemorrhage. He also resuscitates the baby which, as far as the midwife is concerned, is stillborn and has therefore been wrapped in newspaper and put under the bed. The grateful father presents

196

Andrew with a five-guinea cheque as a present. Through a deplorable breach of professional confidence on the part of the local bank manager, Mrs Page learns of the cheque and demands it is paid into the practice account. Andrew gives in his notice.

After Andrew's marriage to the local schoolteacher, Christine, he moves to another Welsh mining town where he falls out with the district nurse because of her old-fashioned treatment of a scalded arm. His popularity sinks further when he confronts a crowded surgery of malingering coal miners and sends back to work the ringleader who has been sick and off work for fifteen years.

Andrew is critical of medical textbooks which contain 'too many old-fashioned conservative ideas'. What he had been taught about medicines he finds unreliable; rightly he concludes that three-quarters of the remedies in his *pharmacopoeia* are useless.

Andrew and Christine move to London where he buys a practice in Paddington with the surgery in the basement of a dark, depressing and run-down house. They have to live frugally. One of his old medical school friends, who has become very grand, invites them to dinner in Queen Anne Street where the other guests include a neighbouring Harley Street surgeon, Mr Ivory, and a consultant physician, neither of whom have higher degrees or hospital appointments. Over brandy the two 'consultants' discuss with enthusiasm the common practice of fee-splitting, whereby a surgeon gave a proportion of his fee to the referring GP, and the financial rewards of injecting useless drugs rather than giving them by mouth. Sadly Andrew is impressed.

He is appointed to a voluntary hospital as an honorary physician to outpatients without access to inpatient beds (a bad arrangement that persisted in many London teaching hospitals until after the NHS). His professional standards are beginning to slip and he dispenses useless medicines, a practice he formerly condemned. Christine is saddened by her husband's mercenary aspirations and by him becoming a favourite of the smart set where he is advised that his practice would flourish better if he visited a good tailor. She is lonely and neglected. Andrew takes rooms in Wimpole Street (three or five guineas a consultation) and continues to run the surgery in Paddington (three shillings and sixpence a consultation) while Christine dispenses his useless medicines. She and Andrew now occupy separate bedrooms.

His private practice looks up after Andrew successfully treats a

197

senior saleswoman from an *haute couture* establishment, who has dermatitis of her hands, and subsequently refers some of her wealthy clients to him. He is called urgently to the *salon* to attend a young customer thought to be having an epileptic fit. In fact she is hyperventilating and over-breathes so much that her hands go into a tetanic spasm which Andrew cures by slapping her face. A local shopkeeper presents with an acute abdominal emergency and asks to be treated privately. Andrew invites Mr Ivory, his less-than-properly-qualified Harley Street colleague, to operate. The patient dies of a massive haemorrhage in the ill-equipped operating theatre of a sleazy nursing home during a dramatic operation. The surgeon pointedly explains that, as the patient did not die *on* the operating table, there is no legal necessity for an inquest nor any obligation to notify the coroner, as would be the case today. Andrew berates Mr Ivory for his incompetence and the surgeon turns his back on Andrew to walk away with an 'ugly look that speaks of unforgiving fury'.

A young woman with tuberculosis, originally referred to Andrew in his outpatient clinic at the hospital, is not doing well. She has been admitted under the care of the senior physician who rejects Andrew's up-to-date suggestion of inducing a pneumothorax, a procedure for resting the lung by cushioning it with a layer of air injected between the lung and the ribcage. Andrew, therefore, moves the patient to a clinic where he induces a pneumothorax under the guidance of a medically unqualified American, with the unusual credentials of being an ex-Harvard medical student, an ex-physicist and an ex-banker. Mr Ivory reports Andrew to the General Medical Council for working with an unqualified practitioner when the pneumothorax was induced. Although advised by his solicitor to adopt a monosyllabic contrite demeanour at the hearing by the GMC, Andrew is provoked into making a dramatic speech in which he points out that many great scientists who had benefited mankind were not medically qualified; he condemns quacks and bogus remedies; he protests at the complacency of the medical establishment who stifle progress; he denounces the 'hopelessly inadequate training doctors get'; he pleads for postgraduate education; he begs for better pay for nurses.

The Citadel had a major impact; it induced suspicion in the public, some believing that all its revelations were true and widely applicable; the less well-to-do became aware of the deficiencies in

198

the medical care they were receiving. The better-off were appalled by the apparent chicanery of private practice and the greed of those in Harley Street. There was resentment among the medical profession that Cronin had revealed bad practices, had over-emphasised fee-splitting and undermined the authority of the GMC. He was rated a traitor. Even *Punch* failed to restore perspective by printing a pastiche on 15 September 1937, *I was a Doctor (with apologies to the medical profession, but none to those who tell tales about it)*.

Many of the problems and injustices that rightly troubled young Dr Manson have today been rectified. Medical education is better although by no means perfect; not so many years ago the Dean of Harvard Medical School explained in an introductory lecture to new students that 'half of what we teach today is wrong, but we don't know which half it is'. We are nowadays perhaps more knowledgeable but it is not just knowledge that makes a good doctor. Textbooks are more up-to-date but with the speed of advances they need constantly replacing and rereading. Every drug in the *pharmacopoeia* nowadays has a defined pharmacological action. After qualifying, practical experience is required of all doctors who must do a year in selected house appointments before their names are added to the medical register. Well-organised vocational training schemes for GPs are compulsory; postgraduate education is widely available for GPs and consultants; the Royal Colleges supervise training posts in hospitals and give accreditation to those who have completed their specialist training. The GMC holds a record of all accredited specialists. Fee-splitting has been unknown for fifty years. Standards of care in all branches of medicine are now being audited and kept under review.

The criticisms expressed by Cronin in *The Citadel* were deeply felt. After his death in Switzerland in 1981 no obituary appeared in the *British Medical Journal* and *The Lancet* afforded him just two lines.

* * *

When first appointed, my senior colleagues at Westminster paid me the compliment, or perhaps had some less generous motive, of asking me to see their more difficult and usually 'undiagnosable' patients. The lay members of the Board of Governors and the

Medical School Council also tested the waters, not by offering themselves as patients but by first seeking my professional advice about the ailments of their servants, business employees, distant relatives, colleagues and finally those closest and dearest – in that order. I was getting used to this baptism of fire when Lord Fleck, who was a distinguished physicist, asked me to see his senior secretary at ICI.

'Miss Paget, marvellous woman, been with us for years, but recently she's become distinctly odd. Our company doctor has seen her a couple of times but he's come up with nothing beyond saying it's her age.' Lord Fleck, who spoke with a broad Scottish brogue, spread his arms in despair. 'But she's not that old – about fifty. Would you be kind enough to give her the once over?'

Two weeks later Miss Paget presented herself in outpatients at eleven o'clock. As I rose to greet her, the diagnosis was obvious: she had a severely underactive thyroid gland and was myxoedematous.

Miss Paget denied that she was ill beyond a little tiredness, but on direct questioning she admitted to many of the symptoms that patients with severe thyroid deficiency have. Yes, she did like the central heating turned up high in her flat because she always felt cold. Well, yes, she *was* constipated but had been for years. She agreed her work was becoming more difficult but people used such complicated words nowadays, and she could not always hear on the telephone.

Unexpectedly Miss Paget suddenly winked at one of the medical students sitting beside me. 'If you ask me,' she said in a slightly slurred croaky voice, 'his lordship doesn't understands half of what's goin' on – past it, he is.'

Such behaviour and such a remark were surely out of character. Nor, having heard Lord Fleck chair several meetings of the Medical School Council, was it true.

Miss Paget was admitted to hospital there and then, not so much because she was suffering from the usual symptoms of severe thyroid hormone deficiency, known as myxoedema, but because of her mental state. She was also an excellent teaching case – for both the medical and the nursing students. She needed no persuasion; her niece would pack a suitcase and bring all that was necessary to the ward.

Shortly after half-past twelve the senior nurse in outpatients said the ward-sister wanted me on the telephone.

200

'I'm having a bit of trouble with Miss Paget,' Sister said. 'She won't eat any lunch because she says it's poisoned.'

I laughed. 'She *must* have myxoedema madness. I'll be with you in a minute.'

Miss Paget was sitting at the table in the centre of the ward with the other up-patients – a plate of untouched macaroni cheese in front of her.

'What's the problem, Miss Paget?'

'I can't eat this; it's poisoned.' She spoke quietly.

'Surely not. Let me taste it.' With a spare fork I spiked some of the macaroni and put it in my mouth. I chewed it slowly and then swallowed. 'It's all right, I promise you. It's done me no harm. Come on, you have a taste.'

Cautiously she did. I went back to finish outpatients.

Just after half-past one when the last patient had gone and the notes were being gathered up, I was summoned to the phone again.

'I'm sorry to bother you again but we've got another problem with Miss Paget...'

'Okay, I'll drop in on my way to lunch.'

A few minutes later I swept into the ward. 'What's the problem now?' I asked, slightly irritated.

'She's undressed – behind those curtains – but refuses to get into bed,' Sister said.

'Why?'

'Because the bed linen's been poisoned.' There was the hint of a smile on Sister's face.

I stared at her in disbelief and then slowly smiled too. 'And to persuade her that the bed linen's all right, I suppose you want me to get into bed. On my own or with her – which would you suggest, Sister?' I laughed. 'Ask the houseman to cope; I'm going to lunch.'

Two months later when Miss Paget returned to work, Lord Fleck was astonished at the change in her. She too was pleased that she felt so much better, taking just two tiny white tablets of thyroxine a day.

* * *

Iodine plays two essential roles in the human body. Firstly it is vital for the proper development of the brain of a foetus during its first three months *in utero*. The iodine, of course, comes from the mother and if she is iodine deficient because of little or no iodine in her diet, the baby will be born with a permanently damaged brain and is known as a cretin. The extent of the disability depends upon the degree of iodine insufficiency and ranges from mild intellectual impairment to idiocy. As the cretinous infant grows, it lacks coordination, has shakiness of the limbs and walks with difficulty. Congenital deafness is common and this leads to mutism, the child never making more than unintelligible grunting noises. The condition is irreversible, but is preventable by ensuring that the pregnant mother has an adequate intake of iodine before and during her pregnancy. Worldwide 1.5 billion people are at risk of iodine deficiency. Cretinism occurs in some five per cent of this population and as many as five times more children have milder degrees of intellectual disability. This is the commonest cause of preventable mental deficiency.

Secondly iodine is an essential constituent of the hormone secreted by the thyroid gland. Deficiency of iodine causes this gland in the neck to enlarge in an unsuccessful attempt to make more hormone which usually fails because it cannot make bricks without straw. Women are most often affected and the World Health Organisation estimates that worldwide 655 million people have enlargement of the thyroid, a goitre, from this cause. Elimination of iodine deficiency is essential to prevent maternal goitre, cretinism and hypothyroidism in the mother and her infant. More than a hundred nations were pledged to correct this deficiency by the year 2000.

Iodine deficiency as a cause of hypothyroidism is uncommon in the western world. By law salt has been fortified with iodine since the 1920s in the USA and at about the same time in Switzerland where only 1 in a 1000 army recruits is now rejected because of the consequences of iodine deficiency as compared with 31 per 1000 before salt was iodised. In developed countries today a simple blood test is routinely carried out on every baby, five to seven days after birth, so that any thyroid deficiency can be detected early and effective treatment initiated at once. In Great Britain hypothyroidism occurs in about one in every 3000 births. The clinical features of this in a newborn baby may not be striking and usually comprise feeding problems and failure to thrive. Constipation is common and the baby may be inactive and sluggish in its movements, and sleeps excessively. There may be enlargement of the tongue, dryness and thickening of the skin, a croaky cry, and scalp hair that is short and coarse. The tummy is often protuberant. Occasionally an unusually flat, bloated, coarse appearance of the face may be instantly recognisable to an experienced doctor or midwife. Infantile hypothyroidism is completely reversible if the thyroid hormone, thyroxine, is given by mouth soon after birth. If the diagnosis and hence treatment are delayed, neurological complications as in cretinism may develop and be permanent.

People tend to think that iodine is a dark-brown liquid in a brown or blue ribbed poisons bottle kept in the family medicine cupboard. Parents used to dab the fluid on their children's cuts and grazes with a swab of cotton-wool. If you have ever experienced this, you will know how much it stings and often this is more painful than the original injury. This brown fluid is not pure iodine, which is a purplish-brown crystalline substance, but tincture of iodine which is a solution of a small amount of iodine in a large amount of alcohol, the main cause of the stinging.

In many parts of the world iodine is relatively plentiful in the soil. It is present in vegetables and cereals cultivated on iodine-containing soil, and also in fish taken from the sea because sea water contains iodine. It is present in milk produced by cows that have grazed on grass grown on iodine-rich soil. Iodine may be partially or totally absent in mountainous regions such as the Andes, Himalayas and the Alps where snow or heavy rain leaches it out of the soil. Iodine deficiency also occurs in central land masses far removed from the sea, such as Central Europe and in the middle of Spain, in Iran, in the Congo and around the Great Lakes in the USA.

It has taken many centuries to connect iodine deficiency with cretinism, with neonatal and adult goitre and with hypothyroidism. In 1600 BC the Chinese found that eating seaweed reduced the size of a goitre. Paracelsus (1493–1541), at one time professor of medicine in Basle, made the important connection between cretinism, goitre and idiocy but had no idea that iodine was implicated. In 1769 an English physician used sea-sponge to cure Derbyshire neck – a goitre then common in the Pennines. The first really clear description of cretinism associated with a goitre came from a French doctor in 1792. The word 'cretin' is derived from Christian because it is, as the French doctor put it, 'a title one gives these idiots because they are incapable of committing a sin' because they are incapable of telling right from wrong. Not until 1811 was iodine found to be present in seaweed and not until 1850 did a French physician show that the iodine content of food and water in goitrous regions was low and that the administration of iodine prevented endemic goitre and cretinism.

In the western world today adult hypothyroidism is seldom due to iodine deficiency and is commonly caused by an autoimmune disease in which the white cells in the blood react against the cells of the thyroid gland in the mistaken belief that the thyroid is 'foreign' and belongs to somebody else, as also occurs in the rejection phenomenon when some tissue or organ from one individual is transplanted into another.

Adult hypothyroidism comes on so slowly that often the patient and those closest to her are unaware of the changes it is inducing. The patient is usually a woman because the disease in the western world is ten times more common in women than in men. In England some five per cent of women over the age of fifty suffer from thyroid deficiency.

The patient becomes slowed down. Her hearing deteriorates and she fails to hear the telephone ring. She feels the cold dreadfully in winter, and in the summer wears thicker clothes than those around her and may take a hot water bottle to bed. Her voice becomes deeper in pitch and her speech slurred. She tends to become bald. Her skin is thickened and rough, her hands podgy and her face bloated. She may lose her eyebrows. The word myxoedema is often used to describe severe cases of hypothyroidism in which the tissue covering the face and fingers becomes puffy and swollen. A severely hypothyroid patient may develop hallucinations or delusions like Miss Paget, the secretary at ICI. This myxoedema madness was first well described in 1888 but did not receive much attention from the medical profession. In 1937 Dr A.J. Cronin wrote a vivid description of it in *The Citadel* and the patient, a Welsh coal-miner, responded well to the thyroid hormone prescribed by bright young Dr Manson who made the diagnosis. Although adult hypothyroidism and myxoedema madness are now well-known to the medical profession, surprisingly often the diagnosis is not made until late in the course of the disease.

* * *

A detailed, but at times inaccurate in the face of modern knowledge,

204

account of the nineteenth-century's views on cretinism is given in Balzac's *The Country Doctor*, first published in 1833. Honoré de Balzac (1799–1850), who added the 'de' to give his name more style, was not a doctor. He trained as a solicitor but at the age of twenty-one abandoned the law to become a writer, and for two years lived in penury in Paris writing sensational novels under a pseudonym. His first really successful book appeared when he was nearly thirty and thereafter he wrote a series of novels which portrayed life at all levels of French society. The material for *The Country Doctor* can only have been gathered by careful observation and intimate knowledge of a doctor who practised in a remote mountain valley.

The reader first meets Monsieur Benassis (his Christian name is never revealed nor is he ever called *Monsieur Le Docteur*) at the age of fifty, a bachelor who has been practising medicine for twelve years in the isolated township of St Laurent-du-Pont at the foot of the Gorges du Guiers Mort in the Grande Chartreuse mountains of France. He is altruistic – 'Rich people shall not have my time by paying for it; it belongs exclusively to the folk here in the valley. I do not care about fame and fortune, and I look for neither praise nor gratitude from my patients'. The community hold him in high regard and there is scarcely anyone who 'does not put his name in their prayers, morning and night'.

Such popularity was not always the case. When Benassis first arrives in the canton, on the fringe of the town on the mountainside is perched a hamlet where thirty families live, amongst whom are a dozen cretins. In the higher end of the Isère valley cretins are even more numerous, we are told. Benassis believes that 'all the favourable conditions for spreading the hideous disease' exist because 'the air is stagnant and the hamlet lies in the valley bottom, close beside a torrent supplied with water by the melted snow'. It was common in those days to consider cretinism a contagious disease and that stagnant air played a role; Benassis was not to know that the water from the 'melted snows' was deficient in iodine. He aims to stop 'this physical and mental contagion' by having the cretins transferred to an asylum some forty miles away where they would be better cared for.

After having himself appointed mayor, Benassis has several of the cretins moved at night to the asylum. This 'act of humanity', as Benassis perceives it, causes the local population to look upon him 'as a monster'. Nevertheless he succeeds in moving the other cretins after dark with the single exception of one who is away from home. When it is the turn of this last cretin to be transferred, the doctor is greeted with a shower of stones from the inhabitants of the hamlet. 'Little better than idiots but freed from the taint of cretinism' (presumably meaning that they were of somewhat impaired intellect but not severely cretinous), they believed 'that the presence of one of these creatures brings luck' and were therefore determined to keep their last 'idiot'. The doctor concedes to their demand on the understanding that if the cretin remains in his hovel he is 'to be fed and cared for as the adopted child of the commune'.

The other inhabitants of the hamlet are moved to new homes, built and paid for by Benassis, in a lower and more open part of the valley. Here he installs an irrigation system; the land becomes more fertile and the cows produce more milk. Unknowingly Benassis had moved the families to soil that is less iodine deficient. Cretinism in the community becomes something of the past except for the one remaining ageing cretin who had never heard or spoken a word of articulate speech.

Today some of Benassis's public health measures would be considered high-handed, nor would they conform with our present government's policy of moving the mentally disturbed out of psychiatric hospitals into the community. The use of iodised salt and the addition of iodate to bread have reduced the incidence of cretinism in many iodine-deficient regions by ensuring that women have an adequate intake. In the United Kingdom iodisation of salt is not legally compulsory as it is in some European countries but the incidence of iodine-deficient diseases is low because iodised salt or sea salt is widely used. Where endemic goitre, cretinism and neonatal hypothyroidism still persist, it is not clear how iodine can be most economically and effectively provided. A single intramuscular injection of iodised oil, providing enough iodine for four or five years, has been used successfully in central Africa and in Papua New Guinea. Oral administration of a single dose of iodised oil is sufficient for six to twelve months, and in some areas iodised salt has proved effective despite competition from cheaper, locally made, salt devoid of iodine.

19

Patients as Deceivers

Soon after I started work at Westminster Hospital in 1954 an invitation came from Professor Derrick Dunlop, a physician at the Royal Infirmary in Edinburgh and Professor of Therapeutics at Edinburgh University, to have lunch with him. After the thalidomide disaster in the early sixties, when hundreds of babies with misshapen or absent limbs were born to mothers who had taken this sedative drug during the early weeks of pregnancy, the government set up a committee to oversee the safety of all new medicines. Before its later wider remit, this committee had few legal powers. Derrick Dunlop, who commanded great respect, was tactful and had powers of subtle persuasion, was the ideal person to chair this new, and to some potentially threatening, regulatory body. Tall and slender, always immaculately dressed – almost a dandy – Derrick had great charm, impeccable manners and affected an engaging slight lisp when he lectured.

The lunch at Wilton's in Jermyn Street, London, was excellent – the Dover sole, perfection. Barely had the Pouilly Fuissé been tasted before Derrick revealed the reason for our meeting. Would I like to be considered for the Chair of Medicine in Edinburgh that had recently become vacant? It was a tempting offer and I accepted an invitation to spend a weekend with him to view the scene more closely.

Derrick lived in a Scottish keep, a slender stone-built tower with a narrow central spiral staircase that led from the living quarters on the first floor to the bedrooms above. On the Friday evening, after a dinner served by a Portuguese manservant, we sat talking in the sitting room with two Springer spaniels lying on either side of the blazing log-fire in a hearth beside which were a pair of small wooden kegs containing malt whiskies of great maturity. Derrick painted an expansive, vivid picture of the life of a professor of medicine in Edinburgh. A lecture every day was expected – to medical students, physiotherapists, pharmacists, nurses and almoners (just changing their name to social workers). Less frequently there would be after-dinner speeches because, he explained, the professor of medicine really was *somebody* in Edinburgh society. Derrick staunchly held the view that Edinburgh medicine transcended medicine anywhere else in the world; unquestionably its medical training was the best. At midnight I climbed the spiral stone staircase to my bedroom. The view through the mullioned window with its leaded panes showed a bleak moonlit landscape. The room was freezing cold. Carefully spreading some pages of *The Times*, read on the train journey north, beneath the lower sheet and on top of the upper sheet, I went to bed with a sweater over my pyjamas – not a comfortable night.

Next morning Derrick took me round the Royal Infirmary. He explained that there were no research laboratories for the department of medicine but plans for them were afoot and soon they would be built between the Victorian ward blocks. Many patients in the male ward had cirrhosis of the liver and Derrick explained, as if this were inevitable, that they worked in whisky distilleries.

After much thought and with regrets I declined the invitation. There was no certainty when the new laboratories would be built (they weren't for many years) and it was a major upheaval to move north with children at school in London and all one's relatives and friends in the south. There were enough pressing problems at Westminster Hospital, which unfortunately had been designed and built just before World War II before the scientific revolution in medicine. It lacked the space to introduce modern technology. As a teaching hospital it had from the students' point of view the advantage of being small and intimate, but it was the only medical school in Britain that still lacked university professorial departments of medicine, surgery and obstetrics. For some years the University Grants Committee, which funded the medical school, had criticised this on their quinquennial visits and in the late fifties threw down the final gauntlet – either establish professorial departments or...

I was appointed Dean of the Medical School, and quickly had to persuade my colleagues, the Medical School Council and the hospital's Board of Governors, to find the forty-two beds and mandatory laboratory space for the first Professor of Medicine, to be shortly followed by the same facilities for the first Professor of Surgery. With difficulty the statutory number of beds was found without unbalancing the needs of patients but a new building had to be built for the laboratories, new lecture theatres and seminar rooms.

* * *

Everyone on the ward – nurses, doctors and patients – tacitly agreed that Mrs Charlewood was 'lovely'. She was aged sixty, childless and her husband, who had been a much respected and always helpful senior clerk in the hospital's finance department, had died four years earlier of cancer. Until she married at the aged of thirty-eight, Mrs Charlewood had been the faithful secretary to a bank manager. She dressed neatly and unostentatiously. Her hair was greying and well groomed. She was polite and made light of her problem.

I had first seen her in outpatients on referral from her GP – a well-known, conscientious and skilful local physician – who reported that Mrs Charlewood had had diarrhoea for nearly three months. Three specimens of stool had failed to show any unusual organisms, parasites or blood. Her symptoms had started about a month after she returned from a package holiday to Switzerland. There had been no improvement with Lomotil. 'Were more sophisticated investigations indicated?' Dr Riddell asked.

Mrs Charlewood had a sad expression, lightened by a ready smile whenever she talked. Although she did not really know, because she had no scales at home, she thought she had lost about fourteen pounds in weight. The diarrhoea was watery and occurred at least three, usually four, times a day. Sometimes it caught her by surprise – 'so embarrassing'. There was no pain, perhaps mild abdominal discomfort but nothing to 'write home about'. Her GP had been so kind, but sadly his treatment had not helped.

Mrs Charlewood was admitted and proved a model patient. She made no demands on the nurses or anyone else. She got up early to help other patients and the nursing staff; she ran errands for Sister and the ward clerk. She smiled at the doctors and became friendly with the medical student who clerked her. Her diarrhoea was duly recorded by the nursing staff on a chart – she was required

209

to use a bedpan each time. She was subjected to instrumental examination of her colon. In the radiology department barium was run into her gastro-intestinal tract from below and from above. Nothing abnormal was found. During the week that these and other investigations took place she ate well and lost no weight.

Despite her diarrhoea Mrs Charlewood looked the picture of health. I began to feel uneasy.

'Is she conning us?' I first asked myself and then the students as we stood in the corridor discussing the diagnosis out of earshot. It was hard to explain my unease – nothing more than an intuitive hunch. We arranged for Mrs Charlewood to have a chest X-ray.

'Sister, while Mrs Charlewood's down in X-ray would you mind looking through her locker, her spongebag, everything and see if she's got some ... er ... some hidden tablets ... anything?' I asked.

The search was not easy without the other patients being aware of what was going on but Sister quietly made it known that Mrs Charlewood's locker was long overdue for a thorough spring-clean. Nothing unusual was found.

My suspicions remained and a specimen of Mrs Charlewood's stool was sent to the Department of Chemical Pathology. In advance I spoke to the professor of the department, an old friend from Hammersmith Hospital days, and explained the problem.

'Joan, could you analyse the stools for traces of a purgative – Senokot, Ex-Lax, Calsalettes – anything you can think of?' I asked.

Next day Joan Zilva phoned. 'That patient you were talking about, Mrs Charlewood – her stools are loaded with magnesium.'

'Magnesium?' I said. 'Magnesium sulphate's one of the oldest purgatives in the book – Epsom Salts. Where's she hiding it?'

We had to search Mrs Charlewood's belongings again. Staff nurse protested at this further intrusion into the patient's privacy and two junior nurses also expressed their concern. 'She's lovely,' they said but the divided nursing staff bowed to Sister's instructions. Again Mrs Charlewood was dispatched to the X-ray department as being the most convenient way of 'losing' a patient for several hours without inciting suspicion.

Mrs Charlewood's locker was searched again – but in vain. It was a junior nurse who solved the problem.

'She's got bath-salts – in the bathroom,' she announced. 'She's always fussing over that jar of hers.'

The glass jar, painted with yellow and white flowers, was large and had a glass lid. It was three-quarters empty. I sniffed the colourless crystals which surprisingly had no smell. I poured some into my palm and took them to Chemical Pathology.

Joan Zilva telephoned at lunchtime. 'Those crystals are magnesium sulphate,' she said with conviction and added crisply, 'The report will be sent to the ward on the evening delivery.'

I arranged to see the patient alone in Sister's office; it was the only place on the ward that provided any privacy. Mrs Charlewood listened in total silence – her face expressionless.

'Thank you. Thank you very much. I'll be leaving now,' was all she said. And leave she did – without another word to her fellow-patients, to Sister, to anyone. She even insisted on carrying her suitcase down the corridor herself.

I telephoned Dr Riddell, who for once was not out seeing patients. 'I'm afraid I've made a cock-up over Mrs Charlewood,' I said, and explained what had happened. 'We know why she has diarrhoea but not discovered why she's taking magnesium sulphate. We haven't helped her – haven't treated her.'

Alick Riddell was understanding and sympathetic. 'Don't worry, old boy,' he said. 'I'll cope. I'll call and see her this evening. Have a drink with her. Poor old girl. She's got no family. Suppose she's still grieving over her husband – sad. I'll find out what friends she's got and get them to rally round. Could find a part-time job for her here in the health centre – keep her occupied. Thanks for calling.'

My dissatisfaction with myself was not mitigated by the muted praise from the house staff and students for reaching the right diagnosis. A woman may be too proud to complain of loneliness, but there is no loss of pride in having diarrhoea – until you are found out.

* * *

That patients should pretend to be ill and deceive their doctor may seem at first sight an enigmatic, irrational quirk of human nature, but with better understanding the reason usually becomes more comprehensible. Even so the deception often fails to evoke the sympathy and understanding in the doctor that it should, because doctors are no less vulnerable to psychological insults than anyone else, and their initial reaction to being deceived is likely to be

211

anger or irritation because of the suffered loss of self-esteem. Any intellectual satisfaction in finally reaching the correct diagnosis, usually after a prolonged struggle, is offset by the sense of waste – waste of the doctor's time and trouble, waste of hospital resources by admitting the patient for weeks (sometimes on more than one occasion), and waste of the extensive and often complex investigations – only to discover that the patient has a non-existent, feigned illness. There also remains the haunting thought that the true diagnosis might have been reached more quickly. The ultimate insult is that the doctor never receives a word of thanks, and may well be exposed to hostility or abuse from the deceiver or the deceiver's relatives.

The best-known patient deceivers are those with the syndrome named after the redoubtable Baron Karl Friedrich Heironymus Münchausen (1720–97), an extravagant liar whose unbelievable exploits are recorded in *Singular Travels, Campaigns and Adventures of Baron Münchausen*, a book written in English by Rudolf Raspe and first published in 1785. Here, among other unlikely stories, is recounted how the indomitable hero is confronted on a steep, narrow, icy ledge in the Arctic by a wounded and enraged polar bear. Poor Baron Münchausen has unfortunately run out of live ammunition, and he sheds tears at the prospect of his imminent death. Fortunately he has the wit to collect his frozen tears, puts them in the barrel of his rifle and with a blank cartridge fires them at the bear who is killed.

The histories of patients with Münchausen's syndrome are sometimes no less unbelievable, and are a matrix of fantasy and falsehood in which grains of truth are imbedded. The patient is most often a male, usually of low socioeconomic status with a lifelong pattern of social maladjustment, but you do not know that yet. Not a word said with persuasive conviction can be believed, but you don't know that either. These patients travel from hospital to hospital under different fictitious names which make it impossible to trace their previous medical records. The history is plausible and from long practical experience the symptoms are accurately portrayed. The patient may complain of pain suggestive of a gastric ulcer and of vomiting blood, evidence for which is exhibited in a jar. If this blood were analysed, which it seldom is, the pathologist would find that it was not human, let alone the patient's, but of animal origin garnered from an abattoir. The same technique is used when the Münchausen patient presents, usually late at night, to the Accident and Emergency Department of a hospital with obvious blood in his urine.

Some present with symptoms typical, almost, of a heart attack which they allege they have had before and beg for heroin or morphia to relieve their pain: seldom are they addicts because they lack the tell-tale marks of drug abuse but they also lack the low blood pressure and evidence of shock that usually accompany a genuine heart attack. A revealing characteristic is that the patient is histrionic and demanding, and may become truculent and aggressive if the self-proffered diagnosis is not immediately accepted without question. Others come with multiple scars which add credence to their story of severe recurrent abdominal pain. I looked after a twenty-five-year-old Irishman in Hammersmith Hospital who had for years suffered excruciating abdominal pains, he said. He had been persuaded by a priest to visit Lourdes but on the journey the pain had become so severe that the priest had diverted him to a hospital in Paris where yet another emergency operation was performed. When we suggested that a clinical photograph of his abdominal scars should be taken, the patient, perhaps fearing the picture might include his face, precipitously and blasphemously took his own discharge.

These patients seldom evoke the sympathy they deserve. Usually they present late at night, waste a lot of medical and nursing time, and, to establish their veracity, clamour for attention. They are likely to be unemployed (and unemployable), lack any trade or skills (although they may deny this) and are prepared, despite innumerable and sometimes unpleasant investigations, to spend several days being cossetted in a hospital bed where they are warm, fed and well looked after.

More subtle deceivers are those, usually with some medical knowledge, who present with evidence of obvious disease which is confirmed by abnormal laboratory results. These patients are usually aged twenty to fifty, are female, and often have medical connections being nurses, laboratory technicians, dieticians, physiotherapists or medical secretaries. Usually they elect to be investigated and treated at a hospital where they do not work, and because of their medical connections they are 'trusted'. Their subterfuges are complex and legion, often dangerous and may involve considerable personal discomfort, even pain. A fever of unknown origin is the most common presentation. This can be achieved most safely by manipulating the thermometer; friction applied to the bulb by rubbing it between the thumb and forefinger or with the tongue can induce a gratifying rise in the mercury column. Others warm the thermometer on a hot water bottle, in a hot drink or on a nearby radiator. Switching identical thermometers is a particularly successful ruse.

For those with access to syringes and needles more dangerous methods of inducing a fever are available. The temperature is raised by injecting contaminated material such as milk, saliva or excreta. Not only is fever induced but abscesses may develop, sometimes leading to fatal septicaemia. Some deceivers mutilate themselves causing chronic infection of a finger that has to be amputated – and then another finger. Dermatitis artefacta is well-known to surgeons whose patient's wound does not heal until an unopenable occlusive dressing is applied. Experienced dermatologists are familiar with the bizarre skin lesions produced by self-applied chemical irritants or with a sharp needle or kitchen knife. Patients with a prolonged factitious fever or an obvious physical lesion that does not heal engender much sympathy in their relatives who become critical of the medical staff who fail to effect a cure. Any hint that the doctors suspect the problem is self-induced usually leads to open hostility and removal of the patient to another hospital.

The most surprising and sadly a now well-recognised and worldwide form of deception, the so called Münchausen syndrome by proxy, is the mother who induces factitious illness in her seemingly much-loved child. The mother, often totally trustworthy in her GP's eyes, may record repeatedly a spurious fever in her offspring. There is more than one reported case of the mother who every afternoon visits in hospital her febrile child with septicaemia and introduces contaminated material into the intravenous antibiotic infusion tube. The child's temperature spikes two hours after her mother's departure and it is this that eventually arouses the doctors' suspicions. More commonly the mother smothers her infant with a pillow for sufficient length of time to induce an epileptic convulsion from lack of oxygen, and then alerts the medical team. Under these circumstances confirmation of the abuse is always unpleasant and may involve calling in the police or using a hidden television camera. Nor can one be sure that the mother, when confronted with the incontrovertible evidence, will admit what she has been doing or, more important, accept the treatment that she so desperately needs.

A different category of deceivers are those who unintentionally but deliberately make themselves ill by taking a prescription medicine in excessive dosage. Usually these are older women who are so convinced of their need for this medication that without their doctor's knowledge they succeed in getting additional supplies, either from an over-solicitous pharmacist or from an old doctor friend. Younger patients may be more Machiavellian and induce illness for which they seek medical attention without revealing their self-medication. The medicines they take are commonly diuretics to increase urine output and so reduce weight or lessen premenstrual tension, or purgatives to keep slim. Some patients, usually working in the medical field, may take anticoagulants that thin their blood and induce bruises or blood in their urine. Rarely, a nurse misappropriates insulin and a syringe and needle to induce unconsciousness by lowering her own blood sugar level.

Management of patient deceivers is never easy. Tactful, sympathetic confrontation in privacy, without condemnation or criticism, is the best course but the patient must be assured of continued support and not left in a therapeutic vacuum. Sometimes the reason for the factitious illness is difficult both for the patient and the doctor to understand. The deceivers may be immature, sexually afraid, lonely or frightened; the majority are seeking companionship or reassurance about their financial future, or need love and caring attention.

20

Private Practice and a Jaundiced Colleague

In 1957, three years after I had joined the staff at Westminster Hospital, I started to engage in private practice. Despite my earlier fears that medical work outside the NHS would diminish, it was in fact increasing.

From its inception in 1948 the NHS was, perhaps surprisingly, the largest provider of facilities for private short-term medical care in Britain – a position it maintained for a quarter of a century. Many NHS hospitals had private beds – in some there were only a few, in others a whole floor was used for private work and in a few a whole wing or a separate building was devoted to private patients. Some people considered this to be socially divisive but it met the undoubted needs of those who were unprepared to wait weeks or months for admission to an ordinary bed or, more important, needed a predetermined date in their busy lives for their admission. Furthermore a private patient was assured that his or her operation would be carried out by the consultant surgeon of their choice rather than by a senior registrar or an even more junior doctor in training.

The Act of 1946 had given hospital consultants the right to private practice but at the time the decision whether or not to undertake this was for some not easy. Those in middle life on the appointed day were accustomed to holding an honorary (unpaid) appointment at their voluntary hospital. They were uncertain of the implications of a salaried, particularly a full-time salaried, service. Would it jeopardise their clinical freedom? A few of my former teachers at St Thomas's continued to be honorary and declined to accept a salary. Most accepted part-time contracts and continued in private practice. Many of my generation thought that the best clinical and research work was done by full-timers, but for several reasons private practice gradually became part of my professional life. Although I was able to fund my research work, which involved a small laboratory, a technician and a research fellow, with grants from the Board of Governors of Westminster Hospital and from a well-known medical charity, no personal income was included. My livelihood was derived solely from the seven-elevenths of the whole-time salary paid by the NHS. Secondly, more and more patients, through their GPs of course, sought my advice. Initially it was mainly colleagues or their wives or children, and they were not content to be seen in an ordinary outpatient clinic. I was also asked to see the patients under the care of other consultants on the private floor at Westminster Hospital. Finally, GPs began to think that I might be helpful to some of their patients who posed diagnostic problems.

Private practice brings rewards more important than the obvious financial one. You have a closer relationship with the patient. There is more time to take the history and you do so yourself, first-hand and not through an intermediary, your house physician, as happens on a public ward. The diagnosis and proposed treatment can be discussed more leisurely. The patient's fears, and sometimes irrational beliefs, can be assuaged. All these considerations certainly increase the job satisfaction with the added bonus that the patient is often medically, and sometimes as a person, 'interesting'.

Private practice conducted from the cramped consulting rooms at Westminster Hospital was unsatisfactory, so in 1960 I took rooms in Wimpole Street and more than rooms – a flat so that I could live 'over the shop'. The property was being vacated by a retiring gynaecologist, who understood my fears. 'It will seem a lot of money at first,' he said. 'But don't be afraid. I remember when I first started here. Bankruptcy seemed just around the corner! Don't worry; it'll be all right. Look out there,' he pointed through the window to an E-type Jaguar parked in the road below, 'I've got two of those,' he said and laughed.

Wimpole Street, rather than Harley Street, was a deliberate choice. In my view, perhaps influenced by *The Citadel*, Harley Street had something of a tarnished reputation, and was more expensive. The public were beginning to learn that having rooms in Harley Street conferred no credentials of expertise or professional excellence; it simply meant that any Tom, Dick or Harry had the money to pay the rent. Wimpole Street had equally elegant houses and consulting

218

rooms, and was just as convenient, or inconvenient, for patients as Harley Street was.

* * *

It had been an enjoyable dinner party. As I helped my senior colleague into his overcoat, I repeated, 'Have a lovely holiday. Let us know how you get on.'

'Send you a picture postcard. I'm sure we'll enjoy ourselves. Thanks for all your advice.'

I closed the front door behind Frank Barton and his wife, Greta, also a doctor, and hoped that in the spring they would have a happy time at the little hotel we'd recommended on a still unspoilt Greek island. Frank was a distinguished academic who had devoted most of his life to running a charitable organisation that furthered the progress of basic and clinical sciences by holding conferences to which carefully selected contributors were invited from all over the world.

Later the Bartons did send a postcard; they were having a lovely time; the hotel and its surroundings were even nicer than our description.

Three weeks after the postcard, Greta telephoned early one Saturday morning.

'Frank's been ill for three days. He's got a fever; he's off his food and I'm worried. When will you come and see him?'

After breakfast I drove to their flat. Frank was cheerful and did not look ill. He'd had a headache with a temperature for the last three nights. His appetite had completely gone. There were no other symptoms, nor on examination were there any abnormal findings.

Greta Barton fluttered in and out of the bedroom. 'What's he got?' she kept asking.

I didn't know, and said so.

'Typhoid fever?' suggested Greta – doctor's wives, particularly if they too are doctors, always fear the worst.

'Could be, I suppose. It's too early to say; it might be almost anything. I've taken some blood to see what the lab finds. Probably won't have the results until Monday, but I'll look in tomorrow.'

I was concerned. It would happen that, on the holiday we'd recommended, Frank got something nasty. On the Monday evening Greta greeted me with, 'What did the blood count show?'

219

'A low white cell count.'

'So it's typhoid fever?'

'It could be, but lots of other diseases are associated with a low white count.' I ignored her question of 'Such as?' and went to the bedroom. Even though the light outside was fading I noticed the change.

'You're jaundiced.'

Frank jumped out of bed and studied his face in the mirror on Greta's dressing-table, pulling down a lower eyelid to see if his conjunctiva was yellow.

'Can't see it myself,' he said, 'but I'm feeling much better and my temperature was down last night. Now you mention it, my urine is rather dark.'

As I took some more blood, I said, 'You're certainly jaundiced, but it's hard to believe you've got infective hepatitis after being in North Africa during the war. You did say you'd never had hepatitis?'

'Never; I must be immune. I was with the Eighth Army all through the North African campaign and up through Italy. I must have had a sub-clinical attack somewhere along the road. You'd think so, wouldn't you?'

The liver function tests confirmed that Frank had some sort of hepatitis. That evening Martin Hynes, the director of the laboratory, telephoned me at home and said he had blood from five other doctors in London and also from four doctors' wives who had all developed jaundice during the previous ten days. 'It looks as though there's an epidemic in doctors and their spouses,' he said.

The Public Health Department, to which all the cases were notified, soon discovered that the epidemic was confined to doctors and their wives who had attended a dinner some three weeks earlier at one of the worshipful companies in the City of London. A hundred and twenty people had sat down to the meal and sixty had subsequently developed jaundice. An attack rate of fifty per cent would be considered highly successful in chemical or germ warfare.

Where had the infection come from? The menu on that summer's evening had been cold *gazpacho* soup, roast duck with orange sauce, broccoli and sauté potatoes, and raspberry *Surprise*. The Medical Officer of Health in the City of London interviewed the chefs, kitchen staff and waiters of the catering company that had supplied the meal. None had been ill or in contact with anyone with jaundice. The source remained unknown.

Three weeks later came a new clue. Another outbreak of hepatitis A occurred in a small group of people who had attended a birthday party in Hampstead. Again there was a high attack rate and they too had eaten raspberry *Surprise*. The dinner had not been provided by the same caterers but the frozen raspberries had come from the same wholesaler who had supplied the City dinner. From the wholesaler the trail led back to a large raspberry farm in Scotland – and there it died.

How the raspberries had become infected remained a mystery until I recounted what had happened when we were having tea with Sister after a ward round. The senior registrar at the time was a Scot who had trained in Aberdeen.

'There're lots of raspberry farms near Perth,' Colin MacIntosh said. 'With students from Dundee I used to pick 'em during the season. It was good money – so much a pound. Nor was it unknown...' Colin hesitated, ... unknown for people to increase the weight of their pickings by pee-ing into the plastic bags.'

'You're serious?'

'Of course.'

'And if one of the pickers were incubating infective hepatitis and excreting the virus in his urine, how many raspberries would he contaminate?'

'I've no idea. The raspberries are all mixed up together before they're spot frozen, and the freezing wouldn't destroy the virus, would it?'

* * *

Every year in Great Britain some 6000 people, usually young adults, fall prey to infective hepatitis. The disease used to be called catarrhal jaundice but nowadays is known as hepatitis A. It starts with a flu-like illness – a headache, generalised aching, loss of appetite, nausea and sometimes vomiting, and a temperature. After a week or so the temperature settles and the patient begins to feel a little better. At this stage some patients may be sufficiently observant to note that their urine has become darker and their stools lighter in colour than usual. Jaundice then appears and over a period of days the yellowness reaches a peak, fades slowly and finally disappears after three or four weeks. Most patients make an uneventful recovery and the mortality in those under the age of sixty is very low – only one death per 4000 patients. In the elderly, however, the condition may progress to liver failure and the mortality in those aged sixty-four or over may be as high at 15 per 1000.

Infective hepatitis is caused by a virus. The incubation period – the time between the virus entering the body and symptoms developing – is about twenty-eight days, and it is during this time when the organism is multiplying in its unsuspecting victim that large amounts of it are excreted in the stools and urine and the patient is most infectious to other people. Transmission may occur by person-to-person contact in families, schools and other institutions, and also from contaminated water or food such as raw or inadequately-cooked shellfish garnered from a seabed polluted with sewage. With improved hygiene and sanitation the incidence of hepatitis A in the western world has fallen and nowadays in Britain and the USA some twenty per cent of cases or more are contracted abroad.

In World War II epidemics of infective hepatitis occurred in the armies on most fronts. In North Africa the Battle of Alamein was in danger of being postponed because of an outbreak in the Eighth Army. Five per cent of the officers as compared with one per cent of the other ranks contracted the disease. General Montgomery attributed the higher incidence in his officers to their monthly ration of a bottle of Scotch and contemplated stopping this. Professor Sam Spooner, a microbiologist who had been one of my tutors at Cambridge, was flown to Egypt to investigate. He pointed out that a soldier had his own mug, plate and cutlery which he washed and kept to himself, whereas an officer ate in a mess with communal plates, glasses and cutlery which were washed by mess servants who used only a small fraction of the meagre ration of two pints of water allocated daily to everyone in the desert.

Although there is no specific treatment, prevention is possible by giving gamma-globulin, which contains antibodies against the virus and is obtained from healthy blood-donors. Injections of gamma-globulin are used to protect those who have been in close contact with a patient during the early stages of the disease and to protect those who are travelling to a high-risk area, but the protection lasts for only about six months.

Fortunately success in culturing the hepatitis A virus has led to the development of an effective vaccine. Three injections over six months give protection for ten years and probably longer.

21

New Horizons

Consultant private practice in the United Kingdom is governed by a few unwritten rules and several conventions, most of which the public at large are unaware of. It is not etiquette for a consultant to see any British patient without him or her being referred by their GP. To do so is to invite difficulties because the patient may not give an accurate account of his or her previous medical history which could be highly relevant. Nor is the patient likely to know what tests have already been done or the results of them. The consultant is also open to the accusation of 'stealing' another doctor's patient. If the patient is insured with one of the private medical insurance companies, it will be clearly stated in the contract that the insurer will reimburse the fee charged by a consultant only if the patient has been referred by their GP. In this context the GP is the gatekeeper, and the cost of medical care would escalate out of control if patients were free to seek consultant advice whenever they felt like it.

For the consultant there are other less clearly recognised conventions. Hippocrates (460–370 BC) advised that doctors should not charge each other and most of us extend this courtesy to a colleague's spouse and dependent children. Nor is it the custom for consultants to charge those in Holy Orders or past or present members of the nursing profession.

As time passed other opportunities to use my training and experience in wider, and often less arduous, fields presented themselves. For example, examining final year medical students is only tedious when you have to read an illegible script; otherwise it is a refreshing and educative undertaking. During the four days we met in Cambridge each summer I learnt much from my fellow examiners and also from the candidates, who provided information about the new frontiers being pushed forward in other teaching hospitals. Had computers been extensively used in those days and the engagement of each examiner committed to hard disk by the secretary to the successive Regius Professors of Physic, first Professor Joe Mitchell and later Lord Butterfield, it seems improbable that I would have been invited to examine there for eighteen consecutive years! Examining for Membership of the Royal College of Physicians was also educative but hard work because better methods of assessing a candidate's knowledge, and deciding what knowledge is required, were constantly being sought.

Success in the private sector brought new opportunities in wider and interesting paramedical activities. The Swiss Reinsurance Company of Zurich opened a London office and Dr Aubrey Leatham, a cardiologist, and I were invited to become their medical advisers. This did not involve the rather dull task of examining healthy people seeking life assurance or scrutinising their proposal forms, but was concerned only with those who had suffered some significant illness in the past or continued to suffer ill-health and were seeking life insurance cover. These proposals from the medically impaired were carefully reviewed with one of the company's knowledgeable lay underwriters and the prognosis, on the which the premium was largely based, was derived from our personal experience and from the Swiss Reinsurance Company's previous worldwide experience. The company also held a week-long annual conference in different parts of the world attended by the medical advisers from their overseas subsidiaries. At these we learnt of the different prognosis experienced in the same disease in other countries because of variations in the severity of a condition and in the quality and availability of medical care.

The Royal College of Physicians put my name forward as a non-executive director of Private Patients Plan, the second largest private health insurance company in the United Kingdom. Since its inception in 1940, PPP has had a strong medical representation on its board, a director being sought from each of the Royal Colleges of Physicians, Surgeons, and Obstetricians and Gynaecologists. Seeing how a commercial organisation operated with a professionally-trained company secretary was eye-opening, and showed how the minutes could reflect accurately and succinctly what was said and what was decided; the contrast with those of most NHS committees was striking.

Every Tuesday afternoon at four-thirty my firm at Westminster Hospital went to the X-ray department to review with the senior radiologist, Dr Peter Kerley, the most interesting films taken during the week of our patients. Peter was an Irishman and one of the doyens of British radiology. He was extremely bright, the author of a two-volume textbook of radiology, a keen fisherman, an ardent race-goer and a *bon viveur.* Early in 1964, just as we were leaving the X-ray viewing room one evening, Peter grasped my arm and said, 'Come and have a drink with Horace Evans and me at his house tomorrow evening.'

Sir Horace (later Lord) Evans was a highly regarded consultant at the London Hospital and was Physician to Her Majesty the Queen. He had a house in Harley Street and when I went there the following evening I was surprised to find Sir Arthur Porritt (later Lord Porritt and Governor-General of New Zealand) who was Serjeant Surgeon to the Queen, Ronald Bodley-Scott, also a Physician to the Queen, and Peter Kerley there. We were standing around chatting when Horace Evans said, 'Would you like to be Physician to the Queen's Household?'

Taken totally by surprise I asked what this entailed and learnt that the Queen's Household comprised many people including the Lord Chamberlain and his staff, her Private Secretary and his assistants, the Master of the Household at Buckingham Palace and the Masters of the other royal residencies and their staffs, the Keeper of the Privy Purse and his accountants, Serjeants-at-Arms, the Lords in Waiting, the Women of the Bedchamber, and many others such as the Poet Laureate, Keepers of the Queen's Archives, and pages, servants, chefs and other kitchen staff, chauffeurs, grooms, ostlers and farriers. The day-to-day medical care of members of the Household was undertaken, I learnt, by a different apothecary in each of the royal residences – in London, Windsor, Sandringham, Holyroodhouse and Balmoral. A sufficiently large number lived in and around the Royal Mews in London to merit the apothecary having a surgery there. As Physician to the Queen's Household I would make myself available as a second opinion to the patients of all the five apothecaries.

A week later I was summoned by the Lord Chamberlain to St James's Palace. Lord Cobbold explained that the appointment was not arduous and that I would be paid a small retainer. Many of the upper echelons of the staff were insured with a private medical insurance company and they should be seen in my consulting rooms; those not insured could be seen at Westminster Hospital.

For the next six years I had the pleasure of seeing many of the people who worked on the 'other side of the green baize door', as I called it, and it was indeed pleasurable because many were poorly and most, from the farriers upwards, were extremely interesting people.

In 1970, after Sir Ronald Bodley-Scott had succeeded Lord Evans as Senior Physician to the Queen, I was invited by the Lord Chamberlain to become a Physician to Her Majesty, but it seemed to me not fair that the Queen should have a doctor, to whom she might take an instinctive dislike, imposed upon her. I told Lord Cobbold that I would of course be delighted to accept the appointment but I thought it only right that Her Majesty, who'd met me once at a cocktail party in Buckingham Palace, should express her wishes. A week later I was invited to tea and the Queen raised the difficult question of whether young people who travelled to distant and outlandish places should have their appendix prophylactically removed. What if they developed an acute appendicitis in some remote part of the world? She must have been satisfied with my advice, which was to do nothing, because a few days later Lord Cobbold confirmed my appointment.

Three years later in 1973 Bodley-Scott retired under a recently introduced rule that the Palace staff should retire at the age of sixty-five. When Lord Cobbold proposed this rule in 1972, he and Bodley-Scott both discovered they were already sixty-five and discretely stayed on another year. Thus for nearly ten years I was Physician to the Queen and Head of her Medical Household.

Such an appointment brings responsibilities beyond looking after the Queen and her immediate family because there are many other members of the Royal Family. They all have their own GP (apothecary), although some preferred to call me in at the first sign of ill-health. Perhaps the most difficult aspect was having to be always available, which meant constantly leaving my telephone number or whereabouts with the switchboard in Buckingham Palace. What a difference today's mobile phones have made!

One issue of concern was the pressure the Queen was subjected to on her overseas visits. The country visited tried to cram in as many engagements as they possibly could, never giving thought to whether the Queen had adequate time to change her clothes between functions, to do her hair or to put her feet up for half an hour. I made it my business to scrutinise the detailed programmes when they were in draft form and, if necessary, make suggestions to the Queen's secretary that would relieve the pressure.

Her Majesty appointed me a Knight Commander of the Victorian Order in 1978 and I was to attend an investiture on Tuesday, 14 February. At 8.30 that morning the Queen telephoned and said she was feeling poorly, as was Prince Philip. I hurried to Buckingham Palace in my morning coat, which caused the Monarch to comment that it was a long time since she had seen her physician in such attire. They both had flu. There was no question of her holding the investiture. Fortunately Prince Charles was able to rearrange his commitments and I was dubbed by him.

* * *

Heads of foreign states may make an official visit to London either as a guest of the Queen and stay at Buckingham Palace or as a guest of the government and then usually stay with their ambassador or at Claridges Hotel. They are likely to ask for special medical arrangements. For example, before the visit of President Giscard d'Estaing of France, his personal physician, a young paediatrician doing his national service, made a brief visit to finalise the medical arrangements. At our first meeting he commented wryly that the British seemed determined not to forget their victories over the French. He knew this because he had arrived at Waterloo station, been driven through Trafalgar Square, seen a statue of Nelson and then passed Wellington Barracks! He asked for a cache of blood, of the correct blood group of course, to be placed at key points during his President's visit – at Gatwick, Victoria station and in the City. He wanted to see the room to which the President would be admitted were he taken suddenly ill or injured. Sir Lynn Lockhart-Mummery, the Serjeant Surgeon, and I showed him the floor in the private wing of St Thomas's where the President would be accommodated. But this was not enough; he must see the décor of the actual room because upon this would depend the colour of the flowers that Madam d'Estaing would send.

Other foreign rulers have required an operating theatre in a central London hospital and a neurosurgeon to be on constant standby during their visit. As medicine progresses the arrangements for such visits become more sophisticated. Some American presidents and Middle Eastern rulers bring an attending Boeing 707 or 747 equipped and staffed as a hospital with a state-of-the-art operating theatre.

Heads of state who seek the advice of a consultant in London are often the leaders of a former British colony. A convenient time for them to visit London seems to be when they attend a meeting of the Commonwealth Prime Ministers, irrespective of where this is held. The appointment is usually arranged through their High Commissioner's office in London, and the head of state is likely to arrive at the consultant's rooms in a fleet of cars accompanied by a personal medical attendant, his wife, several hangers-on including a bodyguard and more unobtrusive members of the Diplomatic Section of the Metropolitan Police. The bodyguard can usually be persuaded to stay in the waiting room during the consultation.

Rulers from the Middle or Far East are more internationally minded and may trawl the rest of Europe and the USA for a second or third opinion. Often they try to entice you to go to them. Such overseas visits are likely to be demanding and time-consuming but with experience one learns how best to manage them. It is prudent to make your own travelling arrangements with a major international airline; that of the nation you are visiting may not be wholly reliable, and worse still is to travel in the ruler's private jet because most life-insurance policies become invalid on a non-scheduled flight. Unless you make your own arrangements for accommodation in a local hotel, you may find yourself a virtual prisoner in the royal palace or presidency, unable to take a walk or eat when you want and unable to leave when your task is complete. In general, Middle and Far Eastern potentates are suspicious of all medical advice and seek multiple sequential opinions from three or more foreign consultants. Consummate tact and diplomacy are required should your diagnosis or method of treatment be at variance with those of the local physicians.

My first professional visit to Cairo was ostensibly to inspect a new military hospital that had been built beside the Nile and to give two lectures, or so the Egyptian ambassador in London said. On arrival in Cairo at midnight (their time; my watch said two o'clock in the morning) there was much discussion with the officials as to whether they should collect me from the hotel at seven-thirty or eight o'clock. In bartering style I proposed ten in the hope that a compromise of nine would be achieved; it was.

Most of the morning was spent looking round the new Maadi hospital which was only half open because of a shortage of nurses. Over a cup of coffee with the British matron, the general in charge announced that it was at this time of year that their President had his annual medical check-up. Would I see him at half past three that afternoon? It was more an order than a request.

The setting was as one might expect. The drawing-room in Coba Palace, where the President lives, was crowded with his personal physician, the professor of medicine from Ein-Shams Hospital, numerous other doctors, several ministers and sundry secretaries and attendants. At first they were averse to me seeing the President alone – in private. Eventually I prevailed and the two of us sat on uncomfortable Louis-Quinze chairs as I took his history and reviewed the laboratory data – each result carefully pasted on a separate page in a large leather-bound volume. For the physical examination we moved to an emergency operating theatre that had been built in the grounds of the palace. The President had two serious diseases and when an hour later he climbed down from the couch, he asked affably if I would see his wife. An hour and a half later she in turn asked if I would see their two teenage children, one of whom proved to have anorexia nervosa. It was ten-thirty at night when, exhausted, I went to collect the key to my room at the reception desk in the Nile Hilton Hotel and found an old friend, Professor René Mach from Geneva, standing there.

'Hello,' I said, 'what are you doing here?'

'Much the same as you, I suspect. I saw the President yesterday. D'you know Professor Poulsen from Copenhagen? He saw him the day before.' He introduced us.

Each of us was required to submit a written medical report and my suggestion that we should write a joint one, while we sat having a well-earned drink in the dimly-lit bar, was welcomed. I don't think the President was too displeased but such patients prefer to have independent reports from each doctor so that they can adopt only those pieces of advice that are the least onerous.

Subsequently we were taken on a tour of Luxor and Aswan in the President's private Russian-made plane, the interior upholstered in red plush with grubby lace antimacassars on the arm-rests. Our guide was Major Mustafa, a fat jolly man and a genial host. On

New Year's Eve we had dinner in the Old Cataract Hotel in Aswan, its walls decorated with faded sepia photographs of short-horn cattle grazing on a Scottish moor. The dining room was packed with Russian technicians who were building the new High Dam hydroelectric power station and looked like Americans of an earlier decade with their crew-cut hair and Rolliflex cameras. The orchestra played contemporary American music. Halfway through the meal Mustafa slipped from his chair on to the floor and had an epileptic fit. All we could do was to put the handle of a spoon across his mouth to stop him biting his tongue. He recovered quickly and explained that his epilepsy was the consequence of the Suez war – 'a Breetish boollet in my brain', as he put it. He was waiting to be posted to the Egyptian embassy in London where he would have it removed, he said and laughed. Two months later, at the National Hospital for Nervous Diseases, he did.

Some overseas visits can be for an unusual reason. We were halfway across France in an aeroplane *en route* to Rome before my companion, an insurance loss-adjuster, finished explaining the reasons for the trip. A well-known Italian film producer was scheduled to start making a new movie in four days' time. Everything was in readiness – the leading actors and actresses were under contract, the cameramen were standing by, the sets and locations in readiness. But the producer had just announced he was ill and was unable to make the film. The loss-adjuster explained that the production was insured with a company in Los Angeles, for which he was acting, and for each day the cameras failed to roll they would have to pay $1.5 million. I was required to give an opinion as to whether or not the producer was so ill that the production must be halted and, if so, for how long.

At breakfast next morning in the hotel, the loss-adjuster called attention to the banner headlines in one of the Roman newspapers which proclaimed that the producer was ill and that under no circumstances could he make the film; it was hinted that he did not like the script nor the leading lady.

The Italian producer and I met in his beautiful villa outside Rome. He spoke perfect English. We talked and I examined him in his study. Beside the couch was a tall chest of drawers on top of which were a dozen grey and gold figurines covered with a thick layer of dust.

'Your Oscars?' I enquired; the film producer laughed.

230

It was a complicated history and became even more involved when I learnt that the film producer had recently learnt that his wife was suffering from a grave disorder of the central nervous system. I could find nothing wrong with him and gained the distinct impression that he had no intention of making the movie.

The loss-adjuster, an Italian lawyer and I had lunch in the nearby villa of the financial director of the film, a saturnine Neapolitan who could well have been cast as a member of the Mafia. I explained that a court of law might not accept my evidence that I could find nothing wrong with the producer. A doctor could not easily *prove* that someone was *well* and conversely we often see undoubtedly ill patients who show no signs of disease and have no abnormal blood tests. There was no way of proving, for example, that a patient did not have clinical depression, but I didn't think this man was depressed. I advised that some sort of financial deal should be struck; it would be cheaper than paying $1.5 million day after day. The cost of the difficult hour-long transatlantic telephone call to the insurance company in California was trivial compared with the settlement but I had made the unpalatable point that proving a negative is not always possible.

* * *

It has been suggested that those in important positions, particularly ministers and politicians, should undergo a compulsory annual medical examination like officers in the armed forces and commercial airline pilots. This may detect a physical illness that could impair their performance or judgement but is less likely to pick up a psychological disorder. A number of questionnaires designed to elicit depression, anxiety, psychosis and neurosis are available but it is unlikely that those most at risk would voluntarily submit to such an examination and who is to say when someone with unusual, even bizarre, ideas, particularly a politician, should be relieved of his or her duties?

An unusual request, which came from the political party's Central Office, was to enquire whether I would see a politician to decide if he were medically fit to be Prime Minister. At the time there were two candidates to head the Party but there were fears that this one might not be able to withstand the gruelling hours that the post demanded. The person in question had, as was well known,

231

a condition of his spine which made many movements difficult and painful. His neck was so rigid that he could not turn his head without twisting his hips. Inevitably he would be seriously handicapped, and often in pain, during question-time in the House of Commons. I agreed to see the politician only on the strict understanding that he was fully aware that my report would be as much to the Central Office as to him as an individual.

The assessment proved too difficult to make in an hour's consultation, and the patient – he was sufficiently handicapped to be considered such – agreed to come into hospital for a few days for further observation. After two days I had with reluctance to tell him and the Party leaders that I thought it most unlikely he would stand the rigours of being Prime Minister. Sadly he died a few months later.

* * *

Another patient of longer standing had a particular problem. Her dentist of many years was retiring. Would I help her find a new one?

'I don't want one of those modern ones,' she said.

'What exactly d'you mean by that?'

'Not somebody with one of those high-speed turbo drills. I once had one in New York – most unpleasant. My present dentist has a nice slow machine that he operates with his foot.'

I couldn't help laughing. 'But they went out with Noah's ark. Nobody uses a treadle foot-drill nowadays.'

'And I didn't like it in New York when a piece of rubber sheeting was put round my tooth before it was drilled – I couldn't breathe properly.'

Thus began the search for a new dentist – but not one with a foot drill. All my colleagues had different ideas of course. I spoke to the Professors of Dentistry in the London Dental Schools and they proposed possible candidates. A series of cocktail parties, each hosted by a different Professor of Dentistry, were given with the potential candidate, unaware of what was going on, included among the guests.

'Come and meet this old student of mine,' one professor said. 'He won the gold medal and was top of his class all the way through.' He introduced us.

232

I talked to the nice young man. His hair was rather ungroomed and hung down over his shoulders; his fingernails were distinctly grimy.

After the guests had gone the professor said, 'Sorry about that chap; not what he used to be; he was always so neatly turned out.'

A month later I sat beside the patient and painted a verbal picture of each of the four shortlisted candidates who ranged from the age of thirty-four to fifty-five. To my surprise she had no hesitation in deciding – and chose the youngest. 'He'll see me out and he's the right age to look after the children,' she said.

Before their first meeting I had had a few words with the new dentist in case he was unfamiliar with protocol. That evening I rang the patient to find out how she'd got on.

'Oh very nicely, I think', she said. 'It was all rather new and strange. What did he mean when he asked whether I liked heavy, medium or light?'

'Heavy, medium or light? I'm afraid I don't know what you're talking about.'

'Well, when he tilted the chair back – I had to lie completely horizontal, very peculiar – he asked whether I liked heavy, medium or light.'

'And what did you say?'

'I said I didn't mind.'

'Most unwise if you didn't know what he meant! I'll give him a ring and call you back.'

I telephoned the dentist who at first didn't know what I was talking about. Then he twigged. 'Oh, I know! I was simply asking whether she liked heavy, medium or light classical music. I've got cassettes for all tastes.'

22

Complementary Medicine and Quacks

The telephone rang; my secretary answered it in her office and then rang me. 'Dr Turner wants a word with you.'

'John Turner here. You probably won't remember but about three years ago you saw a patient of mine, a Mrs Elizabeth Nolan, with an overactive thyroid. Would you mind seeing her again? She's very ill this time, I'm afraid. I've admitted her to the Wimpole Street Hospital. Could you see her this evening? It's urgent.'

'Six o'clock all right? D'you want to be there?'

'Yes. Six o'clock will be fine.'

During the lunch hour, sitting at my desk eating a Scotch egg and salad from a plastic box, I read Mrs Nolan's old notes which my efficient and invaluable Sue had retrieved from one of the filing cabinets in her office. Three years before, Mrs Nolan was aged forty-two, married with three children in their early teens. She had classical, straightforward overactivity of her thyroid gland due to Graves' disease. The history, the physical findings and the lab data left no doubt about the diagnosis. She had lost weight, had a voracious appetite, was sweaty, tired, conscious of her heart beating and a little short of breath.

A copy of my report to Dr Turner at that time had been sent to the patient so that she could learn about her illness and how it was proposed to treat her. Carbimazole, which suppresses hormone formation in the thyroid gland, had been recommended and after about six weeks of this a small dose of the thyroid hormone, thyroxine, would be added to prevent her from going the other way and becoming thyroid deficient. This conventional 'block-and-replace' regime, when given for a year or eighteen months, induces a permanent remission in about fifty per cent of patients. I had offered to see Mrs Nolan again in a year's time, or sooner if there were any problems, but there'd been no further communication from Dr Turner – until now.

At six o'clock I stepped out of the lift on to the landing of the third floor of the Wimpole Street Hospital. In the hallway the garish yellow, brown and black chequered carpet that extended down the corridor as far as the eye could see, induced a transient feeling of giddiness. In the distance Dr Turner was writing at the counter surrounding the nurses' station. He was a young GP in the Knightsbridge area of London and was unusual in having a higher degree in surgery. He had been a surgical registrar at his teaching hospital before deciding that life would be easier and he would more quickly become his own master and earn a better living if he went into general practice.

'After you saw her three years ago I prescribed the carbimazole and then added the thyroxine as you suggested,' Turner said. 'In three months she was much improved. Then her husband went to work in Texas, and he and Mrs Nolan disappeared. I didn't see her again until this morning; they'd flown back overnight from Houston. I'm surprised she made it; she's very ill.'

'What from?'

'The most uncontrolled thyrotoxicosis I've ever seen. Her husband said that she'd been persuaded by some American friends to go to a Chinese herbalist, who apparently has a great reputation in Houston. He stopped the carbimazole and thyroxine, and prescribed some herbal remedy which he guaranteed would put her right – permanently; you remember we could only promise a fifty-fifty cure. She was all right for a time, but then became increasingly unwell. She kept on with the herbalist – flatly refusing to see anyone else, her husband says. Eventually she became so weak she had to go to bed. The herbalist wouldn't visit her at home and with difficulty she was persuaded to go to some sort of Christian Science hospital. She got no better and finally her husband persuaded her to fly back to London to see me. I found...'

'Don't tell me. Let me see for myself.'

As soon as I saw Mrs Nolan, I remembered her because of her striking Titian hair. When first we'd met she was attractive, even beautiful, but now looked very different. She lay propped up in bed breathing fast, almost panting. She was so emaciated that she looked like a famine victim from Africa. Her prominent protruding eyes dominated her emaciated jaundiced face with its sunken cheeks and thin blue lips drawn back across lustreless dry teeth. She was so short of breath that it was a struggle for her to even talk.

'Don't tire yourself. Lie quietly and let me examine you.'

She certainly had severe overactivity of her thyroid gland with a fast irregular pulse and advanced heart failure with swelling due to fluid retention extending from her feet to halfway up her chest-wall. An X-ray showed an enormous heart and fluid surrounding both lungs.

During the ensuing discussion I tried to be gentle and as optimistic as possible under the circumstances. Afterwards, outside the room alone with the husband and John Turner, I said, 'The next few days are going to be critical. The fact that your wife is jaundiced is an index of the severity of her heart failure which is secondary to her overactive thyroid gland. If she gets through the next forty-eight hours or so, it's probable that with the right treatment she'll make a complete recovery.' I emphasised the word 'right' and then, after a pause, added, 'There's no place for herbalism or Christian Science in this situation, I'm afraid, but you already know that.'

Mr Nolan did – only too well. 'Elizabeth,' he explained, 'came under the spell of this man – this herbalist quack. She believed implicitly in him. She wouldn't listen to me, even when it was obvious she was getting worse. She's lost about forty-two pounds, nearly three stone.'

'We understand, of course,' John Turner said quietly. 'Despite the fluid retention, the oedema, she's lost rather more than that according to my scales.'

Together we organised a programme of emergency treatment.

On the way home from the hospital, I reflected on how all this could so easily have been avoided. Heart failure from untreated hyperthyroidism was almost a disease of the past. It very seldom happened nowadays – except when patients rejected the conventional because they did not understand, did not want to understand or, for some inexplicable reason, were afraid.

* * *

In the darkness I groped for the phone. 'Can you come – quickly?' asked Dr Turner. 'I'm sorry to call you...' I clambered out of bed, half-asleep; it was three o'clock in the morning.

She was dead when I got to the hospital. Mrs Nolan's Titian hair had been neatly combed, her eyes were closed, her sunken face turned to the ceiling, and her emaciated freckled arms and hands, with well manicured nails, lying palms down on the counterpane.

As I walked slowly and sadly down the steps of the entrance to the hospital into the stillness of the cold night air, I could not help sighing. 'Tragic,' I thought. 'So unnecessary. Awful for her, and even worse for her husband and their children.'

* * *

Many different terms – 'unorthodox', 'unconventional', 'alternative', 'fringe', 'natural', 'holistic' – have been used to describe methods of treating ill-health that differ from orthodox or conventional medicine. 'Unorthodox' and 'unconventional' are ambiguous, and 'alternative' is inappropriate because few of the unorthodox methods make a serious claim to replace conventional medicine in the treatment of all diseases. 'Complementary' is the best rubric because many patients, while attending their medical practitioner for conventional treatment, concurrently take complementary remedies which they may or may not tell their GP about.

In many countries there has been a resurgence of complementary medicine. In part this is due to the failure of orthodox medicine to meet public expectations and in part to patients becoming dissatisfied with their doctor and with the conventional. They feel, sometimes rightly, that their doctor does not take their complaint as seriously as they think he should, or that he fails to understand them, does not empathise with them or does not devote enough time to them. He fails to provide effective treatment for illnesses that defy modern therapeutic advances and which range from the serious, such as multiple sclerosis, to the minor, such as the irritating common cold. Patients are impatient and expect an instant cure; failing this, they may seek a magical one. Some people are alarmed by the technology of modern medicine and fearful of the real or imagined side-effects of many modern drugs. They are encouraged to seek help from the unconventional by advertisements or by friends who confide how successful the outcome has been but seldom mention and quickly forget the failures. Access to the unorthodox is easy and welcoming; the practitioner is courteous, gives individual attention, listens sympathetically, provides an explanation whether correct or not, offers hope of recovery or relief of symptoms and time is not at a premium.

Every generation has had its patent medicines and its quacks. A century ago iodine lockets were commonly worn to keep at bay a multitude of ills; during the last fifty years copper bracelets have been the fashion to prevent 'rheumatism'. The enhanced interest in complementary medicine today is reflected by the two and a half per cent of the population in the United Kingdom that make some 13 million visits a year to unorthodox practitioners, and in the USA almost a third of all adults do so annually. Conventional doctors may refer patients to medically qualified colleagues who have studied some form of complementary medicine or to those who, not medically qualified, practise some type of unorthodox medicine which is neither registered nor regulated in any way. Seventy years ago a doctor who referred a patient to an unqualified practitioner was in danger of being summoned before the disciplinary committee of the GMC, as described in *The Citadel*. Some conventionally-trained doctors turn to complementary techniques because of the despair invoked by repeated therapeutic failures, usually in not serious but nonetheless irritating diseases for which orthodox medicine is imperfect or even useless. Such symptoms as feeling run-down, tired or lacking energy are as often psychosomatic as caused by organic disease but some doctors still fail to recognise symptoms arising from psychological problems – a defect which usually lies more in their medical education than in themselves. In the face of recurrent therapeutic failure it is not surprising that the exasperated GP, who may lack scientific critique but is caring and dedicated, turns elsewhere for help. If the unorthodox works the first time, the self-confidence it brings is self-perpetuating. After a number of successes, rewarded by the patient's grateful thanks, the uncritical doctor becomes convinced of its efficacy and validity.

The unconventional types of treatment include acupuncture, aromatherapy, chiropracty, herbalism, homoeopathy, iridology, osteopathy, radionics and reflexology. The popularity of each varies from one country to another. Homoeopathy and acupuncture are more often used in England than in the USA where there is a greater interest in herbal medicine, perhaps because of their large American-Chinese population.

Patients who seek help from practitioners of complementary

239

medicine usually suffer from the same complaints – the most common being backache, anxiety, headache, arthritic and musculo-skeletal aches and pains, insomnia, depression, allergies of various types, digestive problems and feeling generally unwell. Even an experienced physician with plenty of time may find the cause of any of these difficult to unravel.

Most varieties of complementary medicine, with the exception of acupuncture and herbalism, have emerged in the last hundred years; many are of unsubstantiated efficacy and all are based on unscientific philosophies. Some make no scientific sense and therefore lack credibility. Effectiveness can only be judged by the scientific method using randomised, preferably double-blind, controlled trials that are rightly demanded in orthodox medicine.

Osteopathy is now legally recognised in the United Kingdom and governed by a statutory body, the General Osteopathic Council, which maintains a register of all osteopaths who are qualified by virtue of having achieved the required standards of education and competence. Such recognition does not necessarily imply that osteopathy can stand alone and cease to be complementary to orthodox medicine. It is not a universal panacea and should predominantly concern itself with disorders that arise as a result of disturbance of the bones, joints, ligaments, muscles and tendons. This was not the case when a bone-setter in the United States, Mr Still, the originator of osteopathy, propounded in 1876 that all diseases are caused by pressure on the arteries, mainly in the spine, because of structural anomalies in the joints. Mr Still had reason to be disenchanted with orthodox medicine; he had lost three of his children from meningitis.

Chiropractors have met with less official acceptance in Britain, although in certain conditions, such as backache, they can be as or more effective than orthodox practitioners. Their therapeutic objectives are more encompassing than in osteopathy, claiming success in the treatment of diabetes, cancer and heart diseases. All diseases, believed the originator of chiropracty, who was described as 'a magnetic healer', were the result of pressure on nerves due to malalignment of the vertebrae in the spine – a very different concept from that of osteopathy.

Nor can acupuncture be looked upon as an alternative to conventional medicine. The recent resurgence of interest in the West for this 2000-year-old Chinese technique largely dates from

240

President Nixon's visit to President Mao in 1970. In 1822 acupuncture had been banned in China by the Emperor and removed from the curriculum of the Imperial Medical College because he deemed it a bar to the progress of medicine. Mao reinstated acupuncture mainly for anaesthetic purposes to save spending money on modern anaesthetic equipment. Acupuncture plays a useful role in the relief of some varieties of pain, particularly musculoskeletal pain, and may also have a beneficial effect in nicotine and other addictive states in which a psychological component is prominent. Whether this benefit is due to the minor physiological changes that have been observed or to a placebo effect remains unclear. Certainly its ability to provide anaesthesia during surgical operations is the result of hypnosis, whether consciously or unconsciously practised by the acupuncturist, rather than the needles themselves.

Homoeopathy has no scientifically sustainable basis. The concept that 'like is cured by like' came from Samuel Hahnemann in 1800. Homoeopathists treat symptoms, not illnesses, by giving infinitesimally diluted remedies which have the great advantage of having no side-effects. Not surprisingly scientists are sceptical of the concept that like cures like; that if you feel you are going to be sick, a substance that itself induces nausea will relieve this symptom. They are even more sceptical of the unbelievable concept that the more a substance is diluted and shaken, the more potent it becomes, even if the dilution is carried to the point when not a molecule of the original substance remains. Nor have satisfactory controlled trials, confirmed by others, shown consistent therapeutic efficacy. Homoeopathists used to say that such trials could not be used because homoeopathic treatment had to be tailored not only to the symptoms (rather than the disease) but also to the individual patient. Nevertheless manufacturers promote homoeopathic medicines for specific diseases irrespective of the constitution of the patient. Most homoeopathic practitioners do not recommended their form of treatment for thyroid diseases, tuberculosis, cancer or benign enlargement of the prostate.

Herbalism has the undeserved image of being 'natural', pure and harmless when in fact herbal preparations contain all manner of substances, ranging from the safe to the toxic; they may be effective in some people but cause serious liver damage in others. Many modern drugs have herbal origins but they have been purified and standardised for human use.

At the far end of the spectrum lies reflexology, for which there is no scientific credibility, and aromatherapy, which is certainly relaxing but it remains unproven whether the different fragrances of the essential oils have specific therapeutic actions.

Iridology is a diagnostic tool as to some extent is radionics. Careful inspection of the iris of the eye is said to be capable of diagnosing the cause of all manner of symptoms. Certainly we learn a lot from examining the back of the eye, the retina, in patients with many diseases such as diabetes, high blood pressure, some infectious conditions and many intracranial disorders, but the iris...

Radionics involves the use of a black box decorated with knobs and dials. Inside the box the 'vibrations' or 'energy' is assessed in a drop of blood or some hair from a human or animal patient. The diagnosis is made from the rate of the vibrations and treatment given by broadcasting the corrected rate to the patient, human or animal, two or three times a day if necessary at a distance of several hundred miles. This device was invented by a Dr Abrams whose obituary in the *Journal of the American Medical Association* in 1924 pronounced him 'The Dean of the 20th century charlatans'.

These diverse, therapeutically improbable forms of treatment which produce beneficial effects in some patients all have something in common. They accentuate the placebo effect – the non-specific benefit that any treatment may engender. Often there are two placebo effects, one produced by the medicine, be it simply coloured water, and the other by the doctor. Practitioners of complementary medicine almost invariably have an unshakeable, almost Messianic belief in their system; they are sincere, committed and often charismatic – all of which enhances their placebo effect.

Those medically qualified doctors who in only a limited way adopt the unorthodox do not see themselves as imposters, swindlers, deceivers or cheats, and nor are they. Sadly not all practitioners who use the unorthodox have such worthy aspirations. Selling hope by making false claims of a certain cure is the hallmark of the charlatan, and a small number of the medical profession promote an ineffective, sometimes dangerous, form of treatment for which they charge exorbitant fees, suggesting that their deceit is financially motivated. Their charisma may sweep unsuspecting, desperate and gullible patients off their feet and convert them to vociferous public-relations protagonists – at least temporarily. Such a quack may have a long and successful innings, whether the potentially dangerous

242

treatment is the injection of ozone to improve well-being, or an unproven ineffective treatment for AIDs, or for a non-existent allergy which may be the alleged cause of every complaint under the sun. It is tragic when patients with some fatal illness search the world at great emotional and financial expense seeking help from such charlatans.

The public deserves better protection than it currently has. The GMC was originally founded, and the Medical Register instituted, to enable the public to distinguish qualified from unqualified practitioners. The GMC has no powers over those who are not medically qualified. Those who are, but use unorthodox methods, are immune unless a patient formally complains that the doctor has acted irresponsibly, made false claims for the efficacy of a particular form of treatment, or has failed to exercise a proper standard of professional care. The legal process for exposing useless or dangerous treatments is slow, difficult and expensive, and applies not to the method of treatment but only to the identified offending practitioner, who is sometimes exposed by the media acting on behalf of a patient or a group of patients.

23

Changes in Sexual Behaviour

The papers on the desk did not incite much enthusiasm. Routine medical examinations for life insurance are usually uninteresting, and the fee paid by the assurance companies is not generous considering the time it takes to do the examination and complete the proforma, even if some of us are a little slow or perhaps obsessionally thorough. Usually I decline the task unless for some special reason – and in this case there was.

The sum assured was £5 million and, since no single insurance company would wish to carry such a big risk, part of it was being shared with a re-insurance company to which I was a medical adviser. Seldom does a private individual insure himself for such a large sum; the annual premium costs too much. Rightly I guessed that the present applicant was being insured by his employers, but not many employees are worth £5 million at the age of seventy-two.

Mr Prentice walked into the consulting room in quick, short, almost dancing steps. He was dressed as of an earlier era – striped grey and black trousers, a black jacket and a white starched butterfly collar with a neat silver-coloured bow-tie. His face had an impish expression, and his thin bony hand gave mine a quick darting handshake.

He related his uneventful medical history briskly; his family history revealed nothing unusual. The examination showed nothing abnormal; the electrocardiogram and the urine analysis were normal. Mr Prentice was insurable at the standard rate for his age.

'Could I ask why your company is insuring you for such a large sum, Mr Prentice?' I asked.

'Of course. I joined the firm after I studied brewing at Birmingham

245

University. I rose to be their chief chemist and retired at the age of sixty-five. I live in St John's Wood in London with my wife. Our two daughters are married. My absorbing hobby is a vintage Rolls-Royce open tourer which I look after myself. To be honest I'm as good a mechanic as I am chemist. Every year the brewery gives a luncheon for its retired executives, an occasion that I much enjoy. Two years ago, during the meal, the new managing director told me how the brewery had made an agreement with an American company to manufacture and market their range of soft drinks in the United Kingdom. The venture had not proved a success; the sales of quinine-water and dry ginger-ale had been most disappointing. I suggested that perhaps this was because the mixers were formulated for the North American palate and were much too sweet for over here. So they enticed me back.

'It took about a year to reformulate the tonic-water to the British palate. Then it had to be test-marketed – in the South East of England. It was a great success and the sales graph shows a continuing upward trend. Now I'm reformulating the dry ginger-ale. Such are the potential profits that the brewery seem to think I'm worth a great deal of money to them.' He laughed.

A year later, encouraged by the satisfactory report to the insurance company, Mr Prentice telephoned to ask if he could have an annual check-up to be charged to his own account. For the next few years he came regularly and I shared in his success and enjoyment of life. Mr Prentice brought a photograph of his ancient Rolls-Royce and called attention to the handbrake rising through its ratchet on the off-side running-board. The dry ginger-ale was selling well and now he was reformulating the American company's ginger-beer.

When he came at the age of seventy-eight Mr Prentice was somewhat subdued; he had something on his mind but despite tactful delving I couldn't discover what it was. As often happens under these circumstances it was not until Mr Prentice was leaving that he hesitated at the door of the consulting room.

'There's a little matter I'd like your advice on,' he said as he turned and sat down again. 'Is it all right for me at my age to have ... er ... to have sexual intercourse?'

He then explained his concern. 'Fifty years ago my closest friend died – suddenly and prematurely. I was his sole executor and I had to look after the affairs of his young childless widow; she lives in Petersfield. Every three months I used to drive there in

246

my old Rolls-Royce, and would arrive at noon. The young widow and I went through her accounts – her pension and stocks and shares, the council rates, the telephone bill – before lunch, and left income-tax matters until the afternoon. Before I drove back to London at four o'clock she always gave me a cup of Earl Grey tea and two macaroons.

'As the years went by, she managed her financial affairs so well that there was less and less for me to do. I only needed to go down twice a year but you know how it is...' Mr Prentice dropped his voice. 'We'd finish the accounts before lunch.' He paused, took a shallow breath and went on, 'We got into the ... er ... habit of going to ... er ... bed in the afternoon; it seemed the natural thing to do. Before driving home I always take a cup of Earl Grey tea and two macaroons.' He did not smile. 'I'm going to Petersfield next week. D'you think it will be all right – safe at my age? I wouldn't like to disappoint her but... I love my wife – we've been married nearly sixty years – and I wouldn't like her or my daughters to know.'

'Of course not.' Nor did I smile. 'I'm sure it'll be perfectly all right.'

Mr Prentice's face broke into a gentle smile; then he rose briskly from the chair and shook hands again before leaving.

It was not a matter we referred to directly on Mr Prentice's subsequent visits; I simply enquired if from time to time he was having a cup of Earl Grey tea and two macaroons.

*　*　*

Civilisation has brought many benefits but one price to be paid for the advantages of living in a modern society is that some rules of sexual behaviour are necessary for the good of the community as a whole. The pleasurable sensations associated with sexual intercourse are not essential to reproduction and during the evolutionary process appear to have been heightened and refined so that courting and orgastic satisfaction are enjoyed by all higher mammals. If human beings were allowed an untrammelled sexual appetite, the birth rate and the population would be liable to exceed the community's territorial, financial and food resources. Venereal disease might spread so widely as to endanger the future health of a hedonistic society. Without loving dedicated parents to look after them too many babies

247

are likely to become a burden on society. Certainly children without a family fare less well than those with one, and there is evidence that later in life they are more likely to threaten the safety of persons and property. Society cannot manage without some organising principles and, in the past, strictures and controls on sexual behaviour stemmed largely from Judaeo-Christian laws and customs which were more related to social stability than to religious doctrine.

Since the end of the nineteenth century, major changes have taken place in the sexual mores of our society. These are less closely correlated with the earlier age of sexual maturity in girls and boys than to changes in societal attitudes and advances in contraception. The depth of religious commitment has declined and the moral principles of Christian and Victorian teaching eroded. Sexual expression has now become separated from its reproductive function; marriage is no longer a necessary precondition to having sexual intercourse; and sex before marriage is virtually universal in western society.

Improved condoms and the oral contraceptive pill are, apart from sterilisation, the most effective methods of birth control ever devised. Television has enhanced knowledge of how other people think, live and behave. In both World Wars I and II strictures on personal behaviour were undermined by the largely unspoken but widespread reassuring fatalism expressed as, 'We're here today and gone tomorrow' or 'If it's got your number on it...' In World War II hostilities were not confined to the armed forces; invasion, enemy occupation and above all repeated air-raids, heralded by wailing sirens, brought the war into the home of every civilian. Husbands and boyfriends were sent overseas; wives and girlfriends were drafted to factories, the land army or the women's forces. Many people experienced three very potent emotions – loneliness, unhappiness and fear of dying.

The weekend tryst of a girl and her boyfriend on a forty-eight-hour pass was shared by millions of war-weary listeners to the wireless as the popular dance bands of the day played and their female crooners sang 'That Lovely Weekend' with its catchy melody and its poignant, if trite but well understood, lyric:

Thank you so much for that lovely weekend.
Those two days of heaven you helped me to spend.
The thrill of your kiss as you stepped off the train,
The smile on your face like the sun after rain.

248

To mark the occasion we went out to dine.
Remember the laughter, the music, the wine?
The drive in the taxi when midnight had flown,
And breakfast next morning? We two were alone.

And now you have gone dear, this letter I pen.
My heart travels with you 'til we meet again.
Keep smiling, my darling, and someday we'll spend
A lifetime as sweet as that lovely weekend.

Had chemists and endocrinologists designed the oral contraceptive pill earlier or the condom been made more widely available, there might have been fewer than the 2 million illegitimate babies born in Great Britain during those war years. Although the non-use of contraception at first intercourse has steadily declined, the number of illegitimate babies born to young girls increases annually in this country.

The prevalence of matrimonial infidelity in married couples varies widely in different cultures and communities. The biological and psychological factors leading to adultery seem unlikely to have altered over the years but today's social attitudes, improved contraception and more frequent opportunistic encounters contribute to its increase. The influence of the media has played its part; in the past the press paid scant attention to such personal matters but now is intent upon revealing the details, where possible the most intimate ones, of the extramarital encounters of those in the public eye. More than a third of all marriages in the United Kingdom end in divorce and about half in the United States, where reputedly half the population are weekly churchgoers. In 1989 adultery was the legally stated grounds for only a third of divorces in England, taking second place to the more favoured 'unreasonable behaviour' as the stated reason in half.

Promiscuity used to be considered the prerogative of the male, although in past centuries it was not unknown for a woman, after ten years of an infertile or unconsummated marriage, to bear as many as five or more children – in some instances each discreetly fathered by different men – without apparent perturbation of her husband or her social milieu. Today it is no surprise that extramarital liaisons are commonly sought by women. Feminists have made their case: women are as libidinous as men and have an equal right to sexual freedom. In 1989 sixty per cent of decrees were granted to women on the grounds of their husband's infidelity and forty per cent to men on grounds of their wife's.

The frequency of extra-marital liaisons is as variable as the number of partners may be. The infidelity may occur only once or twice with the same or a different person; or it may constitute a permanent or semi-permanent relationship within a continuing marriage. Men, particularly those who are separated from their wife, divorced or widowed and aged between 25 and 45, are more likely to become habitual philanderers than women, although there are some notable exceptions.

The incidence of casual sexual intercourse, so firmly frowned upon in the past and which, according to the survey, *Sexual Behaviour in Britain*, is still disapproved of by thirty-five per cent of men and sixty-two per cent of women, is unknown. The commonest cause of casual sexual activity is a sudden overwhelming mutual attraction culminating in a one-night stand often precipitated by the disinhibiting effects of alcohol in a pub or at an office party or at a conference in some foreign sunny clime. Although longer relationships rarely spring from such encounters, more durable and usually more emotionally traumatic is the relationship that develops from shared intellectual interests and prolonged proximity in a business organisation, in politics or among the professions working in a hospital or lawyer's office.

Although unreasonable behaviour or adultery may be the declared legal reason for divorce, nearly always there is long-standing matrimonial disharmony which stems, so psychiatrists say, from a 'serious failure of communication' between husband and wife. This amounts to an inability or an unwillingness to foster common interests and talk to each other, or failure to develop a mutually satisfying sexual rapport. The late Lord Justice Sir Roger Ormrod, a wise and outstanding man who was qualified in both medicine and the law, once pronounced, 'It takes three to make adultery'. The significance of this statement is seldom perceived, let alone admitted, by the injured party. Now that women are credited with hitherto unacknowledged sexual rights and desires, the responsibility for mutual sexual happiness must be shared equally by both partners. It is reassuring to learn from *Sexual Behaviour in Britain* published in 1994 that for eighty per cent of the population the marital ideal remained a heterosexual union with a single partner and that all age groups disapprove of infidelity within marriage.

Sexual activity in old age is governed by both physiological and psychological factors. In women the menopause, heralded by the cessation of the menstrual cycle, is almost invariably accompanied by a reduction if not a total loss in her libido. Well aware of this change, she has to adapt to and accommodate her husband's sexual demands which may decrease more gradually over the years.

In the male, sexual interest often persists and the level of this persistence is usually determined by his previous sexual activity. Many men maintain their virility until the age of sixty or seventy. Not surprisingly problems may arise in male-female sexual relationships. After the menopause loss of libido and of vaginal lubrication makes intercourse unattractive if not physically painful for women. Oestrogen replacement therapy may improve this situation but many women find that vaginal lubrication is necessary. Some women find this unsatisfactory and those of a liberal disposition find it more satisfactory for both parties to masturbate their husband or practice fellatio.

24

Delivery of Health Care

The snow in Austria was particularly plentiful in 1980 and I stamped my ski-boots on the threshold of Haus Hummel to clean them before pushing open the heavily studded door that led to the cellar. Grasping the ornate wrought-iron handrail with a gloved hand I stomped carefully down the steep, wet and slippery tiled stairs. At the bottom, pushing open a second door padded with sound-proofing green baize, a babble of voices loud above the strains of a zither greeted me. The *Tanzbar* was crowded and the wooden banquettes surrounding three sides of the tables were packed with people and littered with anoraks, gloves and woollen hats. The *Keller* was always full after four-thirty when the ski-lifts stopped running. On a podium set against the far wall Fritz Hümmel sat behind his electronically amplified zither playing effortlessly with only an occasional glance at the strings – his face set in a smile as he watched the handful of dancers in their ski-boots clumping around in the centre of the floor.

'Hi, we're over here.' I peered through the subdued lighting and haze of cigarette smoke to see who was calling. 'Over here.'

I waved a hand in acknowledgement and pushed towards the bar to first get a drink. Protecting the stein of beer and its head of froth with a hand, I manoeuvred my way to the table.

David Evans, the senior orthopaedic surgeon at Westminster Hospital, greeted me. 'You are just the person I wanted to see. Come and join us. You know these people?' He introduced three other orthopaedic surgeons, all members of the Orthopaedic Ski Club that met for a week every February in the neighbouring village of Zürs. Membership of the Club was limited to twenty plus their wives, and each morning from nine to ten and each evening before

253

dinner the group discussed ski fractures and injuries. The rest of the day they spent on the slopes.

'D'you know Klaus Garvin?' David Evans asked.

'One of the doctors in Zürs? Not personally, but I know of him.'

'Exactly. He's got heart trouble. I don't understand that kind of thing,' David laughed deprecatingly, 'but he's got some sort of congenital heart disease and now at the age of – I suppose he's about forty-five or fifty, he's short of breath and can't ski any more. He needs expert advice; I told him you'd be here this week and next, and I was sure you wouldn't mind taking a look at him.'

'Of course.'

As the only orthopaedic surgeon in the area of Lech and Zürs in the Austrian Vorarlberg, Klaus Garvin was well-known to his British colleagues who had made him an honorary member of their Club. Whenever clinical commitments allowed, Klaus attended their meetings.

After World War II, when Zürs was being developed as a major ski resort, Klaus had been invited to become the head doctor there. Realising that many of his future patients would be British or American and, while waiting for his house and the connecting ten-bedded hospital to be built on land given him by the village council, Klaus had worked as an unpaid supernumerary senior registrar at the Royal Orthopaedic Hospital at Stanmore in England and for another six months at the Beth Israel Hospital in Boston. The substantial financial outlay had been rewarded. Klaus had learnt Anglo-American surgical techniques but, more important, had made himself known to the leading orthopaedic surgeons in England and the USA by attending their congresses and meetings. When an American broke his leg in Zürs and telephoned home for advice, it was reassuring to be told that he could not be in better hands than those of Klaus Garvin.

That evening over the phone I introduced myself to Dr Garvin and arranged to ski over from Lech the next day to see him at ten o'clock.

It was snowing hard when I rang the front-door bell of the little hospital in Zürs. Dr Garvin, dressed in immaculately laundered white linen trousers and a white jacket with a high collar buttoned neatly round his neck, opened the door.

'It's good of you to come in this awful weather.' He spoke English with hardly the trace of an accent. We shook hands. I guessed we were about the same age. The Austrian doctor was stockily built with a square rubicund face that projected confidence. He looked robustly healthy.

'Please come upstairs. If you don't mind I'd like my wife, Hilda, to hear what you say about me so may I show you to the private part of the house?'

Klaus led the way to a large upstairs sitting room furnished with antique painted Austrian furniture and unwieldy over-stuffed sofas and chairs. Frau Garvin carried in a silver tray with cups and a gold-plated cafetière.

As we drank the coffee Dr Garvin talked about his problem. 'I first learnt I had a heart murmur when I was a medical student at Innsbruck University just before the war. Because I was symptom-free and perfectly fit, nobody did anything about it – in those days there was nothing anyone could do anyway.' Klaus smiled. 'That murmur probably saved my life.'

'Really?'

'In the war I was a doctor in the army and scheduled to go to Russia – to the seige of Stalingrad. Everyone posted to the Eastern Front had to be a hundred per cent fit. Because of my heart murmur I was given a home posting. In 1950 I came here; in the last two years I've become increasingly short of breath. I'm a good skier but I can't ski any more; I'm too short of wind. That's all there is to it.'

There were other questions that needed asking. Klaus Garvin had had slight swelling of his ankles; his appetite was less good; he could not manage heavy suitcases; he slept better with three or four pillows.

Hilda remained behind when Klaus took me downstairs to the professional part of the house to examine him. The cardiac murmur was characteristic and there were signs of early heart failure. He produced an electrocardiogram he had done on himself and also a chest X-ray he'd taken.

We went back upstairs so Hilda could hear what I had to say. I spoke slowly, choosing the words with care because Hilda's English was not as good as her husband's and she was not medically qualified. Furthermore Klaus Garvin was an orthopaedic surgeon and might have forgotten all he'd learnt as a medical student about congenital heart disease.

'Dr Garvin, you've got an atrial septal defect – a so-called hole

255

in the heart – which you were born with.' I went into more detail about the anatomy of the lesion before concluding, 'There's only one thing to do. You should have an operation to close the hole.'

Klaus had anticipated this. 'Where shall I go? Money is really no object. Do I go to the National Heart Hospital in London, to the Mayo Clinic or to Houston?'

I prevaricated. 'I'll telephone you tomorrow when I've had time to think about that.' Half an hour later after we'd drunk a glass of schnapps and eaten some of Hilda's delicious *kuchen*, I walked into the sunshine. It had stopped snowing and two lifts took me from Zürs to the top of the Madloch Joch. From there it was a lovely run in the fresh light snow back to Lech. Walking along the road towards the Berghof Hotel I wondered where Klaus Garvin should go. As far as I knew the results in England and the United States were equally good. Chauvinistically I rather favoured the National Heart Hospital in London; it would certainly be cheaper than flying to America and the hospital charges would be less.

One of the attractions of Lech is the river that runs through the village. As I walked beside it, past the old covered wooden bridge, I saw a vaguely familiar face coming towards me carrying his skis. I smiled and he smiled back. We stopped.

'You're ... you're Harry Scott, the cardiac surgeon from the Montreal General,' I said in belated recognition. We had met several years before when I had been awarded a six-week travelling professorship that had taken me from Quebec to Vancouver via Montreal, Kingston, Toronto, Ottawa and Calgary. We chatted about mutual friends and skiing in Lech where Harry had not been before.

What prompted me I don't know – one's brain sometimes works without conscious direction – but I heard myself saying, 'You wouldn't like to see a patient tomorrow, would you? It's a colleague – the chief doctor in Zürs.'

Harry was slightly taken aback but I explained the problem and we arranged to ski over together the next day.

What a bit of luck, I thought as I continued to the Berghof Hotel. The responsibility for deciding where Klaus should go for surgery would be Harry's and he was better qualified to make the decision.

Next morning we took the *Seilbahn* from Lech to the top of the Rüfikopf and skied to Zürs. Harry Scott went like the wind and, when I pointed out he was a little too fast for me, learnt that he had been a member of the McGill University ski team.

The atmosphere in the Garvin's sitting room was tenser than the day before. Hilda offered us coffee on arrival and then sat anxiously fidgeting while we talked. Harry listened to Klaus's heart and studied the chest X-ray and electrocardiogram. Finally he sat down and beckoned Hilda to draw her chair closer. He rubbed his chin with the palm of his hand as he spoke.

'If I were you, Klaus, and I was adrift floating on a raft in the middle of the Atlantic,' he began, 'I'd paddle towards Europe rather than to North America. When I got to Europe, d'you know what I'd do? I'd go to a city not a hundred kilometres from here – to Zurich. In Zurich is a Swedish heart surgeon, Dr Senning, who's had more experience of atrial septal defects than anyone else in the world.'

Early in April as soon as the season finished Klaus had his operation in Zurich. He fulfilled the prophecy that doctors are liable to have uncommon postoperative complications but, when the snow started to fall again in Zürs in mid-November, he and Hilda returned from their summer home in the South of France ready for the new season. He was well enough to ski but his heart had suffered some long-standing damage.

Unusual and unconventional as the delivery of health care was in this case, the outcome was satisfactory, but it would have been better if the operation had been done years earlier when the surgical technique for repair of atrial septal defects had already been perfected.

* * *

It is not surprising that since its inception the NHS has had to adapt to many changes; it is ironic that in part it is a victim of its own success. Some changes have been made gradually; in the 1960s, for example, more emphasis was rightly given to primary GP care. Formal training for GPs was introduced and improvements made in their remuneration and the funding of their premises; closer links were forged between them and the community health services. The founding of the Royal College of General Practitioners was an important step in raising standards.

The birth of the NHS coincided with advances in the medical sciences that have been more rapid and more prolonged than during any comparable period in the past. From this scientific revolution

257

have sprung new clinical specialities, new and more expensive technologies and drugs, and new methods – preventive and therapeutic – for the relief of all manner of diseases. The reduction in mortality has been particularly striking in the perinatal period and in infancy so that many more of the young survive to adult life. This increase in longevity has been apparent for many years and the number of people aged sixty-five and over had increased by a million or more by 2000. Many of them will become ill, which will cost the NHS more, and in later years they may become infirm and need residential care. In the last fifteen years or so the number of people aged over eighty-five in residential and nursing homes has doubled.

New effective treatments for previously incurable diseases have added to the costs. Whereas forty years ago Hodgkin's disease, or leukaemia, was fatal, now many patients are cured – and live on to die of some other disease. Today the middle-aged man who develops early signs of coronary artery disease or has a non-fatal heart attack is likely as a result of sophisticated investigations and expensive highly-skilled surgery to survive and live another twenty profitable years – time in which to fall victim to other diseases and invoke further health costs. No longer, despite lengthening waiting lists, do patients with osteoarthritis of the hip suffer pain and increasing disability until they are confined to a wheelchair; they have their hip replaced and may live another fifteen or so pain-free years before the prosthesis needs replacing or they have a non-fatal stroke and linger on. Patients in every walk of life and with all manner of diseases have increased expectations and so also, on their behalf, do their doctors. 'We can,' as a President of the Royal College of Physicians wrote in 1994, 'do more and more for patients who increasingly expect more and more to be done for them.' Not only do people expect to benefit from the new medicine, rightly they protest when there are prolonged delays in receiving it. Patients with kidney failure, which forty years ago was inevitably fatal, are treated by expensive renal dialysis three times a week for many years in the hope of receiving a renal transplant and in some cases the prospect of a near-normal life expectancy. Since the early fifties a sequence of increasingly effective drugs have been developed for the control of high blood pressure which previously brought a heavy toll from heart failure and strokes.

Patients are more litigious so that some doctors feel compelled to practise defensive medicine. There seems no other explanation for the increase in the number of Caesarean sections which has risen to around fifteen per cent in England, significantly more than the ten per cent elsewhere in Europe but still much lower than the twenty to twenty-five per cent in the more litigious USA. The operation may be carried out because the obstetrician fears he or she may be sued if the infant is born with brain damage despite the fact, difficult or impossible to prove in a court of law, that often the brain damage was present before labour even started.

The pace of medicine has accelerated greatly. The average length of hospital stay has fallen from about fifty days in 1948 to about ten days in 1990 and is now even less. The total number of NHS beds is half what it was at its peak in 1960 despite an increased population; the number of available beds for acute cases is now *per caput* the lowest in Europe, yet the total number of patients treated has risen annually. The pressure for speed conflicts with the rightly agreed policy that consultants and GPs should make more time available to talk to their patients who must be encouraged to participate fully in the decisions that concern their treatment. Shorter hospital stays – sometimes painfully too short – make the teaching of medical students more difficult and impede the training of junior doctors.

These changes have had far-reaching effects other than financial. The hours that junior hospital doctors work have become punitively long. Sleep deprivation and pressure on time may adversely affect the quality of care they give, their ability to respond appropriately to emergencies and their capacity to learn. Long hours and frequent night calls, particularly involving patients with an uncertain diagnosis or who are in pain, afraid, hostile or dying are taxing to any young doctor even when given adequate support and supervision. Nor in many hospitals are their working and living conditions satisfactory; quarters are often sparse, cold and uncomfortable and the food, particularly at the end of a long stint of being on call, of poor aesthetic and nutritional quality. Everyone agrees that, despite the cost implications, their hours of work must be reduced if the evident stress that half of them suffer is to be avoided. They lose the enthusiasm and self-confidence that came when they qualified and may insulate themselves emotionally from their patients' needs. About a quarter become depressed, their marriages are threatened, they become fearful and isolated; some even regret having ever entered the profession. Today the demands are much greater than

259

forty years ago because medicine is more complex and the throughput of patients much faster. More time is spent on writing notes, filling in forms and chasing the results of X-ray and laboratory investigations. Of course experience increases with the workload but the pressures often crowd out the expected educational advantages.

In 1991 it was agreed that the number of hours a junior hospital doctor worked should be reduced to a maximum of eighty-three per week with a goal of seventy-two hours in 1994, which has not yet been achieved. But who is going to do their work? To increase the number of junior doctors is not the answer because they cannot remain juniors for the rest of their professional lives; there must be future prospects for them in the senior ranks. More consultants at increased cost is the agreed solution, not only to spread the workload and improve the training of the junior doctors but also to make good the serious dearth of consultants that exists in many areas. Nationwide specialist services are inadequate; per head of population Britain has fewer specialists in many specialities – neurology, cardiology, endocrinology and vascular surgery in particular – than any other country in the western world. The money for more consultants has been promised but the implementation has yet to come.

Successive governments have been aware of the financial implications that advances in medical practice have brought and have tried to absorb them without committing more than a small additional fraction of the nation's gross national product to health care. Understandably the Department of Health has sought economies from administrators and from doctors. Over the years management of the NHS has undergone many changes – decentralisation to the periphery followed by Whitehall centralisation and back again, more and then fewer tiers of management, smaller geographical regions and larger ones, replacement of unpaid Boards of Governors by salaried chairmen and remunerated board members – all in search of greater efficiency and economy. Responsibility for the care of many sick people, particularly those discharged from mental hospitals and the elderly infirm, has devolved on local authorities without movement of sufficient funds for them to meet this commitment.

As a profession we are aware that some of our practices are neither efficient nor cost-effective. Regional differences in the rate of hysterectomies, for example, must mean either that in some areas the operation is being carried out unnecessarily or in others

260

it is not being done often enough. Understandably politicians strive to reduce expenditure on health care with the always overriding vote-winning objective of reducing income tax. Originally medicines were free but today the government nets some £500 million a year by imposing prescription charges which are beyond the purse of many low-income earners, particularly if the patient requires several medicines, and despite many patients having diseases that exempt them from making any personal payment. No longer is 'the cradle to grave' ethos honoured to those who were brought up to believe that a lifetime of paying taxes would provide social insurance in old age and infirmity. The public would be less unhappy if this sea change had been openly admitted, and guidance and incentives developed for self-insurance.

The apparently unlimited demand for medical care, increasing dissatisfaction by patients and soaring costs led in 1989 to the introduction of a new commercial stratagem designed to save money and improve efficiency. An internal market was established in which hospitals became 'providers' to compete with each other for the payment of their services by 'purchasers', the local authorities and fundholding GPs. Such an internal market artificially splits the health service into hospitals with their professional staff and into the community and GP services, to the detriment of their paramount common interest – the care of the patient. Commercialisation puts increased emphasis on producing the 'goods' (the number of patients treated) and sacrifices quality for quantity. No two patients with the same disease are identical; the basic treatment may be the same for both but it has to be tailored to the individual whose needs cannot be standardised in the same way as a mass-produced product.

Purchasers may be reluctant to pay the additional costs when their patients are transferred from a local hospital to a more distant one where the best treatment, particularly for uncommon diseases or those requiring 'high tech', is available. This has had an adverse effect on teaching hospitals in which lie the unique opportunity and tradition for close collaboration between scientists and clinicians.

There are profound differences between running a business and operating a service. Whether the new method of organising the NHS will prove financially advantageous and secure maximum effective use of limited resources without reducing the quality of care is already in doubt. New hospital managers have been recruited, some at salaries of £75,000–£100,000 per annum; new assistant

261

managers and secretaries have been followed by clerical staff who submit accounts for the treatment of patients to the purchasers. Formerly the administration of a hospital constituted some five per cent of its running costs but this seems likely to reach twenty per cent – an extra cost which is piously misrepresented as 'increased expenditure on health'. Money may be saved by increased transfer of care to the community and to GPs with a reduction in the use of expensive hospital services. For part of the time some consultants may move from their hospital to see patients in GPs' surgeries but this may prove an uneconomical use of an expensive resource.

Also of major consequence is the adverse effect of the internal market on clinical research. Trials of new drugs and methods of diagnosis and treatment, so essential to progress, often involve a longer stay in hospital, more outpatient clinic visits and additional investigations, all of which increase the costs that the purchaser is understandably reluctant to pay. One major step forward was the setting up by the NHS in 1991 of a department of operational research and development so essential to any major organisation, not least to one with the largest workforce in Europe.

All is not as Dr Andrew Manson in *The Citadel* would wish. Nostrums of unproven efficacy, granted a licence by the Department of Health because of 'traditional usage and bibliographies', are still widely advertised, even on television. A few medically qualified practitioners continue to promote scientifically unproven treatments, often for serious diseases and usually at high cost – a matter seemingly of more concern to the patient's medical insurance company, if the patient has one, than to the GMC which has only recently devised procedures for dealing with practitioners who fail to give satisfactory service, short of 'serious professional misconduct'.

Perhaps we need another Dr Cronin to alert the public to the present defects in our health care system. There is a need, which the profession as a whole is addressing, to improve performance and make postgraduate education a continuing process until retirement. We must show that additional funds will be used for proven effective treatments. A very few specialists and GPs give a less than optimal performance because they have allowed themselves to become out of date, are themselves sick, or lose enthusiasm for their work because of the excessive demands that they deem are made upon them. But the overwhelming problem is the cost of financing the NHS. Better health care for less money by improved efficiency is a laudable and perfectly reasonable governmental aim; savings are already being made by patients spending a shorter time in hospital and by appropriate surgical patients being treated as day cases. Such economies are not enough to meet the surging rise in costs which are inevitable in a society with an increasingly ageing population who therefore suffer more ill-health. The government's programme to improve the health of the nation and thereby reduce the sickness rate is laudable but of unproven – some think unlikely – efficacy; it may prove as unobtainable as the spurious belief held by the founders of the NHS that after the new service had been operating for a few years and the backlog of ill-health repaired, there would in the future be less sickness in the population.

Only six per cent of our gross national product is spent on the NHS, less than other major developed countries in Europe. The difficulty of matching seemingly limited resources to the demands has led to the widely accepted belief that there can never be enough money for the health service. But we must not forget that good health and quick effective treatment are highly treasured and that to the people of Britain the introduction of the NHS was the single most important piece of social legislation introduced in the last century. To many it remains a much prized jewel in the national crown. If income tax has to be reduced to curry political favour, would the electorate be averse to paying a separate health tax applied solely to an NHS that followed the original tenets laid down by its founders? Without more funding the public will suffer as more arbitrary rationing is introduced which is most likely to be directed at older patients, and the medical profession's morale and dedication to the NHS will decline as facilities to help their patients are curtailed.

25

Life Expectancy and Victorian Ill-health

'But why have you let this happen?' Martin Monckton asked belligerently and sat more upright in his chair beside the desk. He was more frightened than angry. His face, rubicund at the best of times, was puce and his hair uncharacteristically dishevelled. He made a conscious effort to control himself.

Before I could answer, he continued. 'Don't forget I first came to you more than thirty years ago. After due diligence I chose you because you were a bit younger than me; I thought we'd grow old together and you'd look after me.'

'I hope I have,' I said quietly. 'May I remind you that your father died at the age of fifty-eight of a heart attack and so did your grandfather. You've done more than three score years and ten – better than either of them. You've had a good run and the end isn't just around the corner as you seem to think.'

'I've tried to stick to a low-cholesterol diet and I quit smoking years ago. Why didn't you put me on garlic pills?'

Martin was an assiduous reader of prophetic unsubstantiated medical reports in the newspapers which he cut out and sent to me with a compliment slip.

'Garlic pills? Because there's no convincing evidence they do any good.'

'Or those fish-oil capsules? There was an article about them in the *Financial Times* the other day explaining why the eskimos didn't get heart disease.'

'You sent it to me. Fish-oil may be okay for lowering triglycerides but your triglycerides have always been normal.'

As Martin paused to gather more ammunition, some of his life history passed through my mind. He was a successful businessman and farmer. He was happily married although he sometimes liked to complain he wasn't and would pointedly quote lines from 'Why Can't Women be Like Us', the song so scornfully sung by Rex Harrison in *My Fair Lady*. He and his rich American wife had two grown-up children, a son and a daughter who were happy and relatively trouble-free. In 1960 he had decided to build in East Anglia a large country house 'suitable for a gentleman', the like of which had not been built this century, he boasted. He took two years off work in the City because nobody else could be trusted to supervise its construction in every detail. The neo-Georgian mansion was indeed magnificent but hardly was it finished, when strolling round the newly landscaped garden, Martin saw, on the far side of a ha-ha, a group of men on the boundary of his property. They were surveyors planning a new motorway. For several years he engaged in an expensive legal battle with the Minister of Transport but lost his appeal and the motorway was built; he did not brood over his defeat. Later he suffered grave losses at Lloyds. Nor had his medical life been without incident.

'Look,' I said. 'Your high blood pressure's been beautifully controlled for thirty years. This has retarded the hardening of your arteries but atherosclerosis is an inevitable part of the ageing process and caused you no problems until a couple of years ago.'

'Well, yes, you did manage that quite well,' conceded Martin graciously.

'Thank you. May I remind you that you were convinced that the pain you then had in your buttock was coming from your hip or your back? You had a consultation in the bar of your golf club and off you went to, admittedly, a perfectly respectable osteopath but three months later you were no better.'

'That wasn't the osteopath's fault – not his line of country, old boy. I had a blocked artery in the pelvis. When finally I came to you, you diagnosed it quickly enough.'

'Yes, once you deigned to come it wasn't difficult to diagnose.'

'I liked that South African bloke who unblocked it with a balloon.' Martin laughed. 'Ha, what a character he is. Did the angioplasty under a local so I could watch on a television screen.'

'Well, there you are. You don't have much to complain about.'

'Except that I can't walk round the farm now without having to stop every three or four hundred yards. Don't know which leg's the worst; one day the pain comes first in one calf and the next in the other.'

266

'How much does it really incommode you? You still shoot?'

'Yes, but I can't walk over plough – anyway, everyone goes by Land Rover nowadays. What are you going to do about it?'

'Your South African pal has looked at the new X-rays, the angiograms, and says he can't help. You haven't got a nice short segment of artery that needs unblocking. The arteries high up in both thighs are narrowed in several places. This time you'll need major surgery but I must warn you it's not only your leg arteries that are furred up; they are much the same everywhere.'

Martin was downcast. 'And you let this happen.'

'You were forty when we first met. Your trouble probably started years ago because of your genes – remember your father and his father. We were only just beginning to learn about cholesterol and probably it's important in only some patients. As a child you used to smother your breakfast cereal with cream, you told me…'

'It was porridge.'

'All right then, porridge. We thought cigarettes only caused cancer; now we know about their deleterious effect on arteries. Don't forget your inheritance; you've got to choose your parents very carefully!' I didn't smile at the corny joke.

Martin seemed mollified. 'All right,' he said, 'I'll just have to soldier on, I suppose, until the operation. Damn'd nuisance. I suppose I'll eventually die of a heart attack or a stroke, won't I?'

I said nothing.

'Well, won't I?' Martin insisted.

'Yes, you probably will. We've all got to die of something.'

'All very well for you to talk; never had anything wrong have you?' Martin's anger dissipated. He stood up and thumped me on the shoulder. 'All right, old boy. Thanks a lot. Fix it all up, will you? Come and have lunch with me at White's one day; I'll give you a ring.'

I tidied up the pile of notes and packed them into my attaché case.

Sister came in to hurry me out of the consulting room which somebody else was waiting to use. 'Look forward to seeing you next week,' she said cheerfully.

'I'm afraid I won't be here next week.' I hesitated in the doorway. 'Not in again for about six weeks, Sister.'

'Lovely to have a proper holiday like that, isn't it? Going skiing?'

'No, as a matter of fact I'm going to have a coronary bypass operation tomorrow,' I confided quietly.

Sister was changing the paper sheet on the examination couch and not listening. 'That's nice, isn't it?' she said.

* * *

Everyone has a unique biological inheritance – unless you have an identical twin – and a less unique environmental background. Knowledge of your ancestry gives some idea of what diseases you may be heir to and what your life expectancy is likely to be – assuming you escape an unpredictable demise in an accident or war. My forbearers had a much harder life in a much less healthy environment than I have. My great-grandfather (1803–1878) was the son of a Shropshire farmer who early in the Industrial Revolution became involved in the iron trade and in 1802 moved to the Black Country where he started a business that was to flourish for 150 years.

The Black Country is not defined geographically nor does it appear on an Ordinance Survey map. It has no county or urban boundaries. People know vaguely that it is somewhere in the Midlands. In fact it's shaped like a lop-sided rectangle, mainly in Staffordshire with a small segment in Worcestershire. Within the area are some major industrial towns, and certain trades became associated with certain towns and still are. Walsall is famous for its brassware and leather goods whereas Willenhall is renowned for its locks, keys and hinges of all shapes and sizes. Once described as the workshop of Britain, the Black Country used to be synonymous with smoke, grime and fog. Its essential assets at the beginning of the Industrial Revolution were coal and iron ore.

In 1814 my great-grandfather, William, at the age of ten decided 'ignorantly', as he later admits in his autobiography, to go to work rather than continue his schooling. He soon realised his mistake but once committed 'there was no deliverance from the yoke'. His first job was to look after a pumping engine that prevented an isolated coal mine from flooding. He worked seven days or nights a week, in shifts of twelve hours or more. It was not hard work but unhappily he was on his own in 'solitary confinement with no companion'. At that young age it is hardly surprising that he had 'timid feelings on dark winter nights, and that every strange noise caused a shock of terror and alarm, especially as unearthly things moved about in the dark'. The engine was located near Hell Lane

268

where William was placed in great moral danger, he writes, because, being so much on his own, he was glad of anyone who would come to play with him, and some of the 'worst – the vilest of the vile – came'.

In those days it was accepted practice for children aged six to fifteen to work in coal mines for twelve-hour shifts. Not until after the report, *The Commission of Enquiry into the State of Children in Employment* appeared was the first Factory Act passed in 1833 forbidding the employment of children under the age of nine, and not until after the Mines Act of 1842 was the use of all child labour forbidden.

When aged fifteen William was promoted to the more responsible task of looking after an engine that drew miners out of the pit but, after two years, wishing to learn a better trade, he became apprenticed to one of his father's blacksmiths. By the age of twenty-one, still living at home, he earned two shillings a week out of which he had to clothe himself. He became a Sunday School teacher and at the age of twenty-four married another Sunday School teacher. A few months after their wedding, his father, aged fifty, died in a matter of days from 'a stoppage in the bowels'.

William took over his father's wrought-iron business but was aware that, although he had the necessary technical knowledge, he lacked managerial experience. Business matters were not made easier by his moral convictions. His father had been in the habit of going on Saturday nights to the public houses to get his bills paid by the colliery managers who had used his firm during the previous week. William was reluctant to follow his father's example because he was well aware of the dangers of alcohol. Public houses stayed open all night and drunkenness was rife. He was determined 'to keep clear of these ruinous places where so many have fallen to rise no more'. He collected his dues on Mondays; this independent action brought him much local respect and later he became a Justice of the Peace.

The workers were 'rough and crude in their speech'. Any new employee was treated with suspicion and called a 'far-comer'. The women and girls came to work in shawls, and their long hair was a great danger because of its liability to be caught in machinery. The workers were happy-go-lucky but loyal to their boss and exerted themselves particularly hard when there was piece-work or a rush job. No canteen facilities existed; for their lunch the workmen brought a pound of ham or beefsteak which they fried on the blade of a shovel held in a furnace or over a blacksmith's hearth. They organised their own recreation. On the rough ground near the factory, foot races were run for purses put up by the backers. Whippet racing and rabbit coursing were favourite sports. Cock fighting, dog fighting and encounters between colliery pugilists, who fought with bare fists, took place almost daily. Badger, bear and bull baiting were rare but 'made sickening and barbarous exhibitions'.

In 1832 William records that the Black Country was 'visited with that dreadful disease, the cholera'. This particular epidemic was introduced from a ship that had docked in Newcastle upon Tyne. The disease was carried south by manual labourers seeking seasonal employment and by itinerant tradesmen, migrants and entertainers. During the first thirty years of the nineteenth century the urban population had trebled making conditions for the spread of cholera ideal. Many unskilled labourers lived with their families in underventilated, overcrowded slums in mean streets near the factories. The buildings were squalid without so much as a single tap to supply running water, which was usually drawn from a communal pump connected to a well. The flushing water closet had not been invented. The shortage of accommodation meant that a whole family might occupy a single room for living, eating and sleeping – its floor thick with dirt and filth. Often on the ground outside a window or a door lay a pile of putrefying, foul-smelling household slops, a source of nourishment for dogs, cats and rats. Stagnant cesspools in back gardens or on common land overflowed to contaminate the water in the wells. By the summer of 1832 cholera had reached the Midlands where 'whole families fell victim, being alive one day and buried the next. The death cart was constantly about with coffins for the dead. Our little chapel was filled with earnest enquiring souls'. The total mortality in England and Wales was recorded as 31,000.

Over a period of twenty-five years William's wife gave birth to fourteen children, only four of whom survived to adult life. The first was stillborn and eight more died in infancy because their mother was unable to feed them. 'In the absence of a wet-nurse, they sank into weakness and died. Everything to assist in feeding and every kind of food was tried without success. The nursing bottle was not in existence in the early part of our married life,' he explains.

Travelling in Victorian times was hazardous. William dislocates his shoulder and fractures a shoulder-blade when his gig overturns after the pony bolts and a wheel hits a curb-stone. On another occasion his wife, eldest son and he are nearly killed when their horse shies, runs the carriage up the banked side of the road and tips it over. The three of them fall under the wheels of an oncoming wagon which stops just in time. William is also involved in a railway accident. The train was travelling 'at the great speed of forty miles an hour' when the fire-box drops off the locomotive and severs the coupling to the first carriage in which he is sitting. The carriage rolls over to lie across the adjacent track where another train smashes into it, killing two passengers. William is not seriously hurt but suffers 'from a great shock, many bruises, a badly shaken nervous system and the action of the heart was altered'.

In 1851 his wife reported, 'I have something on my bosom like a pea. It is so hard.' The doctor 'examined the breast very carefully and sent some ointment to rub on it. But the substance grew very fast and the rubbing made it grow faster... The lump proved to be a cancer of the worst kind'. The breast is removed in the Royal Hospital, Wolverhampton, without the benefit of anaesthesia.

Dr John Snow in London had begun to use ether as an anaesthetic in 1851, and general anaesthesia became more widely applied after he administered chloroform for the birth of Queen Victoria's seventh child, Leopold, on 7 April 1853. Dr Snow records in his diary, 'At twenty minutes past twelve I commenced to give a little chloroform with each pain, by pouring about fifteen minims by measure upon a folded handkerchief ... Her Majesty expressed great relief from the application, the pain being very trifling... The effect of the chloroform was not at any time carried to the extent of quite removing consciousness... The infant was born at thirteen minutes past one... The Queen appeared very cheerful and well, expressing herself much gratified with the effect of the chloroform'. Medical progress is seldom received with universal acclaim and *The Lancet* at the time recorded that 'intense astonishment' had been caused by 'the rumour that Her Majesty was placed under the influence of chloroform, an agent which has unquestionably caused instantaneous death in a considerable number of cases'.

My great-grandfather left no account of his wife's operation in 1851 but a contemporary medical student, John Brown, describes a similar case in *Rab and his Friends and Other Papers and Essays*. John Brown first meets Mrs Ailie Noble when her anxious husband, James, brings her to a hospital in Edinburgh in his cart drawn by an old grey horse and accompanied by their aging mastiff, Rab.

'She's got a kind o' trouble in her breast, doctor,' the carrier tells the medical student. 'Wull ye tak' a look at it?' In the consulting room John examines the right breast carefully as Ailie and James watch with Rab watching all three. 'There it was, that had once been so soft, so shapely, so white, so gracious and bountiful – hard as a stone, a centre of horrid pain.'

Ailie is admitted to the hospital. Her husband stays to nurse her and Rab with his large blunt head and black muzzle watches from under the bed. The surgeon examines Ailie. 'It could be removed – it might never return – it would give her speedy relief – she should have it done.'

The next day the operating room is crowded with students eager to secure good places. The surgeon and his staff of assistants are ready. Ailie walks in 'quickly, but without haste; dressed in her mutch, her neckerchief, her white dimity shortgown, her black bombazeen petticoat, showing her white worsted stockings and her carpet shoes'. One look at her quiets and abates the eager students. Behind her are James and Rab; James sits down some distance away and takes the dog's 'huge and noble head between his knees'.

Ailie steps up and lays herself upon the table. She arranges herself, takes a rapid look at her husband, shuts her eyes and holds John Brown's hand. The operation is started; it is necessarily slow; and 'chloroform – one of God's best gifts to his suffering children – was then unknown. The surgeon does his work. The pale face shows its pain but is still and silent... Rab sees blood flowing from his mistress, and her suffering; he growls and gives now and then a sharp impatient yelp; he would have liked to have done something to that man. But James has him firm.'

It is over: she is dressed, steps gently and decently down from the table, looks for James; then, turning to the surgeon and the students, she curtsies – and in a low, clear voice, begs their pardon if she has behaved ill. The students – all of them – wept like children; the surgeon 'happed her up carefully', and resting on James and John Brown, Ailie goes to her room with Rab following.

For a while all goes well. The students come, quiet and anxious, and surround her bed. Ailie says she likes to see their young, honest faces. The surgeon dresses her, and 'speaks to her in his own short kind way'. But four days postoperatively Ailie has a rigor, the wound is infected, she becomes delirious and dies of septicaemia.

William Bayliss's wife initially fared better. 'The operation was skilfully done and she rapidly recovered. Very soon she looked so well that we hoped that there would be no return of the malady but from what we heard of the nature of cancers we were doubtful.' Alas, as had been feared, the malignancy recurred, spread to the lungs and after some months of suffering 'my dear wife, the mother of my children, was taken from me but we shall meet again for she died in the Lord'. William is desolate – 'no one can tell what it is to lose a dear wife but those who have passed through the trial'.

Happily he finds not only a new wife but a mother for his children because 'as the Lord said long ago, it is not well for a man to be alone'. William appreciates the problems his new wife, a widow, will face with four step-children but they have two children of their own, a daughter and a tall delicate son who at the age of fifteen coughs up blood and five months later is dead of pulmonary tuberculosis.

In his mid-forties William begins to suffer from an environmental disease, chronic bronchitis. 'I could not bear the smoke and sulphur, which were so bad from the furnaces. When the wind was in the east or north-east, I dreaded to go home', he writes. To add to his trouble he develops melancholia; depression, as we would call it today. 'I was constantly depressed in body and mind. There seemed nothing but ruin before me, and that it was better to die than to live. Every little trouble was a mountain. Night and day the difficulties rose before me.' Two events help to relieve his depression. He moves away from the Black Country to avoid the severe atmospheric pollution and he reorganises the management of his business by taking on more executive help.

Eventually he and his wife move to spend his remaining eight years in an attractive house on the hills outside Torquay where surprisingly he found the local children 'very rebellious, far worse than the children in Hell Lane'. He died of pneumonia at the age of seventy-five, his life-span probably shortened by the chronic bronchitis. My great-grandmother's death from cancer of the breast may have had hereditary implications for my two sisters. Pam sadly died of cancer of the breast, as also did Di.

273

William had two sons. The older died of an unknown cause at the age of eighty-five. The younger, my grandfather, died in his sleep at the age of eighty-four of a coronary thrombosis. He had eight children; the five sons, my father and four uncles, all died of coronary artery disease between the ages of seventy-five and eighty-two. His three daughters, my aunts, lived rather longer to die also of coronaries at the ages of eighty, eighty-six and eighty-nine. My paternal grandmother died young, at the age of fifty, of septicaemia, and my mother of a coronary at the age of seventy-seven.

The writing on the family wall is not difficult to read and is in many ways reassuring.